INSTRUCTOR'S SOLUTIONS MANUAL

PAUL LORCZAK

with contributions from

BEVERLY FUSFIELD   CARRIE GREEN

APPLIED BASIC MATHEMATICS

William Clark

Harper College

Robert Brechner

Miami-Dade College

PEARSON

Addison Wesley

Boston San Francisco New York
London Toronto Sydney Tokyo Singapore Madrid
Mexico City Munich Paris Cape Town Hong Kong Montreal

Reproduced by Pearson Addison-Wesley from electronic files supplied by the author.

ISBN-13: 978-0-321-50679-5
ISBN-10: 0-321-50679-0

1 2 3 4 5 6 OPM 11 10 09 08

PEARSON
Addison
Wesley

CONTENTS

Chapter 1 Whole Numbers

Section 1.1 Understanding the Basics of Whole Numbers

Concept Check

2. A system that uses the digits to represent numbers is called the Hindu-Arabic or _decimal_ number system.

4. Any of the numbers 0, 1, 2, 3, 4, 5, 6, 7, 8, 9, 10, 11, 12, 13, 14, 15, … are called the _whole_ numbers.

6. When a number such as 385 is written as $300 + 80 + 5$, we say that the number is written in as _expanded_ notation.

8. In rounding, if the digit to the right of the specified place value is 5 or more, _increase_ the digit in the specified place value by one. Otherwise, the digit remains the same.

10. A _table_ is a collection of data arranged in rows and columns for ease of reference.

Guide Problems

12. For the number 8360, identify the name of each place value.

    Recall the rightmost digit in a whole number is in the ones place, the next digit to the left is in the tens place, the next in the hundreds place, then thousands, and so on.

Digit	Name of each place value
8	thousands
3	hundreds
6	tens
0	ones

In problems 14-28, the place value of the underlined digit is given as the answer. Recall that whole numbers are specified using periods of three place values each. The periods up to the billions period are listed below from leftmost to rightmost. The three place values within each period are also listed from left to right.

Period	Place values		
billions	hundred billions	ten billions	billions
millions	hundred millions	ten millions	millions
thousands	hundred thousands	ten thousands	thousands
ones	hundreds	tens	ones

14. In 4_78_ the 7 is in the *tens* place.

16. In 1_6_30 the 6 is in the *hundreds* place.

18. In 63,4_1_0 the 1 is in the *tens* place.

20. In 19_5_,039 the 5 is in the *thousands* place.

22. In 225,_5_38 the 5 is in the *hundreds* place. Note the underlined 5 is in the hundreds place. The digit 5 to the left of the comma is in the thousands place.

24. In 175,_4_45 the 4 is in the *hundreds* place. Note the underlined 4 is in the hundreds place. The rightmost 4 is in the tens place.

26. In 2,<u>5</u>62,785 the 5 is in the *hundred thousands* place.
Note the rightmost 5 is in the ones place.

28. In 7,962,881,954 the 7 is in the *billions* place.

Guide Problems

30. In word form, 1202 is "one thousand, <u> two </u> <u> hundred </u> two." The digit 2 following the 1 is the hundreds place.

32. In standard form, 5349201 is written <u> 5,349,201 </u>. Commas are used to separate the three digit periods when a number has five or more digits. In word form, the number is " five <u> million </u>, three hundred <u> forty-nine </u> <u> thousand </u>, two hundred <u> one </u>." The digit 5 occupies the millions place, the thousands period consists of 349 read "three hundred forty-one" and the last digit written is the ones digit which is "one" here. Note the word form does not use the word *and*.

In Exercises 34 through 44, the standard notation for the given number is found by separating each period of three digits with a comma whenever the number has more than four digits. If a number has exactly four digits a comma need not be used but both forms are acceptable. The word form of the number is found by writing the name of the number occupying each period (using your knowledge of writing one-, two-, and three digit numbers) followed by the name of the period (in all but the case of the ones period.) In the word form the periods are separated by commas. A period consisting entirely of zeros does not contribute to the word form.

34. 751 standard notation: 751
word form: seven hundred fifty-one

36. 1479 standard notation: 1479 or 1,479
word form: one thousand, four hundred seventy-nine

38. 45000 standard notation: 45,000
word form: forty-five thousand
Note the period 000 is in not part of the word form.

40. 23606 standard notation: 23,606
word form: twenty-three thousand, six hundred six

42. 6555347 standard notation: 6,555,347. For the word form, consider the digits in each period.
digits: 6	word form: six	period: millions
digits: 555	word form: five hundred fifty-five	period: thousands
digits: 347	word form: three hundred forty-seven	period: ones
Word form for 6555347 : six million, five hundred fifty-five thousand, three hundred forty-seven

44. 7228145017 standard notation: 7,228,145,017. For the word form, consider the digits in each period.
digits: 7	word form: seven	period: billions
digits: 228	word form: two hundred twenty-eight	period: millions
digits: 145	word form: one hundred forty-five	period: thousands
digits: 017	word form: seventeen	period: ones
Word form for 7228145017 : seven billion, two hundred twenty-eight million, one hundred forty-five thousand, seventeen

Guide Problems

46. Write 9813 in expanded form.
9813 has 9 thousands, 8 hundreds, 1 ten, and 3 ones
Expanded form: <u> 9000 + 800 + 10 + 3 </u>

In Exercises 48-54, an expanded form is first found as follows. For each digit that is not zero, write the digit followed by the name of the place it occupies separating each digit-word pair with a plus sign. The other expanded form is found by writing each digit-word pair in the sum as a number. For example, "8 tens" is 80 and "5 ten-thousands" is 50,000.

48. In expanded form 695 is
    6 hundreds + 9 tens + 5 ones or $600 + 90 + 5$

50. In expanded form 9689 is
    9 thousands + 6 hundreds + 8 tens + 9
    or $9000 + 600 + 80 + 9$

52. In expanded form 46,273 is
    4 ten thousands + 6 thousands + 2 hundreds
         + 7 tens + 3 ones
    or $40000 + 6000 + 200 + 70 + 3$

54. In expanded form 703,300 is
    7 hundred thousands + 3 thousands + 3 hundreds
    or $700,000 + 3000 + 300$

Guide Problems

56. Round 132,449 to the nearest ten thousand.

    a. What digit is the ten thousands place?
       That is, what digit is the place to which
       you want to round. Here, it is 3.

    b. Which place determines what me must
       do in the ten thousands place?
       The place that determines how we round
       is the place immediately to the right of the
       place we are rounding to. Here the place
       to the right of ten thousands is the <u>thousands</u>
       place.

    c. What digit is in that place? <u>2</u>

    d. Explain what to do next.
       The specified digit, 3, remains the same
       because the digit in the thousands place is
       4 or less. Change each digit to the right of
       of the specified place value to zero.

    e. Write the rounded number. <u>130,000</u>
       As described in part d., the 3 in the ten
       thousands place stays the same and the
       digits to the right: 2,4, 4 and 9, are
       replaced with zeros to yield 130,000.

In Exercises 58-68, the procedure outlined in the Guide Problems is applied to round the given number to the specified place. 1) Locate the digit in the specified place. 2) Identify the digit to the right of the specified digit. 3) Increase the specified digit by one if the digit to the right is 5 or more. Leave the specified digit the same otherwise. 4) Replace all digits to the right of the specified digit with zeros.

58. 12,819 to the nearest hundred
    The digit in the hundreds place is 8.
    The digit to the right is 1 which is
    less than 5. Leave the 8 alone and
    replace the 1 and 9 with zeros to get
    12,800.

60. 591,680 to the nearest hundred thousand
    The digit in the hundred thousands place is 5.
    The digit to the right is 9 which is
    more than 5. Increase the 5 by one and
    replace the 9,1,6,8 with zeros to get
    600,000.

62. 125,516 to the nearest ten
    The 1 in the tens place is followed by
    a 6 so increase that 1 to 2 and zero out
    the 6 to yield the rounded number 125,520.

64. 2,258,932 to the nearest hundred
    The specified digit 9 is followed by 3.
    Round down to 2,258,900.

66. 76,002,009 to the nearest thousand
    The specified digit 2 is followed by 0. Leave the 2 as is and zero out 9 to get 76,002,000.

68. 1,943,477 to the leftmost place value
    The leftmost place value is the millions place which contains a 1. The 9 in the place to the right indicates increase 1 to 2 and use zeros for the remaining places to get 2,000,000.

70. "Three hundred fifty thousand, three hundred twenty-one" in standard notation is 350,321.

72. A revenue of "three hundred twelve billion, four hundred twenty-seven million dollars" in standard notation has 312 in the billions period, 427 in the millions period and 000 in both the thousands and ones period. The standard notation is then $312,427,000,000.

74. The dollar amount $852 has the digits 852 in the ones period so the word form is "eight hundred fifty-two dollars."

76. The number 2,500,000 in word form is "two million, five hundred thousand."

78. The number 318,979,564,000 has the digits 318 in the billions period, 979 in the millions period and 564 in the thousands period. Since the digits in the ones period are all 0, the ones period contributes nothing to the word form. The word form is "three hundred eighteen billion, nine hundred seventy-nine million, five hundred sixty-four thousand."

80. The hundreds place of 13,229 contains the digit 2. The tens place to the right also has a 2 so the hundreds place is unchanged by rounding and the farm has 13,200 cows rounded to the nearest hundred.

82. The billions place in $182,708,000,000 has a digit of 2. The digit to the right, in the hundred millions place, is a 7 so increase the digit 2 to 3 and replace 7 and 8 to the right with zero to get $183,000,000,000 rounded to the nearest billion.

84. From the chart, the average yearly salary with a high school diploma is $27,915. The periods here are the thousands and ones period containing the digit 27 and 915 respectively. The word form is then "twenty-seven thousand, nine hundred fifteen dollars."

86. Workers with an advanced degree earn an average of $74,602 annually. The digit in the ten thousands place is 7 which is followed by a 4 in the thousands place. Since 4 is less than 5, leave the 7 unchanged and zero the remaining digits to get the rounded value of $70,000.

88. A worker with a high school diploma earn, on average, $27,915 a year. In rounding to the nearest ten, the 5 in the ones place indicates to increase the 1 to 2 and zero out the 5 to get $27,920 rounded.

Section 1.2   Adding Whole Numbers

Concept Check

2. Numbers that are added together are known as __addends__.

4. The identity property of addition states that adding __zero__ to a number results in a sum equal to the original number.

6. The associative property of addition states that changing the __grouping__ of the addends does not change the sum.

8. A closed, flat geometric figure in which all sides are line segments is called a __polygon__.

Guide Problems

10. $0 + 41 = \underline{\ 41\ }$

This example demonstrates the addition property of $\underline{\ zero\ }$.

The addition property of zero states that when 0 is added to any number the result is that number. Thus, $0 + 41 = 41$.

12. Show that $(4 + 9) + 12 = 4 + (9 + 12)$.

$$(4 + 9) + 12 = 4 + (9 + 12)$$
$$13 + 12 = 4 + \underline{\ 21\ }$$
$$\underline{\ 25\ } = \underline{\ 25\ }$$

Performing the additions results in a sum of 25 on both sides so the sums are identical. This example demonstrates the $\underline{\text{associative}}$ property of addition.

14. Add $0 + 2000$.
By the addition property of zero, $0 + 2000 = 2000$.

16. Show that $42 + 6 = 6 + 42$.

Since
$$42 + 6 = 48$$
$$6 + 42 = 48$$

both additions result in a sum of 48 and the two sums are identical. This demonstrates the $\underline{\text{commutative}}$ property of addition.

18. Show that $40 + (15 + 5) = (40 + 15) + 5$.

$$40 + (15 + 5) = 40 + 20 = 60$$
$$(40 + 15) + 5 = 55 + 5 = 60$$

Since the additions on both sides result in a sum of 60, the additions are identical. This demonstrates the $\underline{\text{associative}}$ property of addition.

Guide Problems

20.
$$\begin{array}{r} 522 \\ + \ 21 \\ \hline 5\underline{4}3 \end{array}$$

22.
$$\begin{array}{r} 3\overset{1}{1}9 \\ + \ 59 \\ \hline 378 \end{array}$$

In Exercises 24-54, the addition is performed as in the Guide Problems. Starting at the right, the digits in each column are added. If the sum of a column is 9 or less, write the result directly underneath that column. If the sum of a column is ten or more, write the units digits of the column sum underneath that column and carry any remaining digits to the top of the column to the left to be included in that column's sum. Continue this way to the left until all columns have been added.

24.
$$\begin{array}{r} 33 \\ + \ 64 \\ \hline 97 \end{array}$$

26.
$$\begin{array}{r} 50 \\ + \ 35 \\ \hline 85 \end{array}$$

28.
$$\begin{array}{r} 57 \\ + \ 40 \\ \hline 97 \end{array}$$

30.
$$\begin{array}{r} 31 \\ + \ 86 \\ \hline 117 \end{array}$$

32.
$$\begin{array}{r} \overset{\scriptscriptstyle 1}{2}75 \\ +\ 31 \\ \hline 306 \end{array}$$

34.
$$\begin{array}{r} \overset{\scriptscriptstyle 1\ 1}{9}75 \\ +129 \\ \hline 1104 \end{array}$$

36.
$$\begin{array}{r} 4210 \\ +2088 \\ \hline 6298 \end{array}$$

38.
$$\begin{array}{r} \overset{\scriptscriptstyle 1\ \ 1}{3}\,387 \\ +8\,807 \\ \hline 12{,}194 \end{array}$$

40.
$$\begin{array}{r} \overset{\scriptscriptstyle 2\ 1}{3}32 \\ 285 \\ +699 \\ \hline 13\,16 \end{array}$$

42.
$$\begin{array}{r} \overset{\scriptscriptstyle 1}{7}57 \\ 621 \\ +881 \\ \hline 2259 \end{array}$$

44.
$$\begin{array}{r} \overset{\scriptscriptstyle 1\ 2\ 1}{1}419 \\ 280 \\ 467 \\ 41 \\ +\ 500 \\ \hline 2707 \end{array}$$

46.
$$\begin{array}{r} \overset{\scriptscriptstyle 2\ 1\ 1}{9}01 \\ 8\,226 \\ 434 \\ 82 \\ +1\,610 \\ \hline 11{,}253 \end{array}$$

In Exercises 48-54, the addition is first written vertically aligning the numbers so that the corresponding places align. The addition is then performed as in 23-46.

48.
$$\begin{array}{r} \overset{\scriptscriptstyle 1}{6}68 \\ +\ 71 \\ \hline 739 \end{array}$$

50.
$$\begin{array}{r} \overset{\scriptscriptstyle 1\ 1\ 1}{2}378 \\ +6977 \\ \hline 9355 \end{array}$$

52.
$$\begin{array}{r} \overset{\scriptscriptstyle 1\ 1\ 1}{6}92 \\ 171\,3 \\ +3336 \\ \hline 574\,1 \end{array}$$

54.
$$\begin{array}{r} \overset{\scriptscriptstyle 1\ \ 1}{7}13 \\ 1\,919 \\ +8\,223 \\ \hline 10{,}855 \end{array}$$

56. The phrase "increased by" implies addition.
$$\begin{array}{r} \overset{\scriptscriptstyle 1}{3}54 \\ +\ 281 \\ \hline 635 \end{array}$$
The result is 635.

58. The phrase "added to" means addition.
$$\begin{array}{r} \overset{\scriptscriptstyle 1\ 1}{2}99 \\ +\ 125 \\ \hline 424 \end{array}$$
The result is 424.

60. The total of the three numbers is
$$\begin{array}{r} \overset{\scriptscriptstyle 1}{6}63 \\ 518 \\ +\ 613 \\ \hline 1794 \end{array}$$
The result is 1794.

62. The total number of lamps is given by the sum
$$\begin{array}{r} \overset{\scriptscriptstyle 1\ 1\ 1}{3}430 \\ 2779 \\ +3124 \\ \hline 9333 \end{array}$$
. The company manufactured 9333 lamps.

64. The new car price is the sum of the trade-in and the cash payment.
$$\begin{array}{r} \overset{\scriptscriptstyle 1\ 1}{\$}13{,}589 \\ +\ \$3\,650 \\ \hline \$17{,}239 \end{array}$$

Jessy paid $17,239 for her new car.

66. The total number of runners in the two years is the result of the sum below.
$$\begin{array}{r} \overset{\scriptscriptstyle 1\ 1}{4}432 \\ +6\,590 \\ \hline 11{,}022 \end{array}$$

68. The total number of breakfasts, lunches, dinners, and late night meals can be found by adding along each row of the table. The computations are shown below where the sums have been written vertically.

Breakfast	Lunch	Dinner	Late night
$\overset{2\,3}{215}$	$\overset{1\,2}{326}$	$\overset{2\,1}{429}$	$\overset{2\,2}{124}$
238	3 10	432	129
197	349	375	98
184	308	381	103
+ 258	+ 280	+ 402	+ 183
1092	1573	2019	637

70. $\overset{1}{165}$ mg (1 medium quava)

   $+\ 60$ mg (1 medium orange)

   225 mg total

72. Each cup of frozen orange juice contains 75 mg of vitamin C and each guava contains 165 mg. Three cups orange juice and two medium guavas total $75 + 75 + 75 + 165 + 165 = 555$ mg of vitamin C.

74. The perimeter of the figure is the sum of the lengths of the sides. The length of the entire rectangle is $11 + 3 = 14$ in. There are two sides of length 3 in. and two sides of length 14 in. The perimeter is $14 + 3 + 14 + 3 = 34$ in.

76. The number of feet of molding needed is the perimeter of the ceiling or $11 + 11 + 9 + 13 + 9 = 53$ ft.

Cumulative Skills Review

2.   In the number 675,482 the digit 5 is the rightmost digit in the thousands period and so is in the thousands place.

4.   The hundreds digit of in 34,506 is 5 which is followed by a 0. When rounding to hundreds, then, leave the 5 alone and change the digits to the right to zeros to yield 34,500.

6.   In expanded notation , the number 653 can be written as: 6 hundreds + 5 tens + 3 ones
     or as $600 + 50 + 3$.

8.   The digit of 7,559,239 in the ten thousands place is 5. The digit to its right, in the thousands place, is 9. Since 9 is greater than 5, to round to the nearest ten thousand, add one to the ten thousands place to get 6 and replace all digits to the right with zeros to get 7,560,000.

10. a. The value $73,272,210,000 rounded to the nearest million is $73,272,000,000.

     b. The rounded value $73,272,000,000 has a the digits 73 in the billions period and 272 in the millions period. The other periods consist of 000 and do not contribute to the word form. The word form is then "seventy-three billion, two hundred seventy-two million dollars"

Section 1.3   Subtracting Whole Numbers

Concept Check

2. In subtraction, the number from which another number is subtracted is called the __minuend__ .

4. The result of subtracting numbers is known as the __difference__ .

6. If the digits in a column cannot be subtracted to produce a whole number, __borrow__ from the column to the left.

Guide Problems

In problems 7 through 10, no borrowing is required. The digits in each column can be subtracted starting with the rightmost column and proceeding left.

8.
$$\begin{array}{r} 85 \\ -\ 4 \\ \hline \underline{8\,1} \end{array}$$

since $5 - 4 = 1$
and $8 - 0 = 8$.

10.
$$\begin{array}{r} 7\underline{9} \\ -\ 52 \\ \hline 27 \end{array}$$

since $9 - 2 = 7$
and $7 - 5 = 2$.

In problems 12 through 14, the digit at the top of each column is smaller than the digit below it and so borrowing is required. For a given column, a 1 is borrowed from the digit to the left of the top digit and 10 is added to the digit at the top of the column to perform the subtraction.

12.
$$\begin{array}{r} 41 \\ -\ 6 \\ \hline \end{array}$$
is computed as
$$\begin{array}{r} {}^{3}\cancel{4}\,{}^{11}\cancel{1} \\ -\ 6 \\ \hline 3\,5 \end{array}$$

since $11 - 6 = 5$ and $3 - 0 = 3$.

14.
$$\begin{array}{r} 512 \\ -\ 454 \\ \hline \end{array}$$
is computed as
$$\begin{array}{r} {}^{4}\cancel{5}\,{}^{10}\!\cancel{0}\,{}^{12}\cancel{2} \\ -\ 4\,5\,4 \\ \hline 5\,8 \end{array}$$

since $12 - 4 = 8$, $10 - 5 = 5$, and $4 - 4 = 0$.

In problems 16 through 54, subtraction is performed as in the Guide Problems. Subtraction is performed in each column moving from right to left. Borrowing is not needed in problems 16-26 and is employed when necessary after problem 26.

16.
$$\begin{array}{r} 49 \\ -\ 7 \\ \hline 42 \end{array}$$

18.
$$\begin{array}{r} 42 \\ -\ 2 \\ \hline 40 \end{array}$$

20.
$$\begin{array}{r} 71 \\ -\ 11 \\ \hline 60 \end{array}$$

22.
$$\begin{array}{r} 49 \\ -\ 28 \\ \hline 21 \end{array}$$

24.
$$\begin{array}{r} 97 \\ -\ 55 \\ \hline 42 \end{array}$$

26.
$$\begin{array}{r} 29 \\ -\ 24 \\ \hline 5 \end{array}$$

28.
$$\begin{array}{r} {}^{2}\cancel{3}\,{}^{11}\cancel{1} \\ -\ 3 \\ \hline 28 \end{array}$$

30.
$$\begin{array}{r} {}^{6}\cancel{7}\,{}^{13}\cancel{3} \\ -\ 7 \\ \hline 66 \end{array}$$

32.
$$\begin{array}{r} {}^{7}\cancel{8}\,{}^{10}\cancel{0} \\ -\ 3\,6 \\ \hline 44 \end{array}$$

34.
$$\begin{array}{r} {}^{5}\cancel{6}\,{}^{12}\cancel{2} \\ -\ 4\,7 \\ \hline 1\,5 \end{array}$$

36.
$$\begin{array}{r} {}^{3}\cancel{4}\,{}^{15}\cancel{5}\,8 \\ -\ 8\,4 \\ \hline 374 \end{array}$$

38.
$$\begin{array}{r} 748 \\ -\ 30 \\ \hline 718 \end{array}$$

40. $$\begin{array}{r} {\scriptstyle 7\ 14} \\ \not{8}\not{4}9 \\ -\ 355 \\ \hline 494 \end{array}$$

42. $$\begin{array}{r} {\scriptstyle 3\ 17} \\ \not{4}\not{7}9 \\ -\ 184 \\ \hline 295 \end{array}$$

44. $$\begin{array}{r} {\scriptstyle 4\ 12\ 17\ 10} \\ \not{5}\not{3}\not{8}\not{0} \\ -1392 \\ \hline 3988 \end{array}$$

46. $$\begin{array}{r} {\scriptstyle 1\ \ 15} \\ 1\not{2},\not{5}63 \\ -\ 10,963 \\ \hline 1600 \end{array}$$

In Problems 48 through 54, the subtraction is written horizontally. In each case, the first step is to rewrite the problem vertically aligning the corresponding place values in each number.

48. $$\begin{array}{r} {\scriptstyle 11\ 11} \\ \not{1}\not{2}\not{1} \\ -\ 53 \\ \hline 68 \end{array}$$

50. $$\begin{array}{r} {\scriptstyle 5\ 11} \\ 7\not{6}\not{1} \\ -\ 706 \\ \hline 55 \end{array}$$

52. $$\begin{array}{r} {\scriptstyle 6\ 10\ 7\ 13} \\ \not{7}\not{0}\not{8}\not{3} \\ -\ 134 \\ \hline 6949 \end{array}$$

54. $$\begin{array}{r} {\scriptstyle 5\ 10} \\ 15\not{6}\not{0} \\ -\ 1057 \\ \hline 503 \end{array}$$

56. "85 minus 62" means $85-62$.
$$\begin{array}{r} 85 \\ -\ 62 \\ \hline 23 \end{array}$$

58. "349 decreased by 97" means $349-97$.
$$\begin{array}{r} {\scriptstyle 2\ 14} \\ \not{3}\not{4}9 \\ -\ 97 \\ \hline 252 \end{array}$$

60. "243 less than 959" means $959-243$.
$$\begin{array}{r} 959 \\ -\ 243 \\ \hline 716 \end{array}$$

62. "the difference of 45,988 and 12,808" means $45,988-12,808$.
$$\begin{array}{r} 45,988 \\ -\ 12,808 \\ \hline 33,180 \end{array}$$

64. The increase in population is given by $300,000,000-281,421,906$ which is computed below.
$$\begin{array}{r} {\scriptstyle 2\ 9\ 9\ \ 9\ 9\ 9\ \ 9\ 9\ 10} \\ \not{3}\not{0}\not{0},\not{0}\not{0}\not{0},\not{0}\not{0}\not{0} \\ -\ 281,421,906 \\ \hline 18,578,094 \end{array}$$

66. The student population increased from 5440 to 6120. There is an increase of $6120-5440$ or 680 students as computed below.
$$\begin{array}{r} {\scriptstyle 5\ 10\ 12} \\ \not{6}\not{1}\not{2}0 \\ -5440 \\ \hline 680 \end{array}$$

68. The difference in the dollar amounts is
$$\begin{array}{r} {\scriptstyle 2\ \ 12} \\ \$\not{3},\not{2}50,000 \\ -\ \$2,850,000 \\ \hline \$400,000 \end{array}$$
so the prediction exceed the actual profits by \$400,000.

70. a. The population increased by $556,000-541,500=14,500$ people from 2005 to 2006.

b. The difference in population between 2007 and 2006 is $556,000-548,400=7600$ so 7600 people left Melville between 2006 and 2007.

c. The word form of 7600 is "seven thousand, six hundred."

72. First add the amounts that Marlena spent: $\$6+\$44+\$30=\$80$. Then subtract the total spent from the \$150 she began with: $\$150-\$80=\$70$. She had \$70 left.

74. The total number of students majoring in *either* design or retailing is $92 + 105 = 197$. The reminder of the 310 students are fashion modeling majors so $310 - 197 = 113$ students are fashion modeling majors.

76. In 2002 there were 2049 DVDs available and in 2003 there were 4787. Computing the difference

$$
\begin{array}{r}
4\,7\,\overset{7}{\cancel{8}}\,\overset{17}{\cancel{7}} \\
-\;2\,0\,4\,9 \\
\hline
2\,7\,3\,8
\end{array}
$$

There were 2738 fewer DVDs in 2002 than 2003.

Cumulative Skills Review

2.
$$
\begin{array}{r}
\overset{1}{6}\,9\,3 \\
4\,1 \\
+\;1\,0{,}1\,1\,0 \\
\hline
1\,0{,}8\,4\,4
\end{array}
$$

4. To show that $(2 + 3) + 7 = 2 + (3 + 7)$, simplify both sides and show each side is equal to the same number.

$$(2 + 3) + 7 = 2 + (3 + 7)$$
$$5 + 7 = 2 + 10 \qquad \text{(Perform the addition within parentheses first)}$$
$$12 = 12$$

Since both sides are equal to 12, it must be that $(2 + 3) + 7 = 2 + (3 + 7)$.

6.
$$
\begin{array}{r}
\overset{1}{2}\,2\,5 \\
7\,0\,8 \\
+\;\;5\,2 \\
\hline
9\,8\,5
\end{array}
$$

8. The digit in the leftmost place value of 243,559 is a 2. The digit to its right is 4 which is less than five so the 2 remains unchanged when rounding to the leftmost place. Replace all digits to the right of 2 with zeros to get the rounded value of 200,000.

10.
$$
\begin{array}{r}
\overset{1}{3}\,\overset{1}{4}\,8 \\
+\;3\,9\,0\,9 \\
\hline
4\,2\,5\,7
\end{array}
$$

Section 1.4   Multiplying Whole Numbers

Concept Check

2. Numbers being multiplied are known as __factors__ .

4. The multiplication property of zero states that the product of any number and __0, or zero,__ is 0.

6. According to the commutative property of multiplication, $5 \cdot 7 = \underline{\ 7 \cdot 5\ }$.

8. According to the distributive property of multiplication over subtraction, $2(8-3) = 2 \cdot 8 - \underline{\ 2 \cdot 3\ }$.

Guide Problems

10. $13 \cdot 1 = \underline{\ 13\ }$

This example demonstrates the multiplication property of $\underline{\ one\ }$. The multiplication property of one states that the product of any number and 1 is that number.

12. Show that $2(1 \cdot 4) = (2 \cdot 1)4$.

Perform the multiplications on both sides. Evaluate within the parentheses first.
$$2(1 \cdot 4) = (2 \cdot 1)4$$
$$2(\ \underline{4}\ ) = (\ \underline{2}\ )4$$
$$\underline{8} = \underline{8}$$
The results are the same, showing
$$2(1 \cdot 4) = (2 \cdot 1)4.$$
This example demonstrates the $\underline{\ associative\ }$ property of multiplication.

14. Show that $3(5-2) = 3 \cdot 5 - 3 \cdot 2$.

Perform the operations on both sides. On the left side, evaluate within the parentheses first. On the right side, perform the multiplications before the subtraction.
$$3(5-2) = 3 \cdot 5 - 3 \cdot 2$$
$$3(\ \underline{3}\ ) = 15 - \underline{6}$$
$$\underline{9} = \underline{9}$$
The results are the same showing
$$3(5-2) = 3 \cdot 5 - 3 \cdot 2$$
This example demonstrates the $\underline{\ distributive\ }$ property of multiplication over $\underline{\ subtraction\ }$.

16. By the multiplication property of zero, the product of any number and 0 is 0, so
$$92 \cdot 0 = 0.$$

18. By the multiplication property of one, the product of any number and 1 is that number, so $1 \cdot 439 = 439$.

20. Show that $9 \cdot 3 = 3 \cdot 9$.
Compute each side separately.
$$9 \cdot 3 = 3 \cdot 9$$
$$27 = 27$$
The results are the same, showing
$$9 \cdot 3 = 3 \cdot 9$$
This illustrates the commutative property of multiplication.

22. Show that $1(9 \cdot 7) = (1 \cdot 9)7$.
Compute each side separately.
$$1(9 \cdot 7) = (1 \cdot 9)7$$
$$1 \cdot 63 = 9 \cdot 7$$
$$63 = 63$$
The results are the same, showing
$$1(9 \cdot 7) = (1 \cdot 9)7$$
This illustrates the associative property of multiplication.

24. Show that $4(9-3) = 4 \cdot 9 - 4 \cdot 3$.
Compute each side separately.
$$4(9-3) = 4 \cdot 9 - 4 \cdot 3$$
$$4 \cdot 6 = 36 - 12$$
$$24 = 24$$
The results are the same, showing
$$4(9-3) = 4 \cdot 9 - 4 \cdot 3$$
This illustrates the distributive property of multiplication over subtraction.

Guide Problems

26.
$$\overset{4}{5}6$$
$$\times\ 7$$
$$\overline{39\underline{2}}$$

In other words, "7 times 6 is 42. Write the 2 in the ones place of the answer and carry the 4 to the tens column. 7 times 5 is 35 plus the 4 carried over is 39. Write 39 in the hundreds and tens place of the answer."

28.
$$\overset{5}{3}6$$
$$\times\ 9$$
$$\overline{324}$$

Since $9 \times 6 = 54$ a 5 is carried to the tens column.

30.
$$86$$
$$\times\ 13$$
$$\overline{258}$$
$$860$$
$$\overline{1\underline{1}18}$$

32.
$$1216$$
$$\times\ 50$$
$$\overline{60,80\underline{0}}$$

In Problems 34 through 60, multiplication is performed using the techniques of this section. Numbers are not expressed in standard notation until the final answer.

34.
$$41$$
$$\times\ 2$$
$$\overline{82}$$

36.
$$63$$
$$\times\ 2$$
$$\overline{126}$$

38.
$$\overset{2}{5}8$$
$$\times\ 3$$
$$\overline{174}$$

40.
$$\overset{7}{3}9$$
$$\times\ 8$$
$$\overline{312}$$

42.
$$16$$
$$\times\ 33$$
$$\overline{48}$$
$$480$$
$$\overline{528}$$

44.
$$70$$
$$\times\ 75$$
$$\overline{350}$$
$$4900$$
$$\overline{5250}$$

46.
$$740$$
$$\times\ 80$$
$$\overline{59,200}$$

48.
$$407$$
$$\times\ 89$$
$$\overline{3663}$$
$$32560$$
$$\overline{36223}$$

or 36,223

50.
$$1681$$
$$\times\ 60$$
$$\overline{100,860}$$

52.
$$8737$$
$$\times\ 91$$
$$\overline{8737}$$
$$786330$$
$$\overline{795067}$$

or 795,067

In Problems 54 through 60, the problems are given horizontally. In each solution, the problem is first written vertically before multiplying.

54.
$$2014$$
$$\times\ 515$$
$$\overline{10070}$$
$$20140$$
$$1007000$$
$$\overline{1037210}$$

or 1,037,210

56.
$$3906$$
$$\times\ 550$$
$$\overline{195300}$$
$$1953000$$
$$\overline{2148300}$$

or 2,148,300

58.
$$333$$
$$\times\ 34$$
$$\overline{1332}$$
$$9990$$
$$\overline{11322}$$

or 11,322

60.
$$4200$$
$$\times\ 223$$
$$\overline{12600}$$
$$84000$$
$$840000$$
$$\overline{936600}$$

or 936,600

62. Twice 45,000 is

$$\begin{array}{r} 45{,}000 \\ \times\ 2 \\ \hline 90{,}000 \end{array}$$

64. First multiply without dollars

$$\begin{array}{r} 54 \\ \times\ 50 \\ \hline 2700 \end{array}$$ The product of 54 and \$50 is \$2700.

66. First determine 16 times 8. Then multiply the result by 22.

$$\begin{array}{r} \overset{4}{16} \\ \times\ 8 \\ \hline 128 \end{array}\qquad \begin{array}{r} 128 \\ \times\ 22 \\ \hline 256 \\ 2560 \\ \hline 2816 \end{array}$$

16 times 8 times 22 is 2816.

68. Multiply 35 by 8:

$$\begin{array}{r} \overset{4}{35} \\ \times\ 8 \\ \hline 280 \end{array}$$

Sonya earns \$280.

70. First find the total number of mail pieces each week. The average family $18+3+1=22$ pieces per week. Given 52 weeks in a year, the total amount of mail is

$$\begin{array}{r} 22 \\ \times\ 52 \\ \hline 44 \\ 1100 \\ \hline 1144 \end{array}$$ The average family receives 1144 pieces of mail per year.

72. The Bookworm sold 125 dictionaries at \$18 apiece for a total of $\$18\times125=\$2250$.

74. Over 30 days, using 33 gallons per day, the average family will use $30\times33=990$ gallons of water.

76. a. If a wallpaper hanger can hang 110 square feet per hour then he can hang $7\times110=770$ square feet in 7 hours.

   b. From part a., one paper hanger can hang 770 square feet of paper per day, assuming a 7-hour day. Over a 5-day week, one paper hanger can then hang $5\times770=3850$ square feet per week. Since there are 3 paper hangers, the total amount of paper they can hang in a 5-day week is $3\times3850=11{,}550$ square feet.

78. a. The number of square feet in an NCAA or NBA court is

$$\begin{array}{r} 94 \\ \times\ 50 \\ \hline 4700 \end{array}$$ or 4700 square feet.

   b. The number of square feet in a high school court is

$$\begin{array}{r} 84 \\ \times\ 50 \\ \hline 4200 \end{array}$$ or 4200 square feet.

   c. The difference in square feet of a NCAA/NBA and high school court is

$$\begin{array}{r} 4700 \\ -\ 4200 \\ \hline 500 \end{array}$$ or 500 square feet.

80. From the graph, one acre was worth \$1970 in 2005. The value of 260 acres is found by multiplying:

$$\begin{array}{r} 1970 \\ \times\ 260 \\ \hline 118200 \\ 394000 \\ \hline 512200 \end{array}$$ A 260-acre farm was worth \$512,200.

82. In 1997, a 100-acre farm was worth $100 \times \$1270 = \$127,000$. In 2002, the same farm was worth $100 \times \$1650 = \$165,000$. So the 1997 value was $\$165,000 - \$127,000 = \$38,000$ less than the 2002 value.

Cumulative Skills Review

2. The digit in the hundreds place of 9228 is 2. The digit to the right is a 2 which is less than 5. To round to the hundreds place, leave the 2 in the hundreds place as is and zero out the 2 and 8 to the right to get 9200.

4.
$$\begin{array}{r} {}^{7}\cancel{8}\,{}^{13}\cancel{3} \\ -\ 1\ 9 \\ \hline 6\ 4 \end{array}$$

6. The phrase "decreased by" implies subtraction. The result is 387. The computation is shown below.

$$\begin{array}{r} {}^{4}\cancel{5}\,{}^{10}\cancel{1}\,{}^{12}\cancel{2} \\ -\ 1\ 2\ 5 \\ \hline 3\ 8\ 7 \end{array}$$

8. Tim loaded a total of $48 + 43 = 91$ cases.

10. Subtracting the credits earned so far from the number needed gives

$$\begin{array}{r} 64 \\ -\ 22 \\ \hline 42 \end{array}$$

so Sandy needs 42 more credits.

Section 1.5   Dividing Whole Numbers

Concept Check

2. In a division problem, the number being divided is called the dividend .

4. The result of dividing numbers is called the quotient .

6. The quotient of any number and one is the number itself.

8. The quotient of zero and any nonzero number is zero .

10. The number that remains after division is complete is called the remainder .

Guide Problems

12. $64 \div 64 = \underline{1}$

The result is 1 because and the quotient of any nonzero number with itself is always 1.

14. $\dfrac{42}{0} = \underline{\text{undefined}}$

The quotient of any number and 0 is undefined.

16. $91 \div 1 = 91$
Any number divided by one results in that number.

18. $34 \div 34 = 1$
Any number divided by itself results in 1.

20. $0 \div 23 = 0$
Zero divided by any nonzero number is 0.

22. $13 \div 0$
Division by 0 is *undefined*.

24. $\dfrac{49}{0}$
Division by 0 is *undefined*.

26. $\dfrac{0}{29} = 0$
Zero divided by any nonzero number is 0.

28. $31\overline{)0}$ with 0 above — Zero divided by any nonzero number is 0.

30. $0\overline{)93}$ Division by 0 is *undefined*.

Guide Problems

32.
$$15\overline{)50}$$
with 3 above, 45 below

because there are three 15s in 50. Note the problem illustrates one step in the division process and is not a complete division.

34.
$$13\overline{)616} \quad 47\ R\ 5$$
$$\underline{52}$$
$$96$$
$$\underline{91}$$
$$5$$
Since 13 cannot divide 5, 5 is the remainder.

In Problems 36 through 66 division problems that are stated vertically or with a fraction bar are rewritten as long division problems for solving. If the division is straightforward as in problem 35, then the long division format is not used.

36. $21 \div 7 = 3$

38.
$$3\overline{)66} \quad 22$$

40.
$$67\overline{)804} \quad 12$$
$$\underline{67}$$
$$134$$
$$\underline{134}$$

42.
$$32\overline{)544} \quad 17$$
$$\underline{32}$$
$$224$$
$$\underline{224}$$

44. $\begin{array}{r} 71 \\ 46{\overline{\smash{\big)}\,3266}} \\ \underline{322} \\ 46 \\ \underline{46} \end{array}$

46. $\begin{array}{r} 434 \\ 12{\overline{\smash{\big)}\,5208}} \\ \underline{48} \\ 40 \\ \underline{36} \\ 48 \\ \underline{48} \end{array}$

48. $\begin{array}{r} 1000 \\ 1000{\overline{\smash{\big)}\,1000000}} \\ \underline{1000} \end{array}$

50. $\begin{array}{r} 9 \ R \ 5 \\ 9{\overline{\smash{\big)}\,86}} \\ \underline{81} \\ 5 \end{array}$

52. $\begin{array}{r} 12 \ R \ 3 \\ 8{\overline{\smash{\big)}\,99}} \\ \underline{8} \\ 19 \\ \underline{16} \\ 3 \end{array}$

54. $\begin{array}{r} 13 \ R \ 21 \\ 37{\overline{\smash{\big)}\,502}} \\ \underline{37} \\ 132 \\ \underline{111} \\ 21 \end{array}$

56. $\begin{array}{r} 52 \ R \ 9 \\ 16{\overline{\smash{\big)}\,841}} \\ \underline{80} \\ 41 \\ \underline{32} \\ 9 \end{array}$

58. $\begin{array}{r} 19 \ R \ 5 \\ 21{\overline{\smash{\big)}\,404}} \\ \underline{21} \\ 194 \\ \underline{189} \\ 5 \end{array}$

60. $\begin{array}{r} 55 \ R \ 3 \\ 11{\overline{\smash{\big)}\,608}} \\ \underline{55} \\ 58 \\ \underline{55} \\ 3 \end{array}$

62. $\begin{array}{r} 7 \ R \ 1 \\ 63{\overline{\smash{\big)}\,442}} \\ \underline{441} \\ 1 \end{array}$

64. $\begin{array}{r} 33 \ R \ 153 \\ 183{\overline{\smash{\big)}\,6192}} \\ \underline{549} \\ 702 \\ \underline{549} \\ 153 \end{array}$

66. $\begin{array}{r} 24 \ R \ 45 \\ 121{\overline{\smash{\big)}\,2949}} \\ \underline{242} \\ 529 \\ \underline{484} \\ 45 \end{array}$

68. $\begin{array}{r} 299 \\ 4{\overline{\smash{\big)}\,1196}} \\ \underline{8} \\ 39 \\ \underline{36} \\ 36 \\ \underline{36} \end{array}$

70. $\begin{array}{r} 400 \ R \ 10 \\ 19{\overline{\smash{\big)}\,7610}} \\ \underline{76} \\ 10 \end{array}$

72. Use long division.

$\begin{array}{r} 91 \\ 4{\overline{\smash{\big)}\,364}} \\ \underline{36} \\ 4 \\ \underline{4} \end{array}$

The quotient of 364 and 4 is 91.

74. 2380 trees are divided among 35 acres. Dividing

$\begin{array}{r} 68 \\ 35{\overline{\smash{\big)}\,2380}} \\ \underline{210} \\ 280 \\ \underline{280} \end{array}$

gives 68 trees per acre.

76. Determine the number of times
    36 goes into 9000.

$$
\begin{array}{r}
250 \\
36\overline{)9000} \\
72 \\
\overline{180} \\
\underline{180}
\end{array}
$$

The order requires 250 cases.

78. a. $22,464 divided by 468 is

$$
\begin{array}{r}
48 \\
468\overline{)22464} \\
1872 \\
\overline{3744} \\
\underline{3744}
\end{array}
$$

The average was $48 per transaction.

b. $22,464 divided by 6 is

$$
\begin{array}{r}
3744 \\
6\overline{)22464} \\
18 \\
\overline{44} \\
42 \\
\overline{26} \\
24 \\
\overline{24} \\
24
\end{array}
$$

The average was $3744 per day.

80. The insurance rates for 2000 and 2001 were $687 and $723 dollars respectively. The average for the two years is found by adding these amounts, $687 + $723 = $1410 and then dividing by 2, $1410 ÷ 2 = $705.

82. The rates for 2002 through 2005 were $784, $855, $868, and $926. When rounded to the nearest ten, these four values become $780, $860, $870 and $930 respectively. Find their sum $780 + $860 + $870 + $930 = $3440 and divide by four, $3440 ÷ 4 = $860. The average is $860.

Cumulative Skills Review

2.
$$
\begin{array}{r}
\overset{8}{\cancel{9}}\,\overset{16}{\cancel{6}} \\
-\ 2\ 8 \\
\hline
6\ 8
\end{array}
$$

4. The hundreds digit in 1586 is 5. The 8 to the right indicates to round the 5 up to 6 and 0 the digits to the right to get 1600.

6.
$$
\begin{array}{r}
2200 \\
\times\quad 3 \\
\hline
6600
\end{array}
$$

8. The number 8965 has the digit 8 in the thousands period and the digits 965 in the ones period. The word form is "eight thousand, nine hundred sixty-five."

10. There are 19 rows at 11 seats per row, so the total number of seats is $19 \times 11 = 209$.

Section 1.6   Evaluating Exponential Expressions and Applying Order of Operations

Concept Check

2. In exponential notation, the factor that is repeatedly multiplied is called the base .

4. In the expression 10^6, the number 10 is known as the base .

6. Write 5^4 in word form. "five to the fourth power"

8. The result of raising a number to the first power is the number itself.

10. For each of the following, which operation is performed first according to the order of operations?

    a.   addition or division?   division

    b.   evaluate exponential expressions or subtraction?   exponents

    c.   multiplication or operations within parentheses?   operations within parentheses

Guide Problems

12. $4 \cdot 4 = \underline{4^2}$

     The factor being multiplied
     repeatedly is 4 so 4 is the
     base in exponential notation.
     There are two factors of 4 so
     the exponent is 2.

14. $12 \cdot 12 \cdot 12 = 12^{\underline{3}}$

     The base is 12. There are three
     factors of 12 in the product so
     the exponent is 3.

16. $\underline{15} \cdot \underline{15} \cdot \underline{15} \cdot \underline{15} = 15^4$

     The exponential notation 15^4
     means a product consisting
     of four factors of 15.

18. $6 \cdot 6 \cdot 6 \cdot 4 = 6^{\underline{3}} \cdot 4$

     The product on the left consists
     of three factors of 6 and one factor
     of 4. Thus a base of 6 goes with
     the exponent of 3. Remember, even
     though there is one factor of 4, we do
     not write 4^1 since an exponent of 1 is
     implied.

20. $8 \cdot 8 \cdot 8 \cdot 8 \cdot 8$
     There are five factors of 8. So 8
     is the base and 5 is the exponent.
     Exponential notation: 8^5
     Word form: "eight to the fifth power"

22. $4 \cdot 4 \cdot 4 \cdot 4 \cdot 4 \cdot 4 \cdot 4 \cdot 4$
     Exponential notation: 4^8
     Word form: "four to the
     eighth power"

24. $12 \cdot 12$
     Exponential notation: 12^2
     Word form: "twelve to the
     second power" or
     "twelve squared"

26. $7 \cdot 7 \cdot 7 \cdot 7 \cdot 7 \cdot 7 \cdot 7$
     Exponential notation: 7^7
     Word form: "seven to the
     seventh power"

28. $2 \cdot 2 \cdot 2 \cdot 2 \cdot 6 \cdot 6 \cdot 6$

There are four factors of 2 forming 2^4 and three factors of 6 forming 6^3.

The product can be written as $2^4 \cdot 6^3$.

30. $2 \cdot 5 \cdot 5 \cdot 6 \cdot 9 \cdot 9$ or $2 \cdot 5^2 \cdot 6 \cdot 9^2$ 32. $2 \cdot 2 \cdot 5 \cdot 7 \cdot 7 \cdot 7$ or $2^2 \cdot 5 \cdot 7^3$ 34. $3 \cdot 8 \cdot 20 \cdot 20$ or $3 \cdot 8 \cdot 20^2$

Guide Problems

36. $8^1 = \underline{8}$ because a number raised to the first power is always equals the number.

38. $2^5 = \underline{2} \cdot \underline{2} \cdot \underline{2} \cdot \underline{2} \cdot \underline{2} = \underline{32}$ The base is 2 so each factor is equal to 2. The result is 32 since $2^5 = 2 \cdot 2 \cdot 2 \cdot 2 \cdot 2 = 4 \cdot 2 \cdot 2 \cdot 2$ $= 8 \cdot 2 \cdot 2 = 16 \cdot 2 = 32.$

40. $11^0 = 1$

42. $21^1 = 21$

44. $1^{12} = 1$ (1 to any power is 1)

46. $6^2 = 6 \cdot 6 = 36$

48. $7^2 = 49$

50. $5^4 = 5 \cdot 5 \cdot 5 \cdot 5 = 25 \cdot 5 \cdot 5$ $= 125 \cdot 5 = 625$

52. $2^7 = 2 \cdot 2 \cdot 2 \cdot 2 \cdot 2 \cdot 2 \cdot 2$ $= 128$

54. $6^3 = 6 \cdot 6 \cdot 6 = 36 \cdot 6 = 216$

56. $350^1 = 350$

58. $3^5 = 3 \cdot 3 \cdot 3 \cdot 3 \cdot 3 = 9 \cdot 3 \cdot 3 \cdot 3$ $= 27 \cdot 3 \cdot 3 = 81 \cdot 3 = 243$

60. $2050^0 = 1$

62. $25^2 = 25 \cdot 25 = 625$

Guide Problems

64. Simplify $(25 + 92) \div 13$.
$(25 + 92) \div 13$
$\underline{117} \div 13$ Simplify the expression in parentheses first.
$\underline{9}$ No exponents so divide next.

66. Simplify $3^4 - (3 \cdot 24)$.
$3^4 - (3 \cdot 24)$
$3^4 - \underline{72}$ Evaluate within parentheses first.
$\underline{81} - \underline{72}$ Evaluate exponential expressions next.
$\underline{9}$ Lastly, subtract.

In problems 68 through 94, the order of operations is applied to evaluate each given expression. First, expressions within grouping symbols such as ( ) and [ ] are evaluated. Remember, when a fraction bar appears in an expression, as in problem 80, treat the numerator as if it was contained between grouping symbols and similarly with the denominator. Second, evaluate any exponential expressions. Third, evaluate any multiplications and division as they appear from left to right. Fourth, evaluate any additions and subtractions as they appear from left to right.

68. $(25 + 5) - 18$
$30 - 18$
12

70. $7 \cdot 3 + 4 \cdot 3$
$21 + 12$
33

72. $(18 + 32) \div 5$
$50 \div 5$
10

74. $8+0\div4+2^4$
$8+0\div3+16$
$8+0+16$
$8+16$
24

76. $4+10^2\div50$
$4+100\div50$
$4+2$
6

78. $63\div9\cdot4-2+10$
$7\cdot4-2+10$
$28-2+10$
$26+10$
36

80. $\dfrac{5+3^2-2^2}{10\div5}$
$\dfrac{5+9-4}{2}$
$\dfrac{14-4}{2}$
$\dfrac{10}{2}=5$

82. $18\div3^2\cdot5-2(8-3)$
$18\div3^2\cdot5-2\cdot5$
$18\div9\cdot5-2\cdot5$
$2\cdot5-2\cdot5$
$10-10$
0

84. $15\cdot9-(4+1)^3$
$15\cdot9-5^3$
$15\cdot9-125$
$135-125$
10

86. $100+(3+5)^2-50$
$100+8^2-50$
$100+64-50$
$164-50$
114

88. $4^2+4^3+4^0\cdot16$
$16+64+1\cdot16$
$16+64+16$
$80+16$
96

90. $(15^2+15^2)\div50$
$(225+225)\div50$
$450\div50$
9

92. $[(5-3)\div2]+6\cdot3$
$[2\div2]+6\cdot3$
$1+6\cdot3$
$1+18$
19

94. $\dfrac{16\div2^2}{17-15}+88\div(38-3^3)$
$\dfrac{16\div2^2}{17-15}+88\div(38-27)$
$\dfrac{16\div2^2}{17-15}+88\div11$
$\dfrac{16\div4}{2}+88\div11$
$\dfrac{4}{2}+88\div11$
$2+88\div11$
$2+8=10$

96. The area is given by $A=s^2=(12\text{ miles})^2=12\cdot12$ square miles $=144$ square miles.

98. a. The windows are squares with $s=25$ inches. The area of one such window is
$A=s^2=(25\text{ inches})^2=625$ square inches.

b. If there are 60 such windows, the total area, using the result of part a., is 60×625 square inches or 37,500
square inches.

c. From b., 37,500 square inches of tinting material are needed. If each roll contains 2500 square inches then $37,500\div2500$ rolls are needed. Performing the division gives 15 rolls as the necessary number.

Cumulative Skills Review

2.
$$
\begin{array}{r}
89 \\
16\overline{)1424} \\
\underline{128} \\
144 \\
\underline{144} \\
0
\end{array}
$$

4. The average of 54, 36, and 24 is
$$
\frac{54 + 36 + 24}{3} = \frac{114}{3} = 38.
$$

6.
$$
\begin{array}{r}
1563 \\
3\overline{)4689} \\
\underline{3} \\
16 \\
\underline{15} \\
18 \\
\underline{18} \\
9 \\
\underline{9}
\end{array}
$$

8. "One hundred sixty-two thousand, fifty-five" in standard notation is 162,055.

10. The cost of each lamp is found by dividing
$$
\begin{array}{r}
51 \\
78\overline{)3978} \\
\underline{390} \\
78 \\
78
\end{array}
$$
Each lamp cost $51.

Section 1.7   Solving Application Problems

Concept Check

2. The phrase *decreased by* indicates the operation of   subtraction .

4. *Quotient* and *per* are words used to indicate   division .

6. List the steps for solving application problems.

   1.   Read and understand the problem .

   2.   Take inventory .

   3.   Translate the problem .

   4.   Solve the problem .

   5.   Check the solution .

8. *Understand the situation* You are given previous employment information and asked to find the current employment. *Take inventory* The knowns are the previous employment and the number of new hires. The unknown is the current number of employees. *Translate the problem* The word "hired" indicates we add the change in employees to the previous employee count. *Solve the problem* The company currently employs $1342 + 325 = 1667$ people.

10. You know the number of tablets taken at a time (2), the number of times a day (4), and the number of days (12). The words/phrases *times* and *at a time* say multiplication is used. The prescription needs to be for $2 \times 4 \times 12 = 8 \times 12 = 96$ pills.

12. You know the price of the boat and the price of the trailer. The keyword *and* in *boat and trailer* says the costs should be added. The total spent by Bob is $\$15,493 + \$1322 = \$16,815$.

14. a. 20 acres producing 225 pounds per acre will yield a total of $20 \times 225 = 4500$ pounds of strawberries.

    b. Given 4500 pounds (from part a.) *at* $3 per pound, multiply $4500 \times 3 = 13,500$ to find that Max would make $13,500.

    c. From part b., Max can make $13,500 in one growing season. Given 3 growing seasons in a year, he can make $\$13,500 \times 3 = \$40,500$.

16. Given 660 miles total on 55 gallons, the number of miles *per* gallon is found by dividing $660 \div 55 = 12$. The truck can travel 12 miles on one gallon of gas.

18. a. Round 495, 239, 290, 509, and 679 to 500, 200, 300, 500, and 700. An estimate for the total number of pints sold is $500 + 200 + 300 + 500 + 700 = 2200$ pints.

    b. The actual number is $495 + 239 + 290 + 509 + 679 = 2212$ pints.

20. First, determine the number of calories burned per week by doing 1 hour of aerobics. The table says 171 calories are burned for each 30 minutes. Since 1 hour consists of two 30 minute periods, exercising for 1 hour burns $2 \times 171 = 342$. Second, determine the number of calories burned in a year. At 342 calories per week and 52 weeks in a year, the total calories is $342 \times 52 = 17,784$.

22. The phrase how many more indicates a difference and hence subtraction is required. First, consider each activity separately. Jogging for 3 hours will burn $6 \times 338 = 2028$ calories since there 6 thirty minute periods in 3 hours. Walking briskly for 4 hours (8 thirty minute periods) will burn $8 \times 150 = 1200$ calories. The difference is $2028 - 1200 = 828$ so jogging 3 hours burns 828 calories than walking 4 hours.

24. The first part of the problem is determine the total amount to be paid. The total is the bill plus the tip or $\$157 + \$25 = \$182$. The bill *per* person is $\$182 \div 7 = \$26$.

26. First, add the new purchases to Carla's previous balance of $391. $\$391 + \$39 + \$144 + \$219 + \$78 = \$871$ which represents Carla's balance when the bill arrives. Next, subtract the payment to get $\$871 - \$550 = \$321$. Carla's new balance is $321.

28. Start by determining the total expenses for June by adding the individual expense amounts.
    $$\$15,639 + \$1960 + \$909 + \$548 + \$2300 + \$2150 = \$23,506$$
    If this represents one months expenses, then one year would total $12 \times \$23,506 = \$282,702$.

30. To compute miles per gallon, we must divide total miles by gallons used. First, determine the miles traveled by computing the difference in odometer readings. James rode $5689 - 5339 = 350$ miles. He used 14 gallons so he got $350 \div 14 = 25$ miles per gallon.

32. In the second half, Duane scored $2 \cdot 11 = 22$ points. His total points for both halves is then $11 + 22 = 33$.

34. Computing an average first involves addition and then division. Sam's total score for three games is $165 + 188 + 214 = 567$. His average score is $567 \div 3 = 189$.

36. a. The amount of coal in 9 weeks, *at* 7 days per week, *at* 4 shifts per day, *at* 24 tons per shift is $9 \cdot 7 \cdot 4 \cdot 24 = 6048$ tons.

   b. First, compute the amount of coal extracted in one week. The answer to part a. is the amount extracted in 9 weeks so dividing by 9 yields $6048 \div 9 = 672$ tons per week. there are 52 weeks in a year so over one year $52 \times 672 = 34,944$ tons would be extracted.

38. First, compute the total cost of leasing a Focus and leasing an Explorer. The Focus will cost $36 \times \$165 = \$5940$ while the Explorer will cost $36 \times \$259 = \$9324$. The difference is $\$9324 - \$5940 = \$3384$.

40. First, compute the amount saved on three Ford Explorers. The sale price results in a savings of $\$26,830 - \$19,699 = \$7,131$ on *each* car. The savings on three Explorers is $3 \times \$7,131 = \$21,393$. Similarly, the savings on one Expedition is $\$32,315 - \$24,496 = \$7819$ so the savings on four is $4 \times \$7819 = \$31,276$. The total savings is $\$21,393 + \$31,276 = \$52,669$.

Cumulative Skills Review

2. $3 \cdot 9^2 + \dfrac{[2(18-3)]^2}{9}$

   $3 \cdot 9^2 + \dfrac{[2 \cdot 15]^2}{9}$

   $3 \cdot 9^2 + \dfrac{30^2}{9}$

   $3 \cdot 81 + \dfrac{900}{9}$

   $243 + 100$

   343

4. $6 \cdot 6 \cdot 7 \cdot 7 \cdot 7 = 6^2 \cdot 7^3$

6. In 24,339 the 4 is in the rightmost place of the thousands period and so is in the thousands place.

8. Area of a square with side s is given by $A = s^2$. Here $s = 12$ feet. so
   $A = (12 \text{ feet})^2 = 12 \cdot 12$ square feet
   $A = 144$ square feet

10. The phrase "less than" means subtraction so the answer is $932 - 542 = 390$ as computed below:

$$
\begin{array}{r}
{}^{8}\cancel{9}\,{}^{13}\cancel{3}\,2 \\
-\ 5\ 4\ 2 \\
\hline
3\ 9\ 0
\end{array}
$$

Chapter 1 Numerical Facts of Life

The personal balance sheet for Todd and Claudia is filled in below. Next to each entry, in the rightmost column, is either the word "given" or the arithmetic operation used to arrive at the entry. The word "given" indicates that the value entered was given in the statement of the problem as one of the couple's assets or liabilities. All values represent amounts in dollars.

ASSETS			
CURRENT ASSETS			
Checking account	3640		Given
Savings account	4720		Given
Certificates of deposit	18,640		Given
Total Current Assets		27,000	$= 3640 + 4720 + 18,640$
LONG-TERM ASSETS			
Investments			
Retirement plans	67,880		Given
Stocks and bonds	25,550		Given
Mutual funds	15,960		Given
Personal			
Home	225,500		Given
Automobiles	32,300		Given
Personal property	6400		Given
Other	12,100		Given (sailboat)
Other	7630		Given (electronics)
Total Long-Term Assets		393,320	$= 67,880 + 25,550 + 15,960 + 225,500 +$ $32,300 + 6400 + 12,100 + 7630$
TOTAL ASSETS		$420,320	= Total Current Assets + Total Long-Term Assets $= 27,000 + 393,320$

LIABILITIES			
CURRENT LIABILITIES			
Store charge accounts	1940		Given
Credit card accounts	8660		Given
Other current debt	0		Given
Total Current Liabilities		10,600	$= 1940 + 8660 + 0$
LONG-TERM LIABILITIES			
Home mortgage	165,410		Given
Automobile loans	13,200		Given
Other loans	4580		Given (boat loan)
Total Long-Term Liabilities		183,190	$= 165,410 + 13,200 + 4580$
TOTAL LIABILITIES		$193,790	= Total Current Liabilities + Total Long-Term Liabilities $= 10,600 + 183,190$

NET WORTH			
Total Assets	420,320		From the assets table
Total Liabilities	− 193,790		From the liabilities table
NET WORTH		$226,430	= Total Assets − Total Liabilities
			= 420,320 − 193,790

Chapter 1 Review Exercises

1. In the number 5**4**,220, the indicated digit 4 is in the *thousands* place (the rightmost digit in the thousands period.)

2. In the number **7**27, the indicated digit 7 is in the *hundreds* place (the leftmost digit in the ones period.)

3. In the number 7**8**,414,645, the indicated digit 8 is in the *millions* place (the rightmost digit in the millions period.)

4. In the number 334**1**, the indicated digit 1 is in the *ones* place (the rightmost digit in the ones period.)

5. In the number 35,6**8**6, the indicated digit 8 is in the *tens* place (the middle digit in the ones period.)

6. In the number 18,2**8**6,719, the indicated digit 8 is in the *ten thousands* place (the middle digit in the thousands period.)

7. 336
   standard notation: 336
   word form: three hundred thirty-six

8. 8475
   standard notation: 8,475 or 8475
   word form: eight thousand, four hundred seventy-five

9. 784341
   standard notation: 784,341
   word form: seven hundred eighty-four thousand, three hundred forty-one

10. 380633
    standard notation: 380,633
    word form: three hundred eighty thousand, six hundred thirty-three

11. 62646
    standard notation: 62,646
    word form: sixty-two thousand, six hundred forty-six

12. 1326554
    standard notation: 1,326,554
    word form: one million, three hundred twenty-six thousand, five hundred fifty-four

13. 10102
    standard notation: 10,102
    word form: ten thousand, one hundred two

14. 6653634
    standard notation: 6,653,634
    word form: six million, six hundred fifty-three thousand, six hundred thirty-four

15. 4022407508
    standard notation: 4,022,407,508
    word form: four billion, twenty-two million, four hundred seven thousand, five hundred eight

16. The expanded form of 23 is $20 + 3$ or 2 tens + 3 ones.

17. The expanded form of 532 is $500 + 30 + 2$ or 5 hundreds + 3 tens + 2 ones.

18. The expanded form of 109 is $100+9$ or
1 hundred + 9 ones.

19. The expanded form of 26,385 is or
$20,000+6000+300+80+5$ or
2 ten thousands + 6 thousands +
3 hundreds + 8 tens + 5 ones

20. The expanded form of 2,148 is
$2000+100+40+8$ or
2 thousands + 1 hundred + 4 tens +
8 ones

21. The expanded form of 1,928,365 is
$1,000,000+900,000+20,000+8000+300+60+5$
or
1 million + 9 hundred thousands + 2 ten thousands +
8 thousands + 3 hundreds + 6 tens + 5 ones

22. 363,484

The indicated place,
thousands, contains
a 3. Since a 4 is to
the right, round down
to 363,000.

23. 18,136

The indicated place,
tens, contains a 3.
Since a 6 is to the
right, round up to
18,140.

24. 86,614

The indicated place,
ten thousands, contains
an 8. Since a 6 is to the
right, round up to
90,000.

25. 601,927

The indicated place,
hundreds, contains
a 9. Since a 2 is to
the right, round down
to 601,900.

26. 4,829,387

The indicated place,
millions, contains a 4.
Since an 8 is to the
right, round up to
5,000,000.

27. 3,146,844

The indicated place,
hundred thousands,
contains a 1. Since a 4
is to the right, round
down to 3,100,000.

28. 81,084

The indicated place,
tens, contains
an 8. Since a 4 is to
the right, round down
to 81,080.

29. 196,140

The indicated place,
thousands, contains a 6.
Since a 1 is to the
right, round down to
196,000.

30. 42,862,785

The indicated place,
ten millions, contains
a 4. Since a 2 is to the
right, round down to
40,000,000.

31.
$$\begin{array}{r} 30 \\ + 59 \\ \hline 89 \end{array}$$

32.
$$\begin{array}{r} \overset{1}{4}5 \\ + 68 \\ \hline 113 \end{array}$$

33.
$$\begin{array}{r} 319 \\ + 60 \\ \hline 379 \end{array}$$

34.
$$\begin{array}{r} \overset{1}{9}16 \\ + 35 \\ \hline 951 \end{array}$$

35.
$$\begin{array}{r} 414 \\ + 181 \\ \hline 595 \end{array}$$

36.
$$\begin{array}{r} \overset{1}{3}60 \\ 971 \\ + 964 \\ \hline 2295 \end{array}$$

37.
$$\begin{array}{r} \overset{1}{4}3,\overset{1}{8}14 \\ + 71,658 \\ \hline 115,472 \end{array}$$

38.
$$\begin{array}{r} \overset{1}{1}\overset{1}{7}00 \\ 130 \\ 421 \\ 81 \\ + 237 \\ \hline 2569 \end{array}$$

39.
```
      ¹ ¹
       59
      294
     1100
   +   10
   ──────
     1463
```

40.
```
       ¹
      853
      121
        0
   + 2912
   ──────
     3886
```

41.
```
      ¹
       25
        0
       53
      180
   +    0
   ──────
      258
```

42.
```
      ¹
        9
        0
       71
        0
   +  312
   ──────
      392
```

43.
```
     67
   −  3
   ────
     64
```

44.
```
     16
   −  7
   ────
      9
```

45.
```
     89
   − 62
   ────
     27
```

46.
```
     55
   − 32
   ────
     23
```

47.
```
    695
   − 12
   ────
    683
```

48.
```
    386
   − 24
   ────
    362
```

49.
```
    649
   − 226
   ─────
    423
```

50.
```
    867
   − 253
   ─────
    614
```

51.
```
    6 12 12 12
    7̸ 3̸ 3̸ 2̸
   −  4 9 9
   ─────────
      6 8 3 3
```

52.
```
    1565
   − 360
   ─────
    1205
```

53.
```
       9
    2 1̸0 10
    4̸ 3̸ 0̸ 0̸
   −    3 1
   ─────────
      4 2 6 9
```

54.
```
          9
    6 14 1̸0 10
    7̸ 5̸ 0̸ 0̸
   −    9 7 3
   ──────────
      6 5 2 7
```

55.
```
     64
   ×  1
   ────
     64
```

56.
```
     72
   ×  0
   ────
      0
```

57.
```
      63
   ×  25
   ─────
     315
    1260
   ─────
    1575
```

58.
```
      78
   ×  55
   ─────
     390
    3900
   ─────
    4290
```

59.
```
      39
   ×  95
   ─────
     195
    3510
   ─────
    3705
```

60.
```
     342
   ×  37
   ──────
    2394
   10260
   ──────
   12654
```
   or 12,654

61.
```
     318
   ×  40
   ──────
   12,720
```

62.
```
     111
   ×  55
   ─────
     555
    5550
   ─────
    6105
```

63.
```
      18
   ×  45
   ─────
      90
     720
   ─────
     810
```

64.
```
     270
   ×  64
   ──────
    1 080
   16,200
   ──────
   17,280
```

65.
```
     815
   ×  60
   ──────
   48,900
```

66.
```
      2900
   ×   328
   ───────
    23,200
    58,000
   870,000
   ───────
   951,200
```

67. $48 \div 0$ undefined

Division by 0 is always undefined.

68. $0 \div 63 = 0$

0 divided by any nonzero number is 0.

69. $\dfrac{46}{1} = 46$

Dividing any number by 1 gives the number.

70. $\dfrac{79}{79} = 1$

Dividing any nonzero number by itself gives 1.

71.
$$\begin{array}{r} 16 \\ 49\overline{)784} \\ \underline{49} \\ 294 \\ \underline{294} \end{array}$$

72.
$$\begin{array}{r} 21 \\ 42\overline{)882} \\ \underline{84} \\ 42 \\ \underline{42} \end{array}$$

73.
$$\begin{array}{r} 11 \; R\; 2 \\ 4\overline{)46} \\ \underline{4} \\ 6 \\ \underline{4} \\ 2 \end{array}$$

74.
$$\begin{array}{r} 21 \; R\; 26 \\ 29\overline{)635} \\ \underline{58} \\ 55 \\ \underline{29} \\ 26 \end{array}$$

75.
$$\begin{array}{r} 20 \; R\; 4 \\ 14\overline{)284} \\ \underline{28} \\ 4 \end{array}$$
$\dfrac{284}{14}$ is 20 R 4

76.
$$\begin{array}{r} 34 \; R\; 4 \\ 182\overline{)6192} \\ \underline{546} \\ 732 \\ \underline{728} \\ 4 \end{array}$$
$6192 \div 182$ is 34 R 4

77.
$$\begin{array}{r} 4 \; R\; 2 \\ 11\overline{)46} \\ \underline{44} \\ 2 \end{array}$$

78.
$$\begin{array}{r} 31 \; R\; 2 \\ 3\overline{)95} \\ \underline{9} \\ 5 \\ \underline{3} \\ 2 \end{array}$$

79. $7 \cdot 7 \cdot 7 \cdot 7 = 7^4$
Since there are 4
factors of 7.

80. $13 \cdot 13 \cdot 13 = 13^3$
Since there are 3
factors of 13.

81. $17 = 17^1$

82. $5 \cdot 5 \cdot 5 \cdot 5 \cdot 5 \cdot 5$
$= 5^6$

83. $3 \cdot 3 \cdot 5 \cdot 5 \cdot 5 \cdot 11 \cdot 11$
$= 3^2 \cdot 5^3 \cdot 11^2$

84. $5 \cdot 5 \cdot 7 \cdot 17 \cdot 17 \cdot 19$
$= 5^2 \cdot 7 \cdot 17^2 \cdot 19$

85. $2 \cdot 2 \cdot 2 \cdot 2 \cdot 23 \cdot 23 \cdot 29$
$= 2^4 \cdot 23^2 \cdot 29$

86. $11 \cdot 11 \cdot 11 \cdot 19 \cdot 19$
$= 11^3 \cdot 19^2$

87. $7^2 = 7 \cdot 7 = 49$

88. $2^4 = 2 \cdot 2 \cdot 2 \cdot 2$
$= 4 \cdot 2 \cdot 2$
$= 8 \cdot 2 = 16$

89. $39^1 = 39$

90. $3^5 = 3 \cdot 3 \cdot 3 \cdot 3 \cdot 3$
$= 9 \cdot 3 \cdot 3 \cdot 3$
$= 27 \cdot 3 \cdot 3$
$= 81 \cdot 3$
$= 343$

91. $10^3 = 10 \cdot 10 \cdot 10$
$= 100 \cdot 10$
$= 1000$

92. $66^0 = 1$

Any nonzero number
raised to the 0 power
is 1.

93. $19^2 = 19 \cdot 19$
$= 361$

94. $1^{20} = 1$
1 raised to any
power is 1.

95. $10^6 = 10 \cdot 10 \cdot 10 \cdot 10 \cdot 10 \cdot 10$
$= 1,000,000$

96. $6^3 = 6 \cdot 6 \cdot 6$
    $= 36 \cdot 6$
    $= 216$

97. $0^7 = 0$
    0 raised to any
    power (except 0)
    is 0.

98. $2^9 = 2 \cdot 2 \cdot 2 \cdot 2 \cdot 2 \cdot 2 \cdot 2 \cdot 2 \cdot 2$
    $= 512$

99. $9 + 17 \cdot 20$
    $9 + 340$
    349

100. $34 \div 2 + 9(20 + 5)$
    $34 \div 2 + 9 \cdot 25$
    $17 + 225$
    242

101. $20 \div 2^2 + (5 \cdot 4)$
    $20 \div 2^2 + 20$
    $20 \div 4 + 20$
    $5 + 20$
    25

102. $\dfrac{360 \div 6^2}{35 - 25} + 5^3$
    $\dfrac{360 \div 36}{10} + 5^3$
    $\dfrac{10}{10} + 5^3$
    $\dfrac{10}{10} + 125$
    $1 + 125$
    126

103. $8^2 - (8 - 4)^3$
    $8^2 - 4^3$
    $64 - 64$
    0

104. $5 + \left(\dfrac{300}{12} - 4^2\right)^2$
    $5 + \left(\dfrac{300}{12} - 16\right)^2$
    $5 + \left(25 - 16\right)^2$
    $5 + 9^2$
    $5 + 81$
    86

105. $50 \cdot 8^2 \div (10 + 30)^2$
    $50 \cdot 8^2 \div 40^2$
    $50 \cdot 64 \div 1600$
    $3200 \div 1600$
    2

106. $12 + 2[6 - (5 - 2)]$
    $12 + 2[6 - 3]$
    $12 + 2 \cdot 3$
    $12 + 6$
    18

107. $\dfrac{(4 \cdot 3^2)}{18 - 12} \cdot 10$
    $\dfrac{(4 \cdot 9)}{18 - 12} \cdot 10$
    $\dfrac{36}{18 - 12} \cdot 10$
    $\dfrac{36}{6} \cdot 10$
    $6 \cdot 10$
    60

108. $111{,}000 - 500(12 - 6)^3$
    $111{,}000 - 500 \cdot 6^3$
    $111{,}000 - 500 \cdot 216$
    $111{,}000 - 108{,}000$
    3000

109. $3[100 - 8(4) + 9 \div 3 + 7]$
    $3[100 - 32 + 9 \div 3 + 7]$
    $3[100 - 32 + 3 + 7]$
    $3[68 + 3 + 7]$
    $3[71 + 7]$
    $3[78]$
    234

110. $\dfrac{7^2 - 6^2}{(7 + 6)} + 19$
    $\dfrac{7^2 - 6^2}{13} + 19$
    $\dfrac{49 - 36}{13} + 19$
    $\dfrac{13}{13} + 19$
    $1 + 19$
    20

111. a. The hundreds digit of 453,229 is 2 and it is followed by a 2 so round down to get 453,200 gallons.

   b. The number 453,200 has the digits 453 in the thousands period and 200 in the ones period. The word form is "four hundred fifty-three thousand, two hundred."

112. a. Adding the acreage for each crop, the pasture, and the buildings gives a total of
          $450 + 259 + 812 + 18 + 22 + 6 = 1567$ acres.

      b. Using the total of 1567 acres from part a., if 329 acres are sold the number of acres remaining would be
          $1567 - 329 = 1238$.

113. First compute the total yardage for the holes having a given par.
      Par-3: $6 \times 175 = 1050$ yards   Par-4: $7 \times 228 = 1596$ yards   Par-5: $5 \times 340 = 1700$ yards
      The total yardage for all eighteen holes is $1050 + 1596 + 1700 = 4346$ yards.

114. First, compute the total sales for each type of real estate sold.
      Land: $4 \times \$32,500 = \$130,000$ Condominiums: $1 \times \$55,600 = \$55,600$
      Homes: $\$79,200 + \$96,200 = \$175,400$
      Next, add these amounts $\$130,000 + \$55,600 + \$175,400 = \$361,000$.   Sales totaled $361,000.

115. a. The painting has two sides measuring 22 inches and two sides measuring 14 inches. The perimeter is
          $22 + 22 + 14 + 14 = 72$ inches. At \$3 per inch, the cost of a standard frame would be $72 \times \$3 = \$216$.

      b. From part a., the perimeter is 72 inches. At \$4 per inch, the cost of a deluxe frame would be
          $72 \times \$4 = \$288$. This is $\$288 - \$216 = \$72$ more than the standard frame.

116. a. First note that there are two types of costs. The food cost depends on the number of people who attend
          while the remaining costs are fixed regardless of the number of people who attend. The fixed costs total
          $\$1250 + \$700 + \$328 + \$382 + \$1500 = \$4160$. If 160 people attend at a cost of \$16 per person then the
          total cost of food is $160 \times \$16 = \$2560$. Total cost of the party is $\$4160 + \$2560 = \$6720$.

      b. From part a. the total cost is \$6720, the average cost over 160 people is $\$6720 \div 160 = \$42$ per person.

117. Girls work 8 eight hours and do homework 12 hours for a total of $8 + 12 = 20$ hours per week.

118. Boys exercise 7 hours and work 10 hours for a total of $7 + 10 = 17$ hours per week.

119. In one year girls surf and email a total of $52 \times 17 = 884$ hours while boys use $52 \times 16 = 832$ hours. So girls
      surf and email $884 - 832 = 52$ hours more than boys per year. Another way to see this is to note that in any
      given week girls surf and write emails $17 - 16 = 1$ hour more than boys. Over a year (52 weeks) girls surf
      and write emails 52 hours more than boys.

120. Over 52 weeks girls work a total $52 \times 8 = 416$ hours wile boys work $52 \times 10 = 520$ hours. Thus girls work
      $520 - 416 = 104$ fewer hours than boys.

121. Boys and girls together surf and write emails a total of $16 + 17 = 33$ hours per week. Over a year, the total
      time spent surfing and writing emails would be $52 \times 33 = 1716$. The average among boys and girls is then
      $1716 \div 2 = 858$.

122. The total time per week spent by boys and girls doing homework is $8 + 12 = 20$ hours. The average among
      boys and girls is then $20 \div 2 = 10$.

Chapter 1 Assessment Test

1. In the number 6877, the indicated digit 8 is in the *hundreds* place (the leftmost digit in the hundreds period).

2. In the number 2,336,029, the indicated digit 3 is in the *ten thousands* place (the middle digit in the thousands period).

3. $10,000 + 5000 + 800 + 60 + 2$
standard notation: 15,862
word form: fifteen thousand,
    eight hundred sixty-two

4. $100,000 + 20,000 + 3000 + 500 + 9$
standard notation: 123,509
word form: one hundred twenty-three
    thousand, five hundred nine

5. The expanded form of 475 is $400 + 70 + 5$ or 4 hundreds + 7 tens + 5 ones.

6. The expanded form of 1397 is $1000 + 300 + 90 + 7$ or 1 thousand + 3 hundreds + 9 tens + 7 ones.

7. 34,771 rounded to the nearest thousand is 35, 000. The digit in the thousands place is 4 and the digit to its right is 7 so the thousands place is rounded up to 5 and then by zeros.

8. 6,529,398 rounded to the nearest hundred thousands is 6,500,000. The digit in the hundred thousands place is 5 and the digit to its right is 2 so we round down, leaving the thousands place is alone and following it wit with zeros

9.
```
   463    Simply add column wise.
 + 25
 -----
  488
```

10. Write the addition vertically.
```
   ı ı
  652
    0
  257
+ 576
-----
 1485
```

11.
```
  4 11
  ⸉ ⸉
 - 3 4
 ------
   1 7
```

12. Write vertically and subtract columnwise.
```
  782
 - 41
 ----
  741
```

13.
```
    318
 ×   36
 ------
   1908
   9540
 ------
 11,448
```

14. Write vertically and multiply.
```
    3132
 ×    58
 -------
  25,056
 156,600
 -------
 181,656
```

15.
```
         63
    34)2142
       204
       ----
       102
       102
```

16. $\begin{array}{r} 14 \ R\ 1 \\ 7\overline{)99} \\ 7 \\ \hline 29 \\ 28 \\ \hline 1 \end{array}$

17. $13 \cdot 13 \cdot 13$

Each factor is 13 so 13 is the base. There are three factors so the exponent is 3. Exponential notation is 13^3.

18. $3 \cdot 3 \cdot 5 \cdot 5 \cdot 5 \cdot 5 \cdot 7$
      $3^2 \cdot 5^4 \cdot 7$

19. $6^2 = 6 \cdot 6 = 36$

20. $2^4 = 2 \cdot 2 \cdot 2 \cdot 2 = 4 \cdot 2 \cdot 2 = 8 \cdot 2 = 16$

21. $6 + 7 \cdot 2$
      $6 + 14$
      20

22. $64 \div 2^3 + (5 \cdot 7)$
      $64 \div 2^3 + 35$
      $64 \div 8 + 35$
      $8 + 35$
      43

23.   First determine the number of miles Alice traveled in the two days: $238 + 287 = 525$ miles. The odometer reading would have increased by this amount so add 525 to the original odometer reading to get the new reading. $23,414 + 525 = 23,939$ is the new reading.

24.   Since the amount is being split, use division. Since $2,520,000 \div 14 = 180,000,$ each person receives $180,000.

25.   a. Determine how many times 4 *goes into* 420, that is, divide. Since $420 \div 4 = 105$, there are 105 portions.

      b. 225 meals a night at 7 nights a week is $7 \times 225 = 1575$ meals. Since each meal uses 4 ounces of pasta, this is a total of $4 \times 1575 = 6300$ ounces of pasta. A carton consists of 420 ounces so the number of cartons is $6300 \div 420 = 15$.

26.   a. The rectangular section has two sides of length 150 feet and two sides of 110 feet. The perimeter is $150 + 150 + 110 + 110 = 520$ feet.

      b. The area of the rectangular section is $A = lw = (150 \text{ feet})(110 \text{ feet}) = 150 \cdot 110$ square feet or 16,500 square feet.

Chapter 2   Fractions

Section 2.1   Factors, Prime Factorizations, and Least Common Multiples

Concept Check

2. A __composite__ number is a natural number greater than 1 that has more than two factors (divisors).

4. A factorization of a whole number in which each factor is prime is known as a __prime__ __factorization__ .

6. A __multiple__ of a number is the product of the number and any natural number.

8. The smallest multiple shared by a set of two or more numbers is called the __least__ __common__ __multiple__ or __LCM__ .

Guide Problems

10. The following quotients with 25 as the dividend result in a natural number: $25 \div 1 = 25$, $25 \div 5 = 5$ before factors begin to repeat. The factors of 25 are 1, 5, and 25.

12. Among the natural numbers from 1 to 11, only 1 and 11 divide 11 evenly so the factors of 11 are 1 and 11.

14. Find the factors of 9: $9 \div 1 = 9$, $9 \div 2$ does not divide evenly, $9 \div 3 = 3$. Stop with the last division since there is a repeat factor. The factors of 9 are 1, 3, and 9.

16. The following quotients with 21 as the dividend result in a natural number: $21 \div 1 = 21$, $21 \div 3 = 7$, $21 \div 7 = 3$. Note the factors begin to repeat with the last division. The factors of 21 are 1, 3, 7, and 21.

18. The factors of 41 are 1 and 41 as these are the only natural numbers that divide 41 evenly.

20. The following quotients with 34 as the dividend result in a natural number: $34 \div 1 = 34$, $34 \div 2 = 17$, before factors begin to repeat. The factors of 34 are 1, 2, 17, and 34.

22. Find the factors of 18: $18 \div 1 = 18$, $18 \div 2 = 9$, $18 \div 3 = 6$, $18 \div 6 = 3$ are the quotients that divide evenly. Note the factors begin to repeat with the last division. The factors of 18 are 1, 2, 3, 6, 9, and 18.

24. The factors of 83 are 1 and 83 as these are the only natural numbers that divide 83 evenly.

26. Find the factors of 50: $50 \div 1 = 50$, $50 \div 2 = 25$, $50 \div 5 = 10$, $50 \div 10 = 5$ are the quotients that divide evenly. Note the factors begin to repeat with the last division. The factors of 50 are 1, 2, 5, 10, 25, and 50.

28. Find the factors of 32.

$$32 \div 1 = 32 \qquad 32 \div 2 = 16$$
$32 \div 3$ Does not divide evenly.
$32 \div 4 = 8$
$32 \div 5$ Does not divide evenly.
$32 \div 6$ Does not divide evenly.
$32 \div 7$ Does not divide evenly.
$32 \div 8 = 4$ Factors are repeating. Stop.

The factors of 32 are 1, 2, 4, 8, 16, and 32.

30. Find the factors of 84.

$$84 \div 1 = 84 \qquad 84 \div 2 = 42 \qquad 84 \div 3 = 28$$
$$84 \div 4 = 21 \qquad 84 \div 6 = 14 \qquad 84 \div 7 = 12$$

Division by 5, 8, 9, 10, and 11 does not result in a natural number. Since $84 \div 12 = 7$, the factors are repeating and so the search for factors can stop. The factors of 84 are 1, 2, 3, 4, 6, 7, 12, 14, 21, 28, 42, and 84.

32. The only factors of 31 are 1 and 31, so 31 is a prime number.

34. Since $16 \div 2 = 8$, the number 16 has 8 as a factor and is, therefore, composite. Note any even number greater than two will be divisible by two and must be composite.

36. The only factors of 61 are 1 and 61, so 61 is a prime number.

38. Since 5 divides 95 evenly, $95 \div 5 = 19$, the number 95 is composite. The factors of 95 are 1, 5, 19, and 95.

40. Since 7 divides 14 evenly, $14 \div 7 = 2$, the number 14 is composite. The factors of 14 are 1, 2, 7, and 14.

42. The number 125 is divisible by 5 ($125 \div 5 = 25$) and so 125 is composite. The factors of 125 are 1, 5, 25, and 125.

44. The only factors of 37 are 1 and 37, so 37 is a prime number.

46. The number 54 is divisible by 9 ($54 \div 9 = 6$) and so 54 is composite. The factors of 54 are 1, 2, 3, 6, 9, 18, 27, and 54.

48. The only factors of 67 are 1 and 67, so 67 is a prime number.

Guide Problems

50. Find the prime factorization of 24.
    Construct a factor tree for the number 24. The two branches from a particular number are factors whose product is the given number. Continue in this fashion until all branches end with a prime number. These primes constitute the prime factorization of the starting value.

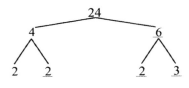

$$24 = \underline{2} \cdot \underline{2} \cdot \underline{2} \cdot \underline{3} = \underline{2}^3 \cdot \underline{3}$$

In problems 52 through 74, a prime factorization is determined using a factor tree. A factor tree is typically not unique. For example, a factor tree for 30 might begin with the factors 5 and 6 or the factors 3 and 10, and so solutions may vary. However any factor tree must lead to the same prime factorization.

52.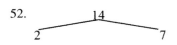

    $14 = 2 \cdot 7$

54.

    $77 = 7 \cdot 11$

56.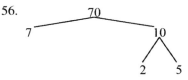

    $70 = 2 \cdot 5 \cdot 7$

58.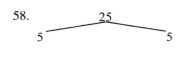

    $25 = 5 \cdot 5 = 5^2$

60.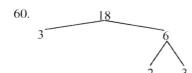

$18 = 2 \cdot 3 \cdot 3 = 2 \cdot 3^2$

62.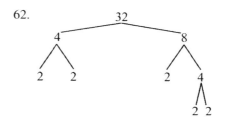

$32 = 2 \cdot 2 \cdot 2 \cdot 2 \cdot 2 = 2^5$

64.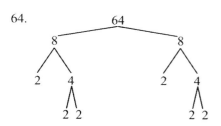

$64 = 2 \cdot 2 \cdot 2 \cdot 2 \cdot 2 \cdot 2 = 2^6$

66.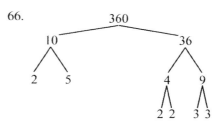

$360 = 2 \cdot 2 \cdot 2 \cdot 3 \cdot 3 \cdot 5 = 2^3 \cdot 3^2 \cdot 5$

68.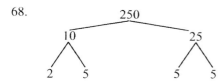

$250 = 2 \cdot 5 \cdot 5 \cdot 5 = 2 \cdot 5^3$

70.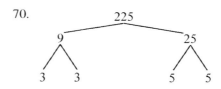

$225 = 3 \cdot 3 \cdot 5 \cdot 5 = 3^2 \cdot 5^2$

72.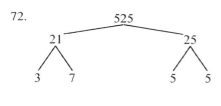

$525 = 3 \cdot 5 \cdot 5 \cdot 7 = 3 \cdot 5^2 \cdot 7$

74.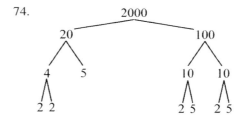

$2000 = 2 \cdot 2 \cdot 2 \cdot 2 \cdot 5 \cdot 5 \cdot 5 = 2^4 \cdot 5^3$

Guide Problems

76. Find the LCM of 3, 4, and 8 by listing multiples.

a. List the first few multiples of each number.

3: 3, 6, <u>9</u>, <u>12</u>, <u>15</u>, <u>18</u>, <u>21</u>, <u>24</u>, ...
4: 4, 8, <u>12</u>, <u>16</u>, <u>20</u>, <u>24</u>, ...
8: 8, 16, <u>24</u>, <u>32</u>, <u>40</u>, <u>48</u>, ...

b. The LCM is the smallest multiple in common to each list. The multiple 24 is the only multiple common to all three lists. What is the LCM?

The LCM of 3, 4, and 8 is <u>24</u>.

78. Find the LCM of 12 and 30 using prime factorization.

    a. Find the prime factorization of each number.

$$12 = 2 \cdot 2 \cdot 3 = 2^2 \cdot 3$$
$$30 = \underline{2} \cdot \underline{3} \cdot \underline{5}$$

    b. The LCM is the product of those prime factors occurring the greatest number of times in any one factorization. What is the LCM?

The greatest number of times that 2 appears in either factorization is __two__ times.

The greatest number of times that 3 appears in either factorization is __one__ times.

The greatest number of times that 5 appears in either factorization is __one__ times.

The LCM of 12 and 30 is
$$\underline{2} \cdot \underline{2} \cdot \underline{3} \cdot \underline{5} = 60 .$$

In problems 80 through 98, either the prime factorization method or the method of listing multiples is used to find the LCM. All problems could be worked by either method although, on occasion, the method of listing multiples may require long lists before a common multiple is found.

80. Prime factorizations:
$$3 = 3, \quad 8 = 2 \cdot 2 \cdot 2 = 2^3$$

The factor 3 appears at most once.
The factor 2 appears at most three times.

LCM of 3 and 8 is $3 \cdot 2^3 = 24$.

82. List multiples:
4: 4, 8, 12, 16, 20, 24, 28, 32, …
7: 7, 14, 21, 28, 35, 42, …
The multiple 28 is common to both lists and is the smallest number common to both lists. The LCM of 4 and 7 is 28.

84. Prime factorizations:
$$9 = 3 \cdot 3 = 3^2$$
$$12 = 2 \cdot 2 \cdot 3 = 2^2 \cdot 3$$
The LCM of 9 and 12 is $2 \cdot 2 \cdot 3 \cdot 3 = 36$.

86. Prime factorizations:
$$24 = 2 \cdot 2 \cdot 2 \cdot 3 = 2^3 \cdot 3$$
$$40 = 2 \cdot 2 \cdot 2 \cdot 5 = 2^3 \cdot 5$$
The LCM of 24 and 40 is $2 \cdot 2 \cdot 2 \cdot 3 \cdot 5 = 120$.

88. List multiples:
8: 8, 16, 24, 32, 40, 48, …
20: 20, 40, 60, 80, …
The LCM of 8 and 20 is 40.

90. List multiples:
12: 12, 24, 36, 48, 60, …
18: 18, 36, 54, 72, …
The LCM of 12 and 18 is 36.

92. Prime factorizations:
$$5 = 5, \quad 8 = 2 \cdot 2 \cdot 2 = 2^3$$
$$16 = 2 \cdot 2 \cdot 2 \cdot 2 = 2^4$$
The LCM of 5, 8, and 16 is $2 \cdot 2 \cdot 2 \cdot 2 \cdot 5 = 80$.

94. Prime factorizations:
$$7 = 7, \quad 21 = 3 \cdot 7$$
$$24 = 2 \cdot 2 \cdot 2 \cdot 3 = 2^3 \cdot 3$$
The LCM of 7, 21, and 24 is $2 \cdot 2 \cdot 2 \cdot 3 \cdot 7 = 168$.

96. Prime factorizations:
$$2 = 2, \quad 12 = 2 \cdot 2 \cdot 3 = 2^2 \cdot 3$$
$$16 = 2 \cdot 2 \cdot 2 \cdot 2 = 2^4$$
The LCM of 2, 12, and 16 is $2 \cdot 2 \cdot 2 \cdot 2 \cdot 3 = 48$.

98. Prime factorizations:
$$8 = 2 \cdot 2 \cdot 2 = 2^3$$
$$12 = 2 \cdot 2 \cdot 3 = 2^2 \cdot 3$$
$$16 = 2 \cdot 2 \cdot 2 \cdot 2 = 2^4$$
$$18 = 2 \cdot 3 \cdot 3 = 2 \cdot 3^2$$
The LCM 8, 12, 16, and 18 is
$$2 \cdot 2 \cdot 2 \cdot 2 \cdot 3 \cdot 3 = 144 .$$

100. Every sixth box gets a red ball and every eighth box gets a blue whistle. The boxes that get both a red ball and a blue whistle correspond to the least common multiple of 6 and 8. Listing multiples of each number,
6: 6, 12, 18, 24, 30, ... and 8: 8, 16, 24, 32, 40, ...
we see the LCM is 24. Every 24th box passing through the assembly line will get both a red ball and a blue whistle.

102. A bell rings every 30 minutes and a buzzer every 40 minutes. The LCM of 30 and 40 can be found with prime factorizations. Since $30 = 2 \cdot 3 \cdot 5$ and $40 = 2 \cdot 2 \cdot 2 \cdot 5$, the LCM of 30 and 40 is $2 \cdot 2 \cdot 2 \cdot 3 \cdot 5 = 120$. Tami will hear the bell and the buzzer simultaneously every 120 minutes or two hours.

Cumulative Skills Review

2. 321,014

4. $8^3 = 8 \cdot 8 \cdot 8 = 64 \cdot 8 = 512$

8. $299 \cdot 1000 = 299,000$

6.
$$\begin{array}{r} 89 \\ 12\overline{)1068} \\ \underline{96} \\ 108 \\ \underline{108} \\ 0 \end{array}$$

$1068 \div 12 = 89$

10. The amount $7540 in word form is "seven thousand five hundred forty dollars"

Section 2.2   Introduction to Fractions and Mixed Numbers

Concept Check

2. The top number in a fraction is called the _numerator_.

4. The line between the numerator and the denominator is known as the _fraction_ _bar_.

6. A fraction in which the numerator is greater than or equal to the denominator is known as an _improper_ fraction.

8. A _complex_ _fraction_ is a quotient of the form $\dfrac{A}{B}$ where A and B are both fractions and where B is not zero.

Guide Problems

10. a. The numerator, 3, is equal to the denominator, 3, so $\dfrac{3}{3}$ is an improper fraction.

b. The number $2\dfrac{3}{10}$ combines a whole number, 2, with a fraction, $\dfrac{3}{10}$, and so is a mixed number.

c. The numerator, 9, is less than the denominator, 22, so $\dfrac{9}{22}$ is a proper fraction.

12. The fraction $\dfrac{1}{16}$ is a proper fraction since 1 is less than 16.

14. The fraction $\dfrac{5}{3}$ is an improper fraction since 5 is greater than 3.

16. The number $12\dfrac{15}{17}$ is a mixed number since it is a whole number combined with a fraction.

18. The fraction $\dfrac{54}{11}$ is an improper fraction since 54 is greater than 11.

20. The fraction $\dfrac{153}{155}$ is a proper fraction since 153 is less than 155.

22. The number $8\dfrac{2}{9}$ is a mixed number since it is a whole number combined with a fraction.

24. One inch on the ruler is divided into 16 equal parts. Three of these parts are shaded. The shaded portion represents the fraction $\dfrac{3}{16}$.

26. The tube of the hypodermic syringe is marked off to consist of 10 equal sections. (Note: There are nine marks that divide the syringe into 10 sections.) Three of the sections are shaded. The fraction shaded is thus $\dfrac{3}{10}$.

28. The rectangle is divided into 16 squares of the same size. All but three of the squares, that is 13 of the squares, have been shaded. The fraction shaded is $\dfrac{13}{16}$.

30. There are seven triangles, of which three have been shaded. The figure represents the fraction $\dfrac{3}{7}$.

32. There are two circles shaded completely. The fourth circle is divided into two parts, one of which is shaded, representing the fraction $\dfrac{1}{2}$. Thus we have two wholes and one-half of a whole together representing the mixed number $2\dfrac{1}{2}$.

34. Each stack consists of five disks. Between the two stacks, a total of eight disks is shaded, so the figure represents the fraction $\dfrac{8}{5}$. Since the first stack is completely shaded and the second stack has three of five disks shaded, the figure also represents the mixed number $1\dfrac{3}{5}$.

36. There a total of 12 tools. There are 5 hammers, 3 screwdrivers and 4 pliers. Thus the fraction represented by hammers is $\dfrac{5}{12}$.

Guide Problems

38. Write $\dfrac{73}{8}$ as a mixed or whole number.

Divide the denominator into the numerator.

$$8\overline{)73} \quad \begin{array}{r} 9 \\ \underline{72} \\ 1 \end{array}$$

The quotient is 9 and the remainder is 1. The quotient is the whole number part of the equivalent mixed number. The fraction part of the mixed number has the remainder as its numerator and the denominator is that of the original fraction. Thus

$$\frac{73}{8} = 9\frac{1}{8}$$

40. Write $9\dfrac{1}{3}$ as an improper fraction.

To convert a mixed number to an improper fraction use the denominator of the fraction part of the mixed number as the denominator of the improper fraction. To find the numerator of the improper fraction, multiply the denominator by the whole number part of the mixed number and add the numerator of the fraction part.

$$9\frac{1}{3} = \frac{9 \cdot 3 + 1}{3} = \frac{28}{3}$$

42. $\begin{array}{r} 6 \\ 8\overline{)48} \\ \underline{48} \\ 0 \end{array}$

$$\frac{48}{8} = 6$$

44. $\begin{array}{r} 10 \\ 11\overline{)114} \\ \underline{110} \\ 4 \end{array}$

$$\frac{114}{11} = 10\frac{4}{11}$$

46. $\begin{array}{r} 7 \\ 6\overline{)43} \\ \underline{42} \\ 1 \end{array}$

$$\frac{43}{6} = 7\frac{1}{6}$$

48. $\begin{array}{r} 18 \\ 3\overline{)54} \\ \underline{3} \\ 24 \\ \underline{24} \\ 0 \end{array}$

$$\frac{54}{3} = 18$$

50. $\begin{array}{r} 9 \\ 7\overline{)63} \\ \underline{63} \\ 0 \end{array}$

$$\frac{63}{7} = 9$$

52. $\begin{array}{r} 8 \\ 3\overline{)26} \\ \underline{24} \\ 2 \end{array}$

$$\frac{26}{3} = 8\frac{2}{3}$$

54. $\begin{array}{r} 7 \\ 17\overline{)124} \\ \underline{119} \\ 5 \end{array}$

$$\frac{124}{17} = 7\frac{5}{17}$$

56. $\begin{array}{r} 9 \\ 11\overline{)104} \\ \underline{99} \\ 5 \end{array}$

$$\frac{104}{11} = 9\frac{5}{11}$$

58. $7\dfrac{2}{3} = \dfrac{7\cdot 3 + 2}{3} = \dfrac{23}{3}$

60. $2\dfrac{5}{8} = \dfrac{2\cdot 8 + 5}{8} = \dfrac{21}{8}$

62. $6\dfrac{2}{3} = \dfrac{6\cdot 3 + 2}{3} = \dfrac{20}{3}$

64. $6\dfrac{5}{6} = \dfrac{6\cdot 6 + 5}{6} = \dfrac{41}{6}$

66. $7\dfrac{2}{13} = \dfrac{7\cdot 13 + 2}{13} = \dfrac{93}{13}$

68. $13\dfrac{1}{4} = \dfrac{13\cdot 4 + 1}{4} = \dfrac{53}{4}$

70. $12\dfrac{2}{9} = \dfrac{12\cdot 9 + 2}{9} = \dfrac{110}{9}$

72. $7\dfrac{1}{10} = \dfrac{7\cdot 10 + 1}{10} = \dfrac{71}{10}$

74. a. Out of 40 questions, you answer 33 correctly. The fraction of the test questions represented by correct answers will have the total number of questions as its denominator and the number of questions answered correctly as its numerator, that is $\dfrac{33}{40}$.

b. If 33 out of 40 questions were answered correctly, then $40 - 33 = 7$ were answered incorrectly. The fraction of wrong answers is then $\dfrac{7}{40}$ of the questions.

76. You attended 5 hours of class on Tuesday. The amount is in hours so to determine the fraction of the day this represents, use the total number of hours in a day, namely 24. The fraction of the day this represents is $\dfrac{5}{24}$.

78. You took 71 pictures out of a possible 215. There are $215 - 71 = 144$ exposures remaining. The fraction the remaining exposures represent is $\dfrac{\text{no. of remaining exposures}}{\text{no. of pictures}} = \dfrac{144}{215}$.

80. a. You have completed four 3-credit courses giving you $4\cdot 3 = 12$ credits. You have also completed three 4-credit courses for another $3\cdot 4 = 12$ credits so you have earned a total of 24 credits. Since you need 63 credits for a degree, your completed course work represents $\dfrac{24}{63}$ of your required credits.

b. You have earned 24 credits leaving you $63 - 24 = 39$ left to earn before you graduate. The fraction of credits remaining before you get your degree is $\dfrac{39}{63}$.

82. If 3373 square feet out of 10,950 square feet is rented then the space that is not rented is

$$\begin{array}{r} 10950 \\ -\quad 3373 \\ \hline 7577 \end{array}$$

The fraction of total space still available is then $\dfrac{7577}{10950}$.

84. a. Public school expenses were \$12,796 and private school expenses were \$30,367. We are asked for the fraction that represents public school expenses as a portion of private school expenses. The phrase "as a portion of private school expenses" indicates the private school expenses represent the total amount, or the denominator. The fraction is then $\dfrac{\$12,796}{\$30,367}$.

b. Since the numerator, \$12,796, is less than the denominator, \$30,367, the fraction in part a is a proper fraction.

c. We are asked for the fraction that represents private school expenses as a portion of public school expenses. The phrase "as a portion of public school expenses" indicates the public school expenses represent the total amount, or the denominator. The fraction is then $\dfrac{\$30,367}{\$12,796}$.

d. Since the numerator, $30,367, is greater than the denominator, $12,796, the fraction in part c is an improper fraction.

Cumulative Skills Review

2.
$$\begin{array}{r} 452 \\ -\ 199 \\ \hline 253 \end{array}$$

4. $7^3 = 7 \cdot 7 \cdot 7 = (7 \cdot 7) \cdot 7 = 49 \cdot 7 = 343$

6.
$$\begin{array}{r} 23 \\ 14\overline{)322} \\ 28 \\ \hline 42 \\ 42 \\ \hline 0 \end{array}$$

$322 \div 14 = 23$

8.
$$\begin{array}{r} 22 \\ \times\ 15 \\ \hline 110 \\ 22 \\ \hline 330 \end{array}$$

$22 \cdot 15 = 330$

10. $143 \cdot 10,000 = 1,430,000$

Section 2.3   Equivalent Fractions

Concept Check

2. A fraction in which the numerator and denominator have no common factor other than 1 is a fraction <u>simplified or reduced</u> to lowest terms.

4. To simplify fractions to lowest terms, <u>divide</u> <u>out</u> any factors common to the numerator and denominator. Use the greatest common factor if you can identify it.

6. To find an equivalent fraction with a larger denominator, <u>multiply</u> the numerator and denominator by the same nonzero whole number.

8. The <u>least</u> <u>common</u> <u>denominator</u> or <u>LCD</u> is the least common multiple (LCM) of all the denominators for a set of fractions.

10. The inequality symbol "<" means "is <u>less</u> than," while the inequality symbol ">" means "is <u>greater</u> than."

Guide Problems

12. Consider the fraction $\dfrac{16}{36}$.

    a. Write the prime factorization of 16.
Use the methods of Section 2.1 such as factor trees.

$$16 = \underline{2} \cdot \underline{2} \cdot \underline{2} \cdot \underline{2}$$

    b. Write the prime factorization of 36.

$$36 = \underline{2} \cdot \underline{2} \cdot \underline{3} \cdot \underline{3}$$

    c. Simplify by dividing out the factors common to the numerator and denominator.

$$\frac{16}{36} = \frac{\overset{1}{\cancel{2}} \cdot \overset{1}{\cancel{2}} \cdot 2 \cdot 2}{\underset{1}{\cancel{2}} \cdot \underset{1}{\cancel{2}} \cdot 3 \cdot 3} = \frac{4}{3 \cdot 3} = \frac{4}{9}$$

So $\dfrac{16}{36} = \dfrac{4}{9}$.

14. Consider the fraction $\dfrac{18}{60}$.

    a. What is the greatest common factor (GCF) of the numerator and denominator of $\dfrac{18}{60}$.

    The greatest common factor of 18 and 60 is 6.

    b. Simplify $\dfrac{18}{60}$ by diving out the GCF.
Divide both the numerator and denominator by the GCF, 6.

$$\frac{18}{60} = \frac{\overset{3}{\cancel{18}}}{\underset{10}{\cancel{60}}} = \frac{3}{10}$$

Problems 16 through 50 employ the following strategy to reduce a given fraction. If the GCF of the numerator and denominator is obvious, then the GCF method is used. If not, the prime factorization method is applied.

16. The GCF of 9 and 24 is 3.

$$\frac{9}{24} = \frac{\overset{3}{\cancel{9}}}{\underset{8}{\cancel{24}}} = \frac{3}{8}$$

18. The GCF of 3 and 27 is 3.

$$\frac{3}{27} = \frac{\overset{1}{\cancel{3}}}{\underset{9}{\cancel{27}}} = \frac{1}{9}$$

20. The GCF of 6 and 15 is 3.

$$\frac{6}{15} = \frac{\overset{2}{\cancel{6}}}{\underset{5}{\cancel{15}}} = \frac{2}{5}$$

22. The GCF of 7 and 77 is 7.

$$\frac{7}{77} = \frac{\overset{1}{\cancel{7}}}{\underset{11}{\cancel{77}}} = \frac{1}{11}$$

24. $24 = 2 \cdot 2 \cdot 2 \cdot 3$
$64 = 2 \cdot 2 \cdot 2 \cdot 2 \cdot 2 \cdot 2$

$$\frac{24}{64} = \frac{\cancel{2} \cdot \cancel{2} \cdot \cancel{2} \cdot 3}{\underset{1}{\cancel{2}} \cdot \underset{1}{\cancel{2}} \cdot \underset{1}{\cancel{2}} \cdot 2 \cdot 2 \cdot 2}$$

$$= \frac{3}{2 \cdot 2 \cdot 2} = \frac{3}{8}$$

26. 13 and 23 are both primes and so have no common factors.

$\dfrac{13}{23}$ is in reduced form.

28. $16 = 2 \cdot 2 \cdot 2 \cdot 2$
$80 = 2 \cdot 2 \cdot 2 \cdot 2 \cdot 5$

$$\frac{16}{80} = \frac{\cancel{2} \cdot \cancel{2} \cdot \cancel{2} \cdot \cancel{2}}{\cancel{2} \cdot \cancel{2} \cdot \cancel{2} \cdot \cancel{2} \cdot 5} = \frac{1}{5}$$

30. $30 = 2 \cdot 3 \cdot 5$
$48 = 2 \cdot 2 \cdot 2 \cdot 2 \cdot 3$

$$\frac{30}{48} = \frac{\cancel{2} \cdot \cancel{3} \cdot 5}{\cancel{2} \cdot 2 \cdot 2 \cdot 2 \cdot \cancel{3}}$$
$$= \frac{5}{2 \cdot 2 \cdot 2} = \frac{5}{8}$$

32. $32 = 2 \cdot 2 \cdot 2 \cdot 2 \cdot 2$
$48 = 2 \cdot 2 \cdot 2 \cdot 2 \cdot 3$

$$\frac{32}{48} = \frac{\cancel{2} \cdot \cancel{2} \cdot \cancel{2} \cdot \cancel{2} \cdot 2}{\cancel{2} \cdot \cancel{2} \cdot \cancel{2} \cdot \cancel{2} \cdot 3} = \frac{2}{3}$$

34. 3 and 17 are both prime numbers and so have no common factors.
$\frac{3}{17}$ cannot be simplified.

36. The GCF of 9 and 39 is 3.

$$\frac{9}{39} = \frac{\overset{3}{\cancel{9}}}{\underset{13}{\cancel{39}}} = \frac{3}{13}$$

38. $77 = 7 \cdot 11$
$84 = 2 \cdot 2 \cdot 3 \cdot 7$

$$\frac{77}{84} = \frac{\cancel{7} \cdot 11}{2 \cdot 2 \cdot 3 \cdot \cancel{7}}$$
$$= \frac{11}{2 \cdot 2 \cdot 3} = \frac{11}{12}$$

40. $63 = 3 \cdot 3 \cdot 7$
$78 = 2 \cdot 3 \cdot 13$

$$\frac{63}{78} = \frac{\cancel{3} \cdot 3 \cdot 7}{2 \cdot \cancel{3} \cdot 13}$$
$$= \frac{3 \cdot 7}{2 \cdot 13} = \frac{21}{26}$$

42. 13 and 53 are both prime. numbers. $\frac{13}{53}$ cannot be simplified.

44. $48 = 2 \cdot 2 \cdot 2 \cdot 2 \cdot 3$
$78 = 2 \cdot 3 \cdot 13$

$$\frac{48}{78} = \frac{\cancel{2} \cdot 2 \cdot 2 \cdot 2 \cdot \cancel{3}}{\cancel{2} \cdot \cancel{3} \cdot 13}$$
$$= \frac{2 \cdot 2 \cdot 2}{13} = \frac{8}{13}$$

46. The GCF of 60 and 62 is 2.

$$\frac{60}{62} = \frac{\overset{30}{\cancel{60}}}{\underset{31}{\cancel{62}}} = \frac{30}{31}$$

48. The GCF of 46 and 72 is 2.

$$\frac{46}{72} = \frac{\overset{23}{\cancel{46}}}{\underset{36}{\cancel{72}}} = \frac{23}{36}$$

50. 37 and 79 are prime numbers and so have no common factors.
$\frac{37}{79}$ cannot be simplified.

Guide Problems

52. Write $\frac{3}{5}$ as an equivalent fraction with a denominator of 35.

Determine the factor that when multiplied by the given denominator, 5, gives the desired denominator, 35. Then multiply both the numerator and denominator by this factor. In this case, the factor is 7.

$$\frac{3}{5} = \frac{3 \cdot 7}{5 \cdot 7} = \frac{21}{35}$$

54. Write $\frac{7}{8}$ as an equivalent fraction with a denominator of 48.

Determine the factor that when multiplied by the given denominator, 8, gives the desired denominator, 48. Then multiply both the numerator and denominator by this factor. In this case, the factor is 6.

$$\frac{7}{8} = \frac{7 \cdot 6}{8 \cdot 6} = \frac{42}{48}$$

56. $\dfrac{3}{4} = \dfrac{?}{24}$

Since $4 \cdot 6 = 24$,

$$\dfrac{3}{4} = \dfrac{3 \cdot 6}{4 \cdot 6} = \dfrac{18}{24}$$

58. $\dfrac{1}{10} = \dfrac{?}{70}$

Since $10 \cdot 7 = 70$,

$$\dfrac{1}{10} = \dfrac{1 \cdot 7}{10 \cdot 7} = \dfrac{7}{70}$$

60. $\dfrac{1}{8} = \dfrac{?}{32}$

Since $8 \cdot 4 = 32$,

$$\dfrac{1}{8} = \dfrac{1 \cdot 4}{8 \cdot 4} = \dfrac{4}{32}$$

62. $\dfrac{1}{3} = \dfrac{?}{24}$

Since $3 \cdot 8 = 24$,

$$\dfrac{1}{3} = \dfrac{1 \cdot 8}{3 \cdot 8} = \dfrac{8}{24}$$

64. $\dfrac{7}{13} = \dfrac{?}{65}$

Since $13 \cdot 5 = 65$,

$$\dfrac{7}{13} = \dfrac{7 \cdot 5}{13 \cdot 5} = \dfrac{35}{65}$$

66. $\dfrac{1}{4} = \dfrac{?}{32}$

Since $4 \cdot 8 = 32$,

$$\dfrac{1}{4} = \dfrac{1 \cdot 8}{4 \cdot 8} = \dfrac{8}{32}$$

68. $\dfrac{8}{11} = \dfrac{?}{77}$

Since $11 \cdot 7 = 77$,

$$\dfrac{8}{11} = \dfrac{8 \cdot 7}{11 \cdot 7} = \dfrac{56}{77}$$

70. $\dfrac{3}{11} = \dfrac{?}{99}$

Since $11 \cdot 9 = 99$,

$$\dfrac{3}{11} = \dfrac{3 \cdot 9}{11 \cdot 9} = \dfrac{27}{99}$$

72. $\dfrac{1}{8} = \dfrac{?}{64}$

Since $8 \cdot 8 = 64$,

$$\dfrac{1}{8} = \dfrac{1 \cdot 8}{8 \cdot 8} = \dfrac{8}{64}$$

74. $\dfrac{2}{3} = \dfrac{?}{120}$

Since $3 \cdot 40 = 120$,

$$\dfrac{2}{3} = \dfrac{2 \cdot 40}{3 \cdot 40} = \dfrac{80}{120}$$

76. $\dfrac{3}{5} = \dfrac{?}{60}$

Since $5 \cdot 12 = 60$,

$$\dfrac{3}{5} = \dfrac{3 \cdot 12}{5 \cdot 12} = \dfrac{36}{60}$$

78. $\dfrac{9}{10} = \dfrac{?}{300}$

Since $10 \cdot 30 = 300$,

$$\dfrac{9}{10} = \dfrac{9 \cdot 30}{10 \cdot 30} = \dfrac{270}{300}$$

80. $\dfrac{2}{9} = \dfrac{?}{180}$

Since $9 \cdot 20 = 180$,

$$\dfrac{2}{9} = \dfrac{2 \cdot 20}{9 \cdot 20} = \dfrac{40}{180}$$

82. $\dfrac{5}{12} = \dfrac{?}{96}$

Since $12 \cdot 8 = 96$,

$$\dfrac{5}{12} = \dfrac{5 \cdot 8}{12 \cdot 8} = \dfrac{40}{96}$$

84. $\dfrac{9}{13} = \dfrac{?}{39}$

Since $13 \cdot 3 = 39$,

$$\dfrac{9}{13} = \dfrac{9 \cdot 3}{13 \cdot 3} = \dfrac{27}{39}$$

86. $\dfrac{6}{11} = \dfrac{?}{55}$

Since $11 \cdot 5 = 55$,

$$\dfrac{6}{11} = \dfrac{6 \cdot 5}{11 \cdot 5} = \dfrac{30}{55}$$

Guide Problems

88. List the fractions $\dfrac{4}{9}$, $\dfrac{1}{3}$, $\dfrac{5}{6}$ in ascending order.

The strategy when ordering or comparing fractions is to first rewrite the fractions as equivalent fractions with the same denominators, the LCD of the fractions. The fractions can then be compared by comparing their numerators.

a. Find the LCD of the fractions. That is, find the LCM of the denominators 9, 3 and 6.

The LCD of $\dfrac{4}{9}$, $\dfrac{1}{3}$, and $\dfrac{5}{6}$ is $\underline{18}$.

b. Write each fraction as an equivalent fraction with the denominator determined in part a.

$$\dfrac{4}{9} = \dfrac{4\cdot 2}{9\cdot \underline{2}} = \dfrac{8}{\underline{18}} \qquad \dfrac{1}{3} = \dfrac{1\cdot 6}{3\cdot \underline{6}} = \dfrac{6}{\underline{18}}$$

$$\dfrac{5}{6} = \dfrac{5\cdot 3}{6\cdot \underline{3}} = \dfrac{15}{\underline{18}}$$

c. Compare the fractions. Since $6 < 8 < 15$,

$$\dfrac{6}{18} < \dfrac{8}{18} < \dfrac{15}{18} \text{ or, in lowest}$$

terms, as $\dfrac{1}{3} < \dfrac{4}{\underline{9}} < \dfrac{5}{\underline{6}}$.

90. LCD of $\dfrac{3}{4}$ and $\dfrac{11}{15}$ is 60.

$$\dfrac{3}{4} = \dfrac{3\cdot 15}{4\cdot 15} = \dfrac{45}{60}$$

$$\dfrac{11}{15} = \dfrac{11\cdot 4}{15\cdot 4} = \dfrac{44}{60}$$

So $\dfrac{44}{60} < \dfrac{45}{60}$ or $\dfrac{11}{15} < \dfrac{3}{4}$.

92. LCD of $\dfrac{7}{12}$ and $\dfrac{11}{18}$ is 36.

$$\dfrac{7}{12} = \dfrac{7\cdot 3}{12\cdot 3} = \dfrac{21}{36}$$

$$\dfrac{11}{18} = \dfrac{11\cdot 2}{18\cdot 2} = \dfrac{22}{36}$$

So $\dfrac{21}{36} < \dfrac{22}{36}$ or $\dfrac{7}{12} < \dfrac{11}{18}$.

94. LCD of $\dfrac{9}{16}$, $\dfrac{5}{8}$, and $\dfrac{7}{12}$ is 48.

$$\dfrac{9}{16} = \dfrac{9\cdot 3}{16\cdot 3} = \dfrac{27}{48}$$

$$\dfrac{5}{8} = \dfrac{5\cdot 6}{8\cdot 6} = \dfrac{30}{48}$$

$$\dfrac{7}{12} = \dfrac{7\cdot 4}{12\cdot 4} = \dfrac{28}{48}$$

So $\dfrac{27}{48} < \dfrac{28}{48} < \dfrac{30}{48}$ or $\dfrac{9}{16} < \dfrac{7}{12} < \dfrac{5}{8}$.

96. LCD of $\dfrac{1}{6}$, $\dfrac{1}{4}$, and $\dfrac{3}{8}$ is 24.

$$\dfrac{1}{6} = \dfrac{1\cdot 4}{6\cdot 4} = \dfrac{4}{24}$$

$$\dfrac{1}{4} = \dfrac{1\cdot 6}{4\cdot 6} = \dfrac{6}{24}$$

$$\dfrac{3}{8} = \dfrac{3\cdot 3}{8\cdot 3} = \dfrac{9}{24}$$

So $\dfrac{4}{24} < \dfrac{6}{24} < \dfrac{9}{24}$ or $\dfrac{1}{6} < \dfrac{1}{4} < \dfrac{3}{8}$.

98. LCD of $\dfrac{1}{5}$, $\dfrac{3}{7}$, and $\dfrac{57}{70}$ is 70.

$$\frac{1}{5} = \frac{1 \cdot 14}{5 \cdot 14} = \frac{14}{70}$$

$$\frac{3}{7} = \frac{3 \cdot 10}{7 \cdot 10} = \frac{30}{70}$$

$$\frac{57}{70} = \frac{57}{70}$$

So $\dfrac{14}{70} < \dfrac{30}{70} < \dfrac{57}{70}$ or $\dfrac{1}{5} < \dfrac{3}{7} < \dfrac{57}{70}$.

100. LCD of $\dfrac{4}{7}$, $\dfrac{3}{14}$, $\dfrac{5}{12}$, and $\dfrac{8}{9}$ is 252.

$$\frac{4}{7} = \frac{4 \cdot 36}{7 \cdot 36} = \frac{144}{252}$$

$$\frac{3}{14} = \frac{3 \cdot 18}{14 \cdot 18} = \frac{54}{252}$$

$$\frac{5}{12} = \frac{5 \cdot 21}{12 \cdot 21} = \frac{105}{252}$$

$$\frac{8}{9} = \frac{8 \cdot 28}{9 \cdot 28} = \frac{224}{252}$$

So $\dfrac{54}{252} < \dfrac{105}{252} < \dfrac{144}{252} < \dfrac{224}{252}$, or

$$\frac{3}{14} < \frac{5}{12} < \frac{4}{7} < \frac{8}{9} .$$

102. If 435 of 1830 students are juniors then there $1830 - 435 = 1395$ students that are not juniors. The fraction represented by the non-juniors in the class is $\dfrac{1395}{1830}$. To simplify this fraction, note $1395 = 3 \cdot 3 \cdot 5 \cdot 31$ and

$1830 = 2 \cdot 3 \cdot 5 \cdot 61$ so $\dfrac{1395}{1830} = \dfrac{\cancel{3} \cdot 3 \cdot \cancel{5} \cdot 31}{2 \cdot \cancel{3} \cdot \cancel{5} \cdot 61} = \dfrac{93}{122}$.

104. a. There are 50 diskettes and 18 are used for a project. The fraction used is $\dfrac{18}{50} = \dfrac{\cancel{18}^{9}}{\cancel{50}_{25}} = \dfrac{9}{25}$.

b. There are 32 diskettes unused represented by the fraction $\dfrac{32}{50} = \dfrac{\cancel{32}^{16}}{\cancel{50}_{25}} = \dfrac{16}{25}$.

106. Out of 24 chocolates, 8 have nuts and 10 have cream filling, leaving 6 pieces. Of these 6 pieces, half are dark solid chocolate, so there 3 dark solid chocolate pieces. The fraction of the box these represent is then

$$\frac{3}{24} = \frac{\cancel{3}^{1}}{\cancel{24}_{8}} = \frac{1}{8} .$$

108. a. There were 60 vehicles sold of which 25 were cars. The cars sold are represented by the fraction

$$\frac{25}{60} = \frac{5 \cdot 5}{2 \cdot 2 \cdot 3 \cdot 5} = \frac{5}{12} .$$

b. There were 60 vehicles sold of which 35 were SUVs. The SUVs sold are represented by the fraction

$$\frac{35}{60} = \frac{5 \cdot 7}{2 \cdot 2 \cdot 3 \cdot 5} = \frac{7}{12} .$$

110. You earned $130. You spent $65 on your car and $19 on school supplies, leaving you with $130 − $65 − $19 = $46 . The fraction of your earnings that this amount represents is

$$\frac{\$46}{\$130} = \frac{\cancel{2} \cdot 23}{\cancel{2} \cdot 5 \cdot 13} = \frac{23}{65} .$$

112. Compare $\frac{2}{3}$ and $\frac{3}{4}$ by converting to equivalent fractions having 12, the LCD, as denominator.

$$\frac{2}{3} = \frac{2 \cdot 4}{3 \cdot 4} = \frac{8}{12} \qquad \frac{3}{4} = \frac{3 \cdot 3}{4 \cdot 3} = \frac{9}{12}$$

The larger fraction is $\frac{9}{12}$ or $\frac{3}{4}$ so Terri's recipe uses more flour.

114. To compare the weights of the items, convert each fraction to an equivalent fraction with denominator 30, the LCD of $\frac{5}{6}, \frac{2}{3}$ and $\frac{3}{5}$.

$$\frac{5}{6} = \frac{5 \cdot 5}{6 \cdot 5} = \frac{25}{30} \qquad \frac{2}{3} = \frac{2 \cdot 10}{3 \cdot 10} = \frac{20}{30} \qquad \frac{3}{5} = \frac{3 \cdot 6}{5 \cdot 6} = \frac{18}{30}$$

The smallest fraction is $\frac{18}{30}$ or, equivalently, $\frac{3}{5}$ of a pound and that is the weight of the smallest item.

Cumulative Skills Review

2.
$$\begin{array}{r} 789 \\ 502 \\ + 1851 \\ \hline 3142 \end{array}$$

4.
$$\frac{3(14-2)+3^2}{5} = \frac{3 \cdot 12 + 3^2}{5} \qquad \text{Simplify within parentheses first.}$$
$$= \frac{3 \cdot 12 + 9}{5} \qquad \text{Simplify exponents.}$$
$$= \frac{36 + 9}{5} \qquad \text{Perform multiplications.}$$
$$= \frac{45}{5} \qquad \text{Simplify above fraction bar.}$$
$$= 9 \qquad \text{Divide.}$$

6.   16607 in standard notation: 16,607
     16607 in word form: sixteen thousand six hundred seven

8.   One hour is 60 minutes, so the fraction of an hour that represents 23 minutes is
$$\frac{23}{60}.$$

10.
$$\begin{array}{r} 31,400 \\ - \quad 451 \\ \hline 30,949 \end{array}$$

Section 2.4   Multiplying Fractions and Mixed Numbers

Concept Check

2.   In multiplying fractions it is often necessary to __simplify__ the result to lowest terms.

4.   In multiplication problems involving a combination of fractions, mixed numbers, and whole numbers, change each mixed number or whole number to an __improper__ fraction. Recall that a whole number n can be written as $\dfrac{n}{1}$.

Guide Problems

6.   Multiply $\dfrac{3}{4} \cdot \dfrac{1}{8}$. Simplify, if possible.

When multiplying fractions, multiply the numerators to find the numerator of the product and multiply the denominators to find the denominator of the product.

$$\frac{3}{4} \cdot \frac{1}{8} = \frac{3}{32}$$

8.   Multiply $\dfrac{5}{12} \cdot \dfrac{8}{15}$. Simplify before multiplying.

Common factors in the numerators and denominators may be divided out.

$$\frac{5}{12} \cdot \frac{8}{15} = \frac{\cancel{5}^{1}}{\cancel{12}_{3}} \cdot \frac{\cancel{8}^{2}}{\cancel{15}_{3}} = \frac{1}{3} \cdot \frac{2}{3} = \frac{2}{9}$$

Here the factor of 5 common to 5 and 15 was divided out as was the 4 common to 8 and 12.

In problems 10 through 48, simplification (if possible) may be done before or after multiplying. Both methods are used in the solutions below. A unique simplified answer must follow from either approach.

10. $\dfrac{1}{3} \cdot \dfrac{1}{5} = \dfrac{1 \cdot 1}{3 \cdot 5} = \dfrac{1}{15}$

12. $\dfrac{3}{5} \cdot \dfrac{1}{4} = \dfrac{3 \cdot 1}{5 \cdot 4} = \dfrac{3}{20}$

14. $\dfrac{3}{5} \cdot \dfrac{2}{7} = \dfrac{3 \cdot 2}{5 \cdot 7} = \dfrac{6}{35}$

16. $\dfrac{4}{9} \cdot \dfrac{5}{7} = \dfrac{4 \cdot 5}{9 \cdot 7} = \dfrac{20}{63}$

18. $\dfrac{2}{5} \cdot \dfrac{8}{9} = \dfrac{2 \cdot 8}{5 \cdot 9} = \dfrac{16}{45}$

20. $\dfrac{5}{6} \cdot \dfrac{7}{12} = \dfrac{5 \cdot 7}{6 \cdot 12} = \dfrac{35}{72}$

22. $\dfrac{5}{9} \cdot \dfrac{4}{5} = \dfrac{\cancel{5}^{1}}{9} \cdot \dfrac{4}{\cancel{5}_{1}} = \dfrac{1 \cdot 4}{9 \cdot 1} = \dfrac{4}{9}$

24. $\dfrac{13}{22} \cdot \dfrac{7}{13} = \dfrac{\cancel{13}^{1}}{22} \cdot \dfrac{7}{\cancel{13}_{1}} = \dfrac{1 \cdot 7}{22 \cdot 1} = \dfrac{7}{22}$

26. $\dfrac{7}{8} \cdot \dfrac{2}{3} = \dfrac{7}{\cancel{8}_{4}} \cdot \dfrac{\cancel{2}^{1}}{3} = \dfrac{7 \cdot 1}{4 \cdot 3} = \dfrac{7}{12}$

28. $\dfrac{4}{9} \cdot \dfrac{6}{13} = \dfrac{4}{\cancel{9}_{3}} \cdot \dfrac{\cancel{6}^{2}}{13} = \dfrac{4 \cdot 2}{3 \cdot 13} = \dfrac{8}{39}$

30. $\dfrac{5}{4} \cdot \dfrac{2}{7} = \dfrac{5 \cdot 2}{4 \cdot 7} = \dfrac{10}{28} = \dfrac{\cancel{10}^{5}}{\cancel{28}_{14}} = \dfrac{5}{14}$

32. $\dfrac{7}{12} \cdot \dfrac{3}{5} = \dfrac{7}{\cancel{12}_{4}} \cdot \dfrac{\cancel{3}^{1}}{5} = \dfrac{7 \cdot 1}{4 \cdot 5} = \dfrac{7}{20}$

34. $\dfrac{2}{5}\cdot\dfrac{5}{8}=\dfrac{\cancel{2}^{1}}{\cancel{5}_{1}}\cdot\dfrac{\cancel{5}^{1}}{\cancel{8}_{4}}=\dfrac{1\cdot 1}{1\cdot 4}=\dfrac{1}{4}$

36. $\dfrac{19}{24}\cdot\dfrac{8}{19}=\dfrac{\cancel{19}^{1}}{\cancel{24}_{3}}\cdot\dfrac{\cancel{8}^{1}}{\cancel{19}_{1}}=\dfrac{1\cdot 1}{3\cdot 1}=\dfrac{1}{3}$

38. $\dfrac{4}{9}\cdot\dfrac{3}{16}=\dfrac{\cancel{4}^{1}}{\cancel{9}_{3}}\cdot\dfrac{\cancel{3}^{1}}{\cancel{16}_{4}}=\dfrac{1\cdot 1}{3\cdot 4}=\dfrac{1}{12}$

40. $\dfrac{5}{24}\cdot\dfrac{18}{25}=\dfrac{\cancel{5}^{1}}{\cancel{24}_{4}}\cdot\dfrac{\cancel{18}^{3}}{\cancel{25}_{5}}=\dfrac{1\cdot 3}{4\cdot 5}=\dfrac{3}{20}$

42. $\dfrac{21}{5}\cdot\dfrac{5}{4}\cdot\dfrac{4}{21}=\dfrac{\cancel{21}^{1}}{\cancel{5}_{1}}\cdot\dfrac{\cancel{5}^{1}}{\cancel{4}_{1}}\cdot\dfrac{\cancel{4}^{1}}{\cancel{21}_{1}}=\dfrac{1\cdot 1\cdot 1}{1\cdot 1\cdot 1}=1$

44. $\dfrac{2}{6}\cdot\dfrac{1}{12}\cdot\dfrac{3}{5}=\dfrac{\cancel{2}^{1}}{\cancel{6}_{3}}\cdot\dfrac{1}{12}\cdot\dfrac{\cancel{3}^{1}}{5}=\dfrac{1\cdot 1\cdot 1}{1\cdot 12\cdot 5}=\dfrac{1}{60}$

46. $\dfrac{6}{7}\cdot\dfrac{1}{3}\cdot\dfrac{3}{14}=\dfrac{\cancel{6}^{3}}{7}\cdot\dfrac{1}{\cancel{3}_{1}}\cdot\dfrac{\cancel{3}^{1}}{\cancel{14}_{7}}=\dfrac{3\cdot 1\cdot 1}{7\cdot 1\cdot 7}=\dfrac{3}{49}$

48. $\dfrac{1}{3}\cdot\dfrac{9}{11}\cdot\dfrac{3}{15}\cdot\dfrac{5}{6}=\dfrac{1}{\cancel{3}_{1}}\cdot\dfrac{\cancel{9}^{3}}{11}\cdot\dfrac{\cancel{3}^{1}}{\cancel{15}_{3}}\cdot\dfrac{\cancel{5}^{1}}{\cancel{6}_{2}}$

  $=\dfrac{1}{11\cdot 2}=\dfrac{1}{22}$

Guide Problems

50. Multiply $1\dfrac{2}{5}\cdot 3\dfrac{1}{3}$.

   a. Change each whole number or mixed number to an improper fraction.

   $1\dfrac{2}{5}=\dfrac{7}{5},\quad 3\dfrac{1}{3}=\dfrac{10}{3}$

   b. Multiply the fractions. Simplify, if possible. Express your answer as a whole number or mixed number, if possible.

   $\dfrac{7}{\cancel{5}_{1}}\cdot\dfrac{\cancel{10}^{2}}{3}=\dfrac{7}{1}\cdot\dfrac{2}{3}=\dfrac{14}{3}=4\dfrac{2}{3}$

52. $1\dfrac{2}{3}=\dfrac{1\cdot 3+2}{3}=\dfrac{5}{3},\quad 2\dfrac{2}{5}=\dfrac{2\cdot 5+2}{5}=\dfrac{12}{5}$

   $1\dfrac{2}{3}\cdot 2\dfrac{2}{5}=\dfrac{5}{3}\cdot\dfrac{12}{5}=\dfrac{\cancel{5}^{1}}{\cancel{3}_{1}}\cdot\dfrac{\cancel{12}^{4}}{\cancel{5}_{1}}=\dfrac{1\cdot 4}{1\cdot 1}=4$

54. $\dfrac{1}{7},\quad 2=\dfrac{2}{1}$

   $\dfrac{1}{7}\cdot 2=\dfrac{1}{7}\cdot\dfrac{2}{1}=\dfrac{1\cdot 2}{7\cdot 1}=\dfrac{2}{7}$

56. $\dfrac{2}{15},\quad 4\dfrac{6}{11}=\dfrac{50}{11}$

   $\dfrac{2}{15}\cdot 4\dfrac{6}{11}=\dfrac{2}{15}\cdot\dfrac{50}{11}=\dfrac{2}{\cancel{15}_{3}}\cdot\dfrac{\cancel{50}^{10}}{11}=\dfrac{20}{33}$

58. $3\dfrac{1}{3}=\dfrac{10}{3},\quad 5\dfrac{1}{4}=\dfrac{21}{4}$

   $3\dfrac{1}{3}\cdot 5\dfrac{1}{4}=\dfrac{10}{3}\cdot\dfrac{21}{4}=\dfrac{\cancel{10}^{5}}{\cancel{3}_{1}}\cdot\dfrac{\cancel{21}^{7}}{\cancel{4}_{2}}=\dfrac{35}{2}=17\dfrac{1}{2}$

60. $4 = \dfrac{4}{1}, \quad \dfrac{5}{8}$

$$4 \cdot \dfrac{5}{8} = \dfrac{4}{1} \cdot \dfrac{5}{8} = \dfrac{\cancel{4}^{\,1}}{1} \cdot \dfrac{5}{\cancel{8}_{2}} = \dfrac{5}{2} = 2\dfrac{1}{2}$$

62. $24 = \dfrac{24}{1}, \quad \dfrac{1}{6}$

$$24 \cdot \dfrac{1}{6} = \dfrac{24}{1} \cdot \dfrac{1}{6} = \dfrac{\cancel{24}^{\,4}}{1} \cdot \dfrac{1}{\cancel{6}_{1}} = 4$$

64. $3\dfrac{4}{5} = \dfrac{19}{5}, \quad 3\dfrac{3}{4} = \dfrac{15}{4}$

$$3\dfrac{4}{5} \cdot 3\dfrac{3}{4} = \dfrac{19}{5} \cdot \dfrac{15}{4} = \dfrac{19}{\cancel{5}_{1}} \cdot \dfrac{\cancel{15}^{\,3}}{4} = \dfrac{57}{4} = 14\dfrac{1}{4}$$

66. $3\dfrac{3}{11} = \dfrac{36}{11}, \quad 2\dfrac{1}{5} = \dfrac{11}{5}$

$$3\dfrac{3}{11} \cdot 2\dfrac{1}{5} = \dfrac{36}{11} \cdot \dfrac{11}{5} = \dfrac{36}{\cancel{11}_{1}} \cdot \dfrac{\cancel{11}^{\,1}}{5} = \dfrac{36}{5} = 7\dfrac{1}{5}$$

68. $\dfrac{2}{11}, \quad 5 = \dfrac{5}{1}$

$$\dfrac{2}{11} \cdot 5 = \dfrac{2}{11} \cdot \dfrac{5}{1} = \dfrac{10}{11}$$

70. $2\dfrac{3}{13} = \dfrac{29}{13}, \quad 3 = \dfrac{3}{1}$

$$2\dfrac{3}{13} \cdot 3 = \dfrac{29}{13} \cdot \dfrac{3}{1} = \dfrac{87}{13} = 6\dfrac{9}{13}$$

72. $3\dfrac{1}{2} = \dfrac{7}{2}, \quad 3\dfrac{3}{4} = \dfrac{15}{4}, \quad \dfrac{1}{5}$

$$3\dfrac{1}{2} \cdot 3\dfrac{3}{4} \cdot \dfrac{1}{5} = \dfrac{7}{2} \cdot \dfrac{15}{4} \cdot \dfrac{1}{5} = \dfrac{7}{2} \cdot \dfrac{\cancel{15}^{\,3}}{4} \cdot \dfrac{1}{\cancel{5}_{1}} = \dfrac{21}{8} = 2\dfrac{5}{8}$$

74. $2\dfrac{1}{2} = \dfrac{5}{2}, \quad 5 = \dfrac{5}{1}, \quad 2\dfrac{3}{5} = \dfrac{13}{5}$

$$2\dfrac{1}{2} \cdot 5 \cdot 2\dfrac{3}{5} = \dfrac{5}{2} \cdot \dfrac{5}{1} \cdot \dfrac{13}{5} = \dfrac{\cancel{5}^{\,1}}{2} \cdot \dfrac{5}{1} \cdot \dfrac{13}{\cancel{5}_{1}} = \dfrac{65}{2} = 32\dfrac{1}{2}$$

76. a. If the truck holds 5200 gallons and is $\dfrac{3}{16}$ full, the number of gallons on board is

$$\dfrac{3}{16} \cdot 5200 = \dfrac{3}{16} \cdot \dfrac{5200}{1} = \dfrac{3}{\cancel{16}_{1}} \cdot \dfrac{\cancel{5200}^{\,325}}{1} = 3 \cdot 325 = 975 \,.$$

   b. The truck now picks up an additional $\dfrac{1}{4}$ of a tank. The number of gallons added is

$$\dfrac{1}{4} \cdot 5200 = \dfrac{1}{4} \cdot \dfrac{5200}{1} = \dfrac{1}{\cancel{4}_{1}} \cdot \dfrac{\cancel{5200}^{\,1300}}{1} = 1300 \text{ so the total number of gallons on board is } 975 + 1300 = 2275 \,.$$

78. a. The regular price of \$460 is reduced by $\dfrac{1}{4}$ or by $\dfrac{1}{4} \cdot 460 = \dfrac{1}{4} \cdot \dfrac{460}{1} = \dfrac{1}{\cancel{4}_{1}} \cdot \dfrac{\cancel{460}^{\,115}}{1} = 115$. The sale price is

   then $\$460 - \$115 = \$345$.

   b. The store offers an additional $\dfrac{1}{4}$ off if the television is dented or scratched. From part (a), we know this

   means an additional \$115 off of the sale price or a new price of $\$345 - \$115 = \$230$.

80. Lloyd earned $\frac{5}{8}$ of his single day's pay or $\frac{5}{8} \cdot 120 = \frac{5}{8} \cdot \frac{120}{1} = \frac{5}{\overset{}{\underset{1}{\cancel{8}}}} \cdot \frac{\overset{15}{\cancel{120}}}{1} = 5 \cdot 15 = 75$ or \$75.

82. Recall that distance is equal to the rate multiplied by time. The rate is 88 miles per hour and the elapsed time is $3\frac{3}{4}$ hours. The total distance is $88 \cdot 3\frac{3}{4} = \frac{88}{1} \cdot \frac{15}{4} = \frac{\overset{22}{\cancel{88}}}{1} \cdot \frac{15}{\underset{1}{\cancel{4}}} = 22 \cdot 15 = 330$ miles.

84. The number of CPAs in the firm is $\frac{3}{7} \cdot 161 = \frac{3}{7} \cdot \frac{161}{1} = \frac{3}{\underset{1}{\cancel{7}}} \cdot \frac{\overset{23}{\cancel{161}}}{1} = 3 \cdot 23 = 69$.

86. Since 1 inch represents $4\frac{1}{2}$ feet, then $5\frac{1}{4}$ represents $5\frac{1}{4} \cdot 4\frac{1}{2}$ feet. Calculating this product gives $5\frac{1}{4} \cdot 4\frac{1}{2} = \frac{21}{4} \cdot \frac{9}{2} = \frac{189}{8} = 23\frac{5}{8}$. The length of the wall is $23\frac{5}{8}$ feet.

88. The increase in Stan's earnings is $\frac{1}{5} \cdot 25,500 = \frac{1}{5} \cdot \frac{25,500}{1} = \frac{1}{\underset{1}{\cancel{5}}} \cdot \frac{\overset{5100}{\cancel{25,500}}}{1} = 5100$ or \$5100.

90. The number of Fords in the parking lot is $\frac{3}{5} \cdot 4800 = \frac{3}{5} \cdot \frac{4800}{1} = \frac{3}{\underset{1}{\cancel{5}}} \cdot \frac{\overset{960}{\cancel{4800}}}{1} = 3 \cdot 960 = 2880$.

92. a. Drive C would get $\frac{2}{5} \cdot 140 = \frac{2}{5} \cdot \frac{140}{1} = \frac{2}{\underset{1}{\cancel{5}}} \cdot \frac{\overset{28}{\cancel{140}}}{1} = 2 \cdot 28 = 56$ gigabytes.

    b. Drive D would get $\frac{3}{5} \cdot 140 = \frac{3}{5} \cdot \frac{140}{1} = \frac{3}{\underset{1}{\cancel{5}}} \cdot \frac{\overset{28}{\cancel{140}}}{1} = 3 \cdot 28 = 84$ gigabytes. Note this result could have been found by noting that drive D would get the remaining storage $140 - 56 = 84$.

94. a. There are 60 rooms each requiring $25\frac{3}{4}$ square yards of carpeting. The total amount of carpeting needed is $60 \cdot 25\frac{3}{4} = \frac{60}{1} \cdot \frac{103}{4} = \frac{\overset{15}{\cancel{60}}}{1} \cdot \frac{103}{\underset{1}{\cancel{4}}} = 15 \cdot 103 = 1545$ square yards.

    b. Each square yard costs $\$2 + \$8 = \$10$. The total cost is $1545 \cdot \$10 = \$15,450$.

96. Since the recipe is designed for a total of 4 people and must be increased to accommodate 15 people, the

quantity of each ingredient must be multiplied by $\dfrac{15}{4}$.

a. $24 \cdot \dfrac{15}{4} = \dfrac{\overset{6}{\cancel{24}}}{1} \cdot \dfrac{15}{\cancel{4}} = 90$ ounces

b. $2\dfrac{4}{5} \cdot \dfrac{15}{4} = \dfrac{\overset{7}{\cancel{14}}}{\underset{1}{\cancel{5}}} \cdot \dfrac{\overset{3}{\cancel{15}}}{\underset{2}{\cancel{4}}} = \dfrac{21}{2} = 10\dfrac{1}{2}$ cups

c. $\dfrac{2}{3} \cdot \dfrac{15}{4} = \dfrac{\overset{1}{\cancel{2}}}{\underset{1}{\cancel{3}}} \cdot \dfrac{\overset{5}{\cancel{15}}}{\underset{2}{\cancel{4}}} = \dfrac{5}{2} = 2\dfrac{1}{2}$ cups

d. $7\dfrac{1}{2} \cdot \dfrac{15}{4} = \dfrac{15}{2} \cdot \dfrac{15}{4} = \dfrac{225}{8} = 28\dfrac{1}{8}$ ounces

e. $\dfrac{3}{4} \cdot \dfrac{15}{4} = \dfrac{45}{16} = 2\dfrac{13}{16}$ teaspoons

f. $2 \cdot \dfrac{15}{4} = \dfrac{\overset{1}{\cancel{2}}}{1} \cdot \dfrac{15}{\underset{2}{\cancel{4}}} = \dfrac{15}{2} = 7\dfrac{1}{2}$ eggs

Cumulative Skills Review

2. $\begin{array}{r} 4393 \\ -\,1220 \\ \hline 3173 \end{array}$

4. If Warren ate 5 pieces out of 12, then he did not eat 7 pieces. The fraction of the total number of slices these represent is $\dfrac{7}{12}$.

6.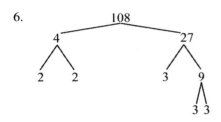

$108 = 2 \cdot 2 \cdot 3 \cdot 3 \cdot 3 = 2^2 \cdot 3^3$

8. The GCF of 9 and 72 is 9 so divide out 9 to get

$\dfrac{9}{72} = \dfrac{\overset{1}{\cancel{9}}}{\underset{8}{\cancel{72}}} = \dfrac{1}{8}$.

10. The amount you have left in your account is $\$520 - \$55 - \$160 = \$305$. The fraction of your original balance this represents is

$\dfrac{305}{520} = \dfrac{\overset{1}{\cancel{5}} \cdot 61}{2 \cdot 2 \cdot 2 \cdot \underset{1}{\cancel{5}} \cdot 13} = \dfrac{61}{2 \cdot 2 \cdot 2 \cdot 13} = \dfrac{61}{104}$

Section 2.5   Dividing Fractions and Mixed Numbers

Concept Check

2. The __reciprocal__ of the fraction $\dfrac{a}{b}$ is the fraction $\dfrac{b}{a}$ where $a \neq 0$ and $b \neq 0$.

4. To divide a combination of fractions, whole numbers, or mixed numbers, change any whole numbers or mixed numbers to __improper__ fractions.

Guide Problems

6. Divide $\dfrac{5}{8} \div \dfrac{15}{16}$.

   a. Identify the reciprocal of the divisor.

   The divisor here is $\dfrac{15}{16}$.

   The reciprocal of $\dfrac{15}{16}$ is

   $\dfrac{16}{15}$.

   b. Rewrite the division problem as a multiplication problem. Replace the operation of division with multiplication and replace the divisor with its reciprocal.

   $\dfrac{5}{8} \div \dfrac{15}{16} = \dfrac{5}{8} \cdot \dfrac{16}{15}$

   c. Multiply the dividend by the reciprocal of the divisor. Multiply using the methods of Section 2.4.

   $$\dfrac{5}{8} \cdot \dfrac{16}{15} = \dfrac{\cancel{5}}{\cancel{8}} \cdot \dfrac{\cancel{16}^{2}}{\cancel{15}_{3}} = \dfrac{1}{1} \cdot \dfrac{2}{3} = \dfrac{2}{3}$$

   so $\dfrac{5}{8} \div \dfrac{15}{16} = \dfrac{2}{3}$.

8. The divisor is $\dfrac{8}{13}$ and its reciprocal is $\dfrac{13}{8}$.

   Rewrite as a multiplication problem and evaluate.

   $$\dfrac{12}{13} \div \dfrac{8}{13} = \dfrac{12}{13} \cdot \dfrac{13}{8} = \dfrac{\cancel{12}^{3}}{\cancel{13}_{1}} \cdot \dfrac{\cancel{13}^{1}}{\cancel{8}_{2}} = \dfrac{3}{2} = 1\dfrac{1}{2}$$

10. The divisor is $\dfrac{4}{5}$ and its reciprocal is $\dfrac{5}{4}$.

   Rewrite as a multiplication problem and evaluate.

   $$\dfrac{6}{11} \div \dfrac{4}{5} = \dfrac{6}{11} \cdot \dfrac{5}{4} = \dfrac{\cancel{6}^{3}}{11} \cdot \dfrac{5}{\cancel{4}_{2}} = \dfrac{15}{22}$$

12. $\dfrac{1}{3} \div \dfrac{2}{3} = \dfrac{1}{3} \cdot \dfrac{3}{2} = \dfrac{1}{\cancel{3}} \cdot \dfrac{\cancel{3}^{1}}{2} = \dfrac{1}{2}$

14. $\dfrac{1}{2} \div \dfrac{1}{3} = \dfrac{1}{2} \cdot \dfrac{3}{1} = \dfrac{3}{2} = 1\dfrac{1}{2}$

16. $\dfrac{4}{7} \div \dfrac{8}{11} = \dfrac{4}{7} \cdot \dfrac{11}{8} = \dfrac{\cancel{4}^{1}}{7} \cdot \dfrac{11}{\cancel{8}_{2}} = \dfrac{11}{14}$

18. $\dfrac{1}{3} \div \dfrac{4}{5} = \dfrac{1}{3} \cdot \dfrac{5}{4} = \dfrac{5}{12}$

20. $\dfrac{1}{9} \div \dfrac{2}{3} = \dfrac{1}{9} \cdot \dfrac{3}{2} = \dfrac{1}{\cancel{9}_{3}} \cdot \dfrac{\cancel{3}^{1}}{2} = \dfrac{1}{6}$

22. $\dfrac{3}{5} \div \dfrac{12}{25} = \dfrac{3}{5} \cdot \dfrac{25}{12} = \dfrac{\cancel{3}^{1}}{\cancel{5}_{1}} \cdot \dfrac{\cancel{25}^{5}}{\cancel{12}_{4}} = \dfrac{5}{4} = 1\dfrac{1}{4}$

24. $\dfrac{1}{4} \div \dfrac{5}{9} = \dfrac{1}{4} \cdot \dfrac{9}{5} = \dfrac{9}{20}$

26. $\dfrac{4}{9} \div \dfrac{1}{9} = \dfrac{4}{9} \cdot \dfrac{9}{1} = \dfrac{4}{\cancel{9}_{1}} \cdot \dfrac{\cancel{9}^{1}}{1} = \dfrac{4}{1} = 4$

28. $\dfrac{1}{5} \div \dfrac{1}{8} = \dfrac{1}{5} \cdot \dfrac{8}{1} = \dfrac{8}{5} = 1\dfrac{3}{5}$

30. $\dfrac{2}{3} \div \dfrac{1}{4} = \dfrac{2}{3} \cdot \dfrac{4}{1} = \dfrac{8}{3} = 2\dfrac{2}{3}$

32. $\dfrac{5}{12} \div \dfrac{5}{6} = \dfrac{5}{12} \cdot \dfrac{6}{5} = \dfrac{\cancel{5}^{1}}{\cancel{12}_{2}} \cdot \dfrac{\cancel{6}^{1}}{\cancel{5}_{1}} = \dfrac{1}{2}$

34. $\dfrac{3}{4} \div \dfrac{1}{12} = \dfrac{3}{4} \cdot \dfrac{12}{1} = \dfrac{3}{\cancel{4}_{1}} \cdot \dfrac{\cancel{12}^{3}}{1} = \dfrac{9}{1}$

Guide Problems

36. Divide $8\dfrac{8}{9} \div 6\dfrac{2}{3}$.

a. Change each whole number or mixed number to an improper fraction.
Here both the dividend and divisor are mixed numbers.

$$8\frac{8}{9} = \frac{80}{9}, \quad 6\frac{2}{3} = \frac{20}{3}$$

b. Identify the reciprocal of the divisor.

The divisor has been rewritten as $\dfrac{20}{3}$.

The reciprocal of $\dfrac{20}{3}$ is $\dfrac{3}{20}$.

c. Rewrite the division problem as a multiplication problem. Replace the operation of division with multiplication and replace the divisor with its reciprocal.

$$\frac{80}{9} \div \frac{20}{3} = \frac{80}{9} \cdot \frac{3}{20}$$

d. Multiply the dividend by the reciprocal of the divisor. Multiply using the methods of Section 2.4.

$$\frac{80}{9} \cdot \frac{3}{20} = \frac{\overset{4}{\cancel{80}}}{\underset{3}{\cancel{9}}} \cdot \frac{\overset{1}{\cancel{3}}}{\underset{1}{\cancel{20}}} = \frac{4}{3} \cdot \frac{1}{1} = \frac{4}{3} = 1\frac{1}{3}$$

so $\dfrac{5}{8} \div \dfrac{15}{16} = \dfrac{2}{3}$.

38. Rewrite mixed numbers as improper fractions.

$$31\frac{1}{2} = \frac{31 \cdot 2 + 1}{2} = \frac{63}{2}, \quad 1\frac{1}{2} = \frac{1 \cdot 2 + 1}{2} = \frac{3}{2}$$

$$31\frac{1}{2} \div 1\frac{1}{2} = \frac{63}{2} \div \frac{3}{2}$$

Rewrite the division problem as a multiplication problem using the reciprocal of the divisor.

$$31\frac{1}{2} \div 1\frac{1}{2} = \frac{63}{2} \div \frac{3}{2} = \frac{63}{2} \cdot \frac{2}{3} = \frac{\overset{21}{\cancel{63}}}{\underset{1}{\cancel{2}}} \cdot \frac{\overset{1}{\cancel{2}}}{\underset{1}{\cancel{3}}}$$

$$= \frac{21}{1} \cdot \frac{1}{1} = 21$$

40. $3\dfrac{1}{2} \div 2\dfrac{4}{5} = \dfrac{7}{2} \div \dfrac{14}{5} = \dfrac{7}{2} \cdot \dfrac{5}{14}$

$$= \frac{\overset{1}{\cancel{7}}}{2} \cdot \frac{5}{\underset{2}{\cancel{14}}} = \frac{1}{2} \cdot \frac{5}{2}$$

$$= \frac{5}{4} = 1\frac{1}{4}$$

42. $178\dfrac{1}{2} \div 3\dfrac{1}{2} = \dfrac{357}{2} \div \dfrac{7}{2} = \dfrac{357}{2} \cdot \dfrac{2}{7}$

$$= \frac{\overset{51}{\cancel{357}}}{\underset{1}{\cancel{2}}} \cdot \frac{\overset{1}{\cancel{2}}}{\underset{1}{\cancel{7}}} = \frac{51}{1} \cdot \frac{1}{1}$$

$$= \frac{51}{1} = 51$$

44. $\dfrac{2}{3} \div 1\dfrac{2}{5} = \dfrac{2}{3} \div \dfrac{7}{5} = \dfrac{2}{3} \cdot \dfrac{5}{7}$

$= \dfrac{10}{21}$

46. $45 \div 1\dfrac{1}{2} = \dfrac{45}{1} \div \dfrac{3}{2} = \dfrac{45}{1} \cdot \dfrac{2}{3}$

$= \dfrac{\overset{15}{\cancel{45}}}{1} \cdot \dfrac{2}{\underset{1}{\cancel{3}}} = \dfrac{15}{1} \cdot \dfrac{2}{1}$

$= \dfrac{30}{1} = 30$

48. $2 \div 3\dfrac{1}{6} = \dfrac{2}{1} \div \dfrac{19}{6} = \dfrac{2}{1} \cdot \dfrac{6}{19} = \dfrac{12}{19}$

50. $\dfrac{3}{2} \div 3 = \dfrac{3}{2} \div \dfrac{3}{1} = \dfrac{3}{2} \cdot \dfrac{1}{3}$

$= \dfrac{\overset{1}{\cancel{3}}}{2} \cdot \dfrac{1}{\underset{1}{\cancel{3}}} = \dfrac{1}{2} \cdot \dfrac{1}{1}$

$= \dfrac{1}{2}$

52. $84\dfrac{1}{3} \div 3\dfrac{2}{3} = \dfrac{253}{3} \div \dfrac{11}{3} = \dfrac{253}{3} \cdot \dfrac{3}{11}$

$= \dfrac{\overset{23}{\cancel{253}}}{\underset{1}{\cancel{3}}} \cdot \dfrac{\overset{1}{\cancel{3}}}{\underset{1}{\cancel{11}}} = \dfrac{23}{1} \cdot \dfrac{1}{1}$

$= 23$

54. $36\dfrac{2}{3} \div 3\dfrac{2}{3} = \dfrac{110}{3} \div \dfrac{11}{3} = \dfrac{110}{3} \cdot \dfrac{3}{11}$

$= \dfrac{\overset{10}{\cancel{110}}}{\underset{1}{\cancel{3}}} \cdot \dfrac{\overset{1}{\cancel{3}}}{\underset{1}{\cancel{11}}} = \dfrac{10}{1} \cdot \dfrac{1}{1}$

$= 10$

56. $\dfrac{3}{8} \div 1 = \dfrac{3}{8} \div \dfrac{1}{1} = \dfrac{3}{8} \cdot \dfrac{1}{1} = \dfrac{3}{8}$

58. $50 \div 2\dfrac{1}{2} = \dfrac{50}{1} \div \dfrac{5}{2} = \dfrac{50}{1} \cdot \dfrac{2}{5}$

$= \dfrac{\overset{10}{\cancel{50}}}{1} \cdot \dfrac{2}{\underset{1}{\cancel{5}}} = \dfrac{10}{1} \cdot \dfrac{2}{1}$

$= 20$

60. $\dfrac{2}{3} \div 4\dfrac{2}{3} = \dfrac{2}{3} \div \dfrac{14}{3} = \dfrac{2}{3} \cdot \dfrac{3}{14}$

$= \dfrac{\overset{1}{\cancel{2}}}{\underset{1}{\cancel{3}}} \cdot \dfrac{\overset{1}{\cancel{3}}}{\underset{7}{\cancel{14}}} = \dfrac{1}{1} \cdot \dfrac{1}{7} = \dfrac{1}{7}$

62. We need to know how many $\dfrac{3}{8}$ there are in $4\dfrac{1}{2}$. First note $4\dfrac{1}{2} = \dfrac{9}{2}$ so $4\dfrac{1}{2} \div \dfrac{3}{8}$ is computed as

$\dfrac{9}{2} \div \dfrac{3}{8} = \dfrac{9}{2} \cdot \dfrac{8}{3} = \dfrac{\overset{3}{\cancel{9}}}{\underset{1}{\cancel{2}}} \cdot \dfrac{\overset{4}{\cancel{8}}}{\underset{1}{\cancel{3}}} = 12$. Thus we can mix 12 gallons.

64. Vanity Homes, Inc. wishes to divide $126\dfrac{1}{2}$ acres into parcels of size $1\dfrac{3}{8}$ acres. The number of parcels will

be $126\dfrac{1}{2} \div 1\dfrac{3}{8} = \dfrac{253}{2} \div \dfrac{11}{8} = \dfrac{253}{2} \cdot \dfrac{8}{11} = \dfrac{\overset{23}{\cancel{253}}}{\underset{1}{\cancel{2}}} \cdot \dfrac{\overset{4}{\cancel{8}}}{\underset{1}{\cancel{11}}} = \dfrac{23}{1} \cdot \dfrac{4}{1} = 92$.

66. The number of $3\dfrac{4}{5}$ pound boxes of nails that can be made from 608 pounds of nails is

$$608 \div 3\frac{4}{5} = \frac{608}{1} \div \frac{19}{5} = \frac{608}{1} \cdot \frac{5}{19} = \frac{\overset{32}{\cancel{608}}}{1} \cdot \frac{5}{\underset{1}{\cancel{19}}} = \frac{32}{1} \cdot \frac{5}{1} = 160 \,.$$

68. a. We need to know how many lengths of $4\dfrac{1}{5}$ feet make up a roll of 840 feet. This number is

$$840 \div 4\frac{1}{5} = \frac{840}{1} \div \frac{21}{5} = \frac{840}{1} \cdot \frac{5}{21} = \frac{\overset{40}{\cancel{840}}}{1} \cdot \frac{5}{\underset{1}{\cancel{21}}} = \frac{40}{1} \cdot \frac{5}{1} = 200 \,.$$ So 200 circuit boards can be made.

    b. Since a roll of wire costs \$2400 and 200 circuit boards can be made from a roll. The cost per circuit
    board is $\dfrac{\$2400}{200} = \$12$.

70. The number of boxes is given by $350 \div \dfrac{5}{8} = \dfrac{350}{1} \div \dfrac{5}{8} = \dfrac{350}{1} \cdot \dfrac{8}{5} = \dfrac{\overset{70}{\cancel{350}}}{1} \cdot \dfrac{8}{\underset{1}{\cancel{5}}} = 70 \cdot 8 = 560$.

Cumulative Skills Review

2. Since the numerator, 3, is less than the denominator, 52, the fraction is proper.

4.   143
      219
    + 99
    ─────
      461

6. $\dfrac{105}{135} = \dfrac{3 \cdot 5 \cdot 7}{3 \cdot 3 \cdot 3 \cdot 5} = \dfrac{\cancel{3} \cdot \cancel{5} \cdot 7}{\cancel{3} \cdot 3 \cdot 3 \cdot \cancel{5}} = \dfrac{7}{3 \cdot 3} = \dfrac{7}{9}$

8.   5637
    − 5290
    ─────
      347

    $5637 - 5290 = 347$

10. In two days you have traveled $215 + 150 = 365$ miles. You have $600 - 365 = 235$ miles remaining. The
    fraction of the entire trip the miles remaining represent is
    $$\frac{235}{600} = \frac{\cancel{5} \cdot 47}{\cancel{5} \cdot 120} = \frac{47}{120} \,.$$

Section 2.6   Adding Fractions and Mixed Numbers

Concept Check

2. To add like fractions, add the __numerators__ and write this sum over the common the __denominator__ .
   Simplify, if possible.

4. When adding mixed numbers, we first add the __fraction__ parts and then add the __whole numbers__ .

6. An alternate method for adding mixed numbers is to change each mixed number to an __improper__ fraction
   and then add.

Guide Problems

8. Add $\dfrac{3}{17} + \dfrac{8}{17}$.

The fractions have the same denominators and so are like fractions. To add like fractions, add the numerators and use the denominator 17 as the denominator of the result.

$$\frac{3}{17} + \frac{8}{17} = \frac{3+8}{17} = \frac{11}{17} \text{ . Note no simplification is possible.}$$

In each of problems 10–24, the fractions being added are like fractions. The denominator of the sum is the same as the denominator of each fraction. The numerator of the sum is found by adding the numerators of the fraction. The resulting fraction is then simplified if possible.

10. $\dfrac{5}{9} + \dfrac{2}{9} = \dfrac{5+2}{9} = \dfrac{7}{9}$

12. $\dfrac{4}{15} + \dfrac{9}{15} = \dfrac{4+9}{15} = \dfrac{13}{15}$

14. $\dfrac{7}{18} + \dfrac{1}{18} = \dfrac{7+1}{18} = \dfrac{8}{18} = \dfrac{2 \cdot 4}{2 \cdot 9} = \dfrac{4}{9}$

16. $\dfrac{7}{36} + \dfrac{11}{36} = \dfrac{7+11}{36} = \dfrac{18}{36} = \dfrac{18 \cdot 1}{18 \cdot 2} = \dfrac{1}{2}$

18. $\dfrac{5}{14} + \dfrac{9}{14} = \dfrac{5+9}{14} = \dfrac{14}{14} = 1$

20. $\dfrac{4}{5} + \dfrac{3}{5} = \dfrac{4+3}{5} = \dfrac{7}{5} = 1\dfrac{2}{5}$

22. $\dfrac{5}{6} + \dfrac{5}{6} + \dfrac{3}{6} = \dfrac{5+5+3}{6} = \dfrac{13}{6} = 2\dfrac{1}{6}$

24. $\dfrac{8}{9} + \dfrac{4}{9} + \dfrac{7}{9} = \dfrac{8+4+7}{9} = \dfrac{19}{9} = 2\dfrac{1}{9}$

Guide Problems

26. Add $\dfrac{3}{8} + \dfrac{5}{6}$.

The fractions being added have different denominators and so are unlike fractions. The strategy is as follows.

a. Find the LCD of the fractions.
    Since $8 = 2 \cdot 2 \cdot 2$ and $6 = 2 \cdot 3$, the LCD is $2 \cdot 2 \cdot 2 \cdot 3 = \underline{24}$.

b. Write each fraction as an equivalent fraction with the LCD found in part a. The LCD is 24.

For the fraction $\dfrac{3}{8}$, multiply by $\dfrac{3}{3}$ to obtain a denominator of 24. Similarly multiply $\dfrac{5}{6}$ by $\dfrac{4}{4}$.

$$\frac{3}{8} \cdot \frac{3}{3} = \frac{3 \cdot 3}{8 \cdot 3} = \frac{9}{\underline{24}} \qquad\qquad \frac{5}{6} \cdot \frac{4}{4} = \frac{5 \cdot 4}{6 \cdot 4} = \frac{20}{\underline{24}}$$

c. Add the fractions. The fractions have been expressed as equivalent like fractions and can be added using the usual strategy for like fractions.

$$\frac{3}{8} + \frac{5}{6} = \frac{9}{24} + \frac{20}{24} = \frac{29}{\underline{24}} \text{ .}$$

The result is an improper fraction and can be written as a mixed number: $\dfrac{29}{24} = 1\dfrac{5}{24}$.

In each of problems 28 – 42, the fractions being added are unlike fractions. In each case, the LCD of the fractions is found, then each fraction is expressed as an equivalent fraction with the LCD as denominator. The resulting like fractions are added. The result is then simplified if possible.

28. $\dfrac{3}{7}+\dfrac{1}{14}$ The LCD of 7 and 14 is 14.

Write as equivalent fractions.

$\dfrac{3}{7}\cdot\dfrac{2}{2}=\dfrac{6}{14}\qquad\dfrac{1}{14}=\dfrac{1}{14}$

Add.

$\dfrac{3}{7}+\dfrac{1}{14}=\dfrac{6}{14}+\dfrac{1}{14}=\dfrac{7}{14}=\dfrac{7\cdot1}{7\cdot2}=\dfrac{1}{2}$

30. $\dfrac{5}{8}+\dfrac{5}{24}$ The LCD of 8 and 24 is 24.

Write as equivalent fractions.

$\dfrac{5}{8}\cdot\dfrac{3}{3}=\dfrac{15}{24}\qquad\dfrac{5}{24}=\dfrac{5}{24}$

Add.

$\dfrac{5}{8}+\dfrac{5}{24}=\dfrac{15}{24}+\dfrac{5}{24}=\dfrac{20}{24}=\dfrac{4\cdot5}{4\cdot6}=\dfrac{5}{6}$

32. $\dfrac{1}{6}+\dfrac{1}{12}$ LCD $= 12$

$\dfrac{1}{6}+\dfrac{1}{12}=\dfrac{1}{6}\cdot\dfrac{2}{2}+\dfrac{1}{12}=\dfrac{2}{12}+\dfrac{1}{12}=\dfrac{3}{12}=\dfrac{1}{4}$

34. $\dfrac{1}{4}+\dfrac{7}{8}$ LCD $= 8$

$\dfrac{1}{4}+\dfrac{7}{8}=\dfrac{1}{4}\cdot\dfrac{2}{2}+\dfrac{7}{8}=\dfrac{2}{8}+\dfrac{7}{8}=\dfrac{9}{8}=1\dfrac{1}{8}$

36. $\dfrac{4}{5}+\dfrac{5}{6}+\dfrac{1}{10}$ LCD $= 30$

$\dfrac{4}{5}+\dfrac{5}{6}+\dfrac{1}{10}=\dfrac{4}{5}\cdot\dfrac{6}{6}+\dfrac{5}{6}\cdot\dfrac{5}{5}+\dfrac{1}{10}\cdot\dfrac{3}{3}=\dfrac{24}{30}+\dfrac{25}{30}+\dfrac{3}{30}=\dfrac{52}{30}=\dfrac{26}{15}=1\dfrac{11}{15}$

38. $\dfrac{2}{3}+\dfrac{3}{6}+\dfrac{4}{9}$ LCD $= 18$

$\dfrac{2}{3}+\dfrac{3}{6}+\dfrac{4}{9}=\dfrac{2}{3}\cdot\dfrac{6}{6}+\dfrac{3}{6}\cdot\dfrac{3}{3}+\dfrac{4}{9}\cdot\dfrac{2}{2}=\dfrac{12}{18}+\dfrac{9}{18}+\dfrac{8}{18}=\dfrac{29}{18}=1\dfrac{11}{18}$

40. $\dfrac{3}{8}+\dfrac{4}{5}+\dfrac{11}{20}$ LCD $= 40$

$\dfrac{3}{8}+\dfrac{4}{5}+\dfrac{11}{20}=\dfrac{3}{8}\cdot\dfrac{5}{5}+\dfrac{4}{5}\cdot\dfrac{8}{8}+\dfrac{11}{20}\cdot\dfrac{2}{2}=\dfrac{15}{40}+\dfrac{32}{40}+\dfrac{22}{40}=\dfrac{69}{40}=1\dfrac{29}{40}$

42. $\dfrac{1}{6}+\dfrac{11}{12}+\dfrac{8}{15}$ LCD $= 60$

$\dfrac{1}{6}+\dfrac{11}{12}+\dfrac{8}{15}=\dfrac{1}{6}\cdot\dfrac{10}{10}+\dfrac{11}{12}\cdot\dfrac{5}{5}+\dfrac{8}{15}\cdot\dfrac{4}{4}=\dfrac{10}{60}+\dfrac{55}{60}+\dfrac{32}{60}=\dfrac{97}{60}=1\dfrac{37}{60}$

Guide Problems

44. Add $11\dfrac{1}{2}+17\dfrac{3}{5}$.

The strategy for adding mixed numbers whose fraction parts are unlike fractions is as follows.

a. Find the LCD of the fraction parts. In this case the LCD is the LCM of the denominators 2 and 5.

Therefore, the LCD $= \underline{\underline{10}}$.

b. Write the fraction part of each mixed number as an equivalent fraction with the LCD found in part a. Rewrite each mixed number using the equivalent fraction part.

$$11\frac{1}{2} = 11\frac{1\cdot\underline{5}}{2\cdot\underline{5}} = 11\frac{5}{\underline{10}} \qquad 17\frac{3}{5} = 17\frac{3\cdot\underline{2}}{5\cdot\underline{2}} = 17\frac{6}{\underline{10}}$$

c. Add the fraction parts and then add the whole number parts. Simplify, if possible.

$$11\frac{5}{\underline{10}}$$
$$+\ 17\frac{6}{\underline{10}}$$
$$\overline{\rule{3cm}{0.4pt}}$$
$$28\frac{11}{\underline{10}} \qquad \text{(because } \frac{5}{10}+\frac{6}{10}=\frac{11}{10} \text{ and } 11+17=28 \text{)}$$

Note the fraction part of the result is an improper fraction. Rewrite this number so the fraction is proper.

$$28\frac{11}{10} = 28 + \frac{11}{\underline{10}} = 28 + 1\frac{1}{\underline{10}} = 29\frac{1}{\underline{10}}$$

The last step above can be thought of as addition of mixed numbers where the first number has a fraction part of zero.

46. $\dfrac{3}{7}+2\dfrac{3}{14}$ The LCD of $\dfrac{3}{7}$ and $\dfrac{3}{14}$ is 14. Rewrite fractional parts.

$$\frac{3}{7} = \frac{3\cdot2}{7\cdot2} = \frac{6}{14}$$

$$\frac{6}{14}$$
$$+\ 2\frac{3}{14}$$
$$\overline{\rule{2.5cm}{0.4pt}}$$
$$2\frac{9}{14}$$

48. $\dfrac{7}{15}+2\dfrac{13}{18}$ The LCD of $\dfrac{7}{15}$ and $\dfrac{13}{18}$ is 90. Rewrite fractional parts.

$$\frac{7}{15} = \frac{7\cdot6}{15\cdot6} = \frac{42}{90}, \qquad 2\frac{13}{18} = 2\frac{13\cdot5}{18\cdot5} = 2\frac{65}{90}$$

$$\frac{42}{90}$$
$$+\ 2\frac{65}{90}$$
$$\overline{\rule{2.5cm}{0.4pt}}$$
$$2\frac{107}{90} = 2+1+\frac{17}{90} = 3\frac{17}{90}$$

Alternate method:

$$\frac{7}{15}+2\frac{13}{18} = \frac{7}{15}+\frac{49}{18} = \frac{7\cdot6}{15\cdot6}+\frac{49\cdot5}{18\cdot5}$$
$$= \frac{42}{90}+\frac{245}{90} = \frac{287}{90} = 3\frac{17}{90}$$

50. $\dfrac{2}{7}+5\dfrac{1}{2}$ The LCD of $\dfrac{2}{7}$ and $\dfrac{1}{2}$ is 14.

Rewrite fractional parts.

$\dfrac{2}{7}=\dfrac{2\cdot2}{7\cdot2}=\dfrac{4}{14},\qquad 5\dfrac{1}{2}=5\dfrac{1\cdot7}{2\cdot7}=5\dfrac{7}{14}$

$$\begin{array}{r}\dfrac{4}{14}\\ +\;5\dfrac{7}{14}\\ \hline 5\dfrac{11}{14}\end{array}$$

52. $\dfrac{12}{35}=\dfrac{12\cdot2}{35\cdot2}=\dfrac{24}{70},\qquad 2\dfrac{1}{10}=2\dfrac{1\cdot7}{10\cdot7}=2\dfrac{7}{70}$

$$\begin{array}{r}\dfrac{24}{70}\\ +\;2\dfrac{7}{70}\\ \hline 2\dfrac{31}{70}\end{array}$$

54. $2\dfrac{7}{10}=2\dfrac{7\cdot10}{10\cdot10}=2\dfrac{70}{100}$

$$\begin{array}{r}4\dfrac{13}{100}\\ +\;2\dfrac{70}{100}\\ \hline 6\dfrac{83}{100}\end{array}$$

56. $6\dfrac{1}{8}+6\dfrac{3}{4}=\dfrac{49}{8}+\dfrac{27}{4}=\dfrac{49}{8}+\dfrac{27\cdot2}{4\cdot2}$

$=\dfrac{49}{8}+\dfrac{54}{8}=\dfrac{103}{8}=12\dfrac{7}{8}$

58. $12\dfrac{1}{3}+4\dfrac{1}{6}=\dfrac{37}{3}+\dfrac{25}{6}=\dfrac{37\cdot2}{3\cdot2}+\dfrac{25}{6}$

$=\dfrac{74}{6}+\dfrac{25}{6}=\dfrac{99}{6}=16\dfrac{3}{6}=16\dfrac{1}{2}$

60. $22\dfrac{1}{2}+38\dfrac{2}{3}+17\dfrac{1}{3}$

The LCD of $\dfrac{1}{2}$, $\dfrac{2}{3}$ and $\dfrac{1}{3}$ is 6.
Rewrite fractional parts.

$22\dfrac{1}{2}=22\dfrac{1\cdot3}{2\cdot3}=22\dfrac{3}{6},\quad 38\dfrac{2}{3}=38\dfrac{2\cdot2}{3\cdot2}=38\dfrac{4}{6}$

$17\dfrac{1}{3}=17\dfrac{1\cdot2}{3\cdot2}=17\dfrac{2}{6}$

$$\begin{array}{r}22\dfrac{3}{6}\\ 38\dfrac{4}{6}\\ +\;17\dfrac{2}{6}\\ \hline 77\dfrac{9}{6}=77+1\dfrac{3}{6}=78\dfrac{3}{6}=78\dfrac{1}{2}\end{array}$$

62. $5\dfrac{1}{3}+10\dfrac{1}{2}+15\dfrac{1}{2}$

The LCD of $\dfrac{1}{2}$ and $\dfrac{1}{3}$ is 6.
Rewrite fractional parts.

$5\dfrac{1}{3}=5\dfrac{1\cdot2}{3\cdot2}=5\dfrac{2}{6},\quad 10\dfrac{1}{2}=10\dfrac{1\cdot3}{2\cdot3}=10\dfrac{3}{6}$

$15\dfrac{1}{2}=15\dfrac{1\cdot3}{2\cdot3}=15\dfrac{3}{6}$

$$\begin{array}{r}5\dfrac{2}{6}\\ 10\dfrac{3}{6}\\ +\;15\dfrac{3}{6}\\ \hline 30\dfrac{8}{6}=30+1\dfrac{2}{6}=31\dfrac{2}{6}=31\dfrac{1}{3}\end{array}$$

64. $3\dfrac{3}{5} = 3\dfrac{12}{20}, \quad 2\dfrac{1}{4} = 2\dfrac{5}{20}, \quad 5\dfrac{3}{10} = 5\dfrac{6}{20}$

$$3\dfrac{12}{20}$$

$$2\dfrac{5}{20}$$

$$+ \quad 5\dfrac{6}{20}$$

$$10\dfrac{23}{20} = 10 + 1\dfrac{3}{20} = 11\dfrac{3}{20}$$

66. $1\dfrac{2}{5} = 1\dfrac{12}{30}, \quad 1\dfrac{5}{6} = 1\dfrac{25}{30}, \quad 6\dfrac{1}{2} = 6\dfrac{15}{30}$

$$1\dfrac{12}{30}$$

$$1\dfrac{25}{30}$$

$$+ \quad 6\dfrac{15}{30}$$

$$8\dfrac{52}{30} = 8 + 1\dfrac{22}{30} = 9\dfrac{22}{30} = 9\dfrac{11}{15}$$

68. $\dfrac{1}{5} = \dfrac{12}{60}, \quad 2\dfrac{1}{3} = 2\dfrac{20}{60}, \quad 1\dfrac{1}{4} = 1\dfrac{15}{60}$

$$\dfrac{12}{60}$$

$$2\dfrac{20}{60}$$

$$+ \quad 1\dfrac{15}{60}$$

$$3\dfrac{47}{60}$$

70. $1\dfrac{1}{3} = 1\dfrac{8}{24}, \quad 1\dfrac{3}{8} = 1\dfrac{9}{24}, \quad 5\dfrac{19}{24} = 5\dfrac{19}{24}$

$$1\dfrac{8}{24}$$

$$1\dfrac{9}{24}$$

$$+ \quad 5\dfrac{19}{24}$$

$$7\dfrac{36}{24} = 7 + 1\dfrac{12}{24} = 8\dfrac{12}{24} = 8\dfrac{1}{2}$$

72. The total weight is $\dfrac{1}{2} + \dfrac{2}{3} = \dfrac{1 \cdot 3}{2 \cdot 3} + \dfrac{2 \cdot 2}{3 \cdot 2} = \dfrac{3}{6} + \dfrac{4}{6} = \dfrac{7}{6} = 1\dfrac{1}{6}$ pounds.

74. The fraction completed is $\dfrac{1}{8} + \dfrac{1}{5} + \dfrac{1}{4} = \dfrac{1 \cdot 5}{8 \cdot 5} + \dfrac{1 \cdot 8}{5 \cdot 8} + \dfrac{1 \cdot 10}{4 \cdot 10} = \dfrac{5}{40} + \dfrac{8}{40} + \dfrac{10}{40} = \dfrac{23}{40}$.

76. Alicia lost a total of $4\dfrac{1}{2} + 3\dfrac{3}{8} + 6\dfrac{3}{4}$ pounds. Using the alternate method of adding mixed numbers and the LCD of 8 gives a total of

$$4\dfrac{1}{2} + 3\dfrac{3}{8} + 6\dfrac{3}{4} = \dfrac{9}{2} + \dfrac{27}{8} + \dfrac{27}{4} = \dfrac{9 \cdot 4}{2 \cdot 4} + \dfrac{27}{8} + \dfrac{27 \cdot 2}{4 \cdot 2}$$

$$= \dfrac{36}{8} + \dfrac{27}{8} + \dfrac{54}{8} = \dfrac{117}{8} = 14\dfrac{5}{8} \text{ pounds.}$$

78. The total amount of rainfall is $3\dfrac{7}{8} + 4\dfrac{3}{8} = 7\dfrac{10}{8} = 7 + 1\dfrac{2}{8} = 8\dfrac{2}{8} = 8\dfrac{1}{4}$ inches.

80. a. Jennifer worked $4\dfrac{3}{5} + 3\dfrac{3}{4} + 5 = 4\dfrac{12}{20} + 3\dfrac{15}{20} + 5 = 12\dfrac{27}{20} = 13\dfrac{7}{20}$ hours last week.

   b. Jennifer will work $7\dfrac{1}{2}$ more than her $13\dfrac{7}{20}$ hours from part a. or

$$13\dfrac{7}{20} + 7\dfrac{1}{2} = 13\dfrac{7}{20} + 7\dfrac{10}{20} = 20\dfrac{17}{20} \text{ hours.}$$

c. Combining the answers to a. and b. gives a total of $13\frac{7}{20} + 20\frac{17}{20} = 33\frac{24}{20} = 34\frac{4}{20} = 34\frac{1}{5}$ hours.

Cumulative Skills Review

2. LCD is the abbreviation for <u>least</u> <u>common</u> <u>denominator</u>.

4. $\frac{3}{4} \cdot \frac{5}{12} = \frac{\overset{3}{\cancel{3}}}{4} \cdot \frac{5}{\underset{4}{\cancel{12}}} = \frac{3}{4} \cdot \frac{5}{4} = \frac{15}{16}$

6.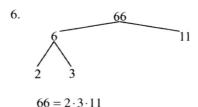

$66 = 2 \cdot 3 \cdot 11$

8. $(3+8)+7 = 3+(8+7)$ by the Associative property for addition.

10. The next job requires $3\frac{1}{2} \cdot 4\frac{1}{6} = \frac{7}{2} \cdot \frac{25}{6} = \frac{175}{12} = 14\frac{7}{12}$ gallons of paint.

Section 2.7   Subtracting Fractions and Mixed Numbers

Concept Check

2. When subtracting fractions with different denominators, we must find the <u>LCD</u> of the fractions, write each fraction as an <u>equivalent</u> fraction with this denominator, and then subtract the resulting like fractions.

4. When subtracting mixed numbers, if the fraction part of the first mixed number is less than the fraction part of the second mixed number, then borrow 1 from the whole number of the first mixed number and add it in the form of $\frac{LCD}{LCD}$ to the fraction part.

6. An alternate method for subtracting mixed numbers is to change each mixed number to an <u>improper</u> fraction and then subtract.

Guide Problems

8. Subtract $\frac{6}{7} - \frac{1}{7}$.

$\frac{6}{7} - \frac{1}{7} = \frac{6-1}{7}$ (Keep common denominator)

$\frac{6-1}{7} = \frac{5}{7}$ (Subtract numerators)

10. $\frac{25}{36} - \frac{18}{36} = \frac{25-18}{36} = \frac{7}{36}$

12. $\frac{7}{12} - \frac{1}{12} = \frac{7-1}{12} = \frac{6}{12} = \frac{6 \cdot 1}{6 \cdot 2} = \frac{1}{2}$

14. $\frac{5}{6} - \frac{1}{6} = \frac{5-1}{6} = \frac{4}{6} = \frac{2 \cdot 2}{2 \cdot 3} = \frac{2}{3}$

16. $\frac{18}{37} - \frac{14}{37} = \frac{18-14}{37} = \frac{4}{37}$

18. $\frac{11}{36} - \frac{5}{36} = \frac{11-5}{35} = \frac{6}{36} = \frac{6 \cdot 1}{6 \cdot 6} = \frac{1}{6}$

20. $\dfrac{19}{56} - \dfrac{11}{56} = \dfrac{19-11}{56} = \dfrac{8}{56} = \dfrac{8 \cdot 1}{8 \cdot 7} = \dfrac{1}{7}$

Guide Problems

22. Subtract $\dfrac{3}{5} - \dfrac{1}{4}$.

    a. Find the LCD of the fraction. The LCD is the least common multiple of the numbers that appear in the denominators of the two fractions. The denominators here are 5 and 4 and their least common multiple is 20, so the LCD is $\underline{20}$.

    b. Write each fraction as an equivalent fraction with the LCD found in part a. Each fraction must be multiplied by a fraction equivalent to 1 that yields a fraction with the LCD, 20, as its denominator.

    $$\dfrac{3}{5} = \dfrac{3}{5} \cdot \dfrac{4}{\underline{4}} = \dfrac{3 \cdot 4}{5 \cdot 4} = \dfrac{12}{\underline{20}} \quad \text{and} \quad \dfrac{1}{4} = \dfrac{1}{4} \cdot \dfrac{5}{\underline{5}} = \dfrac{1 \cdot 5}{4 \cdot 5} = \dfrac{5}{\underline{20}}$$

    c. Subtract the fractions. The two fractions have been written as equivalent fraction having like denominators. Subtract by keeping the like denominator and subtracting the numerators.

    $$\dfrac{3}{5} - \dfrac{1}{4} = \dfrac{12}{\underline{20}} - \dfrac{5}{\underline{20}} = \dfrac{12-5}{20} = \dfrac{7}{\underline{20}}$$

24. $\dfrac{7}{8} - \dfrac{15}{32}$. The LCD is the LCM of 8 and 32 which is 32.

    $$\dfrac{7}{8} - \dfrac{15}{32} = \dfrac{7}{8} \cdot \dfrac{4}{4} - \dfrac{15}{32} = \dfrac{28}{32} - \dfrac{15}{32} = \dfrac{13}{32}$$

26. $\dfrac{1}{2} - \dfrac{7}{20}$. The LCD is the LCM of 2 and 20 which is 20.

    $$\dfrac{1}{2} - \dfrac{7}{20} = \dfrac{1}{2} \cdot \dfrac{10}{10} - \dfrac{7}{20} = \dfrac{10}{20} - \dfrac{7}{20} = \dfrac{3}{20}$$

28. $\dfrac{9}{14} - \dfrac{3}{8}$. The LCD is the LCM of 8 and 14 which is 56.

    $$\dfrac{9}{14} - \dfrac{3}{8} = \dfrac{9}{14} \cdot \dfrac{4}{4} - \dfrac{3}{8} \cdot \dfrac{7}{7} = \dfrac{36}{56} - \dfrac{21}{56} = \dfrac{15}{56}$$

30. $\dfrac{3}{5} - \dfrac{1}{2}$. The LCD is the LCM of 2 and 5 which is 10.

    $$\dfrac{3}{5} - \dfrac{1}{2} = \dfrac{3}{5} \cdot \dfrac{2}{2} - \dfrac{1}{2} \cdot \dfrac{5}{5} = \dfrac{6}{10} - \dfrac{5}{10} = \dfrac{1}{10}$$

32. $\dfrac{3}{8} - \dfrac{1}{6}$. The LCD is the LCM of 6 and 8 which is 24.

    $$\dfrac{3}{8} - \dfrac{1}{6} = \dfrac{3}{8} \cdot \dfrac{3}{3} - \dfrac{1}{6} \cdot \dfrac{4}{4} = \dfrac{9}{24} - \dfrac{4}{24} = \dfrac{5}{24}$$

34. $\dfrac{9}{10}-\dfrac{7}{8}$. The LCD is the LCM of 10 and 8 which is 40.

$$\frac{9}{10}-\frac{7}{8}=\frac{9}{10}\cdot\frac{4}{4}-\frac{7}{8}\cdot\frac{5}{5}=\frac{36}{40}-\frac{35}{40}=\frac{1}{40}$$

Guide Problems

36. Subtract $28\dfrac{5}{8}-5\dfrac{1}{8}$. The fractional part of the first mixed number, $\dfrac{5}{8}$, is greater than $\dfrac{1}{8}$, the fractional part of the second mixed number. Thus, the subtraction can be formed by subtracting the fractional parts $\left(\dfrac{5}{8}-\dfrac{1}{8}\right)$ and then subtracting the whole number parts $(28-5)$.

$$28\frac{5}{8}$$
$$-5\frac{1}{8}$$
$$\overline{}$$
$$\underline{23\frac{4}{8}}=23\frac{1}{2}\quad\text{Note the result could be simplified.}$$

Note in problems 38 through 44, the fractional part of the first mixed number is greater than or equal to the fractional part of the second mixed number. Further the fractions are like fractions. The subtraction is performed by subtracting fractional parts and subtracting whole number parts.

38.
$$4\frac{11}{15}$$
$$-\;1\frac{1}{15}$$
$$\overline{}$$
$$3\frac{10}{15}=3\frac{2}{3}$$

40. In the subtraction below, the second mixed number has a whole number part of 0.
$$2\frac{16}{17}$$
$$-\;\frac{12}{17}$$
$$\overline{}$$
$$2\frac{4}{17}$$

42.
$$2\frac{5}{8}$$
$$-\;\frac{3}{8}$$
$$\overline{}$$
$$2\frac{2}{8}=2\frac{1}{4}$$

44.
$$7\frac{1}{7}$$
$$-\;2\frac{1}{7}$$
$$\overline{}$$
$$5$$

Note the fractional part of the answer is $\dfrac{1}{7}-\dfrac{1}{7}=0$ so the answer is a whole number.

Guide Problems

46. Subtract $16\dfrac{1}{8}-9\dfrac{3}{8}$.

a. Because the fraction part of the first mixed number is less than the fraction part of the second mixed number, 1 must be borrowed from the whole number of the first mixed number in the form of

$\dfrac{LCD}{LCD}$ and added to the fraction part of the first mixed number. The two fraction parts are like fractions with denominators of 8. So 8 is the LCD. The first mixed number is rewritten as

$$16\frac{1}{8} = 15 + 1 + \frac{1}{8} = 15 + \frac{8}{8} + \frac{1}{8} = 15\frac{9}{8}$$

b. With the equivalent version of the first mixed number, the subtraction can be performed by first subtracting the fractional parts and then subtracting the whole number parts.

$$
\begin{array}{r}
15\dfrac{9}{8} \\[2mm]
-\ 9\dfrac{3}{8} \\[1mm]
\hline
6\dfrac{6}{8} = 6\dfrac{3}{4}
\end{array}
\quad \text{Simplify the result}
$$

In problems 48 through 54, the approach is the same. The fraction parts have unlike denominators but the fraction part of the minuend is smaller than that of the subtrahend. The first mixed number is rewritten by borrowing 1 from its whole number part before the subtraction is done. Also the subtraction may be written horizontally or vertically but is performed the same, subtract the whole number parts and subtract the fraction parts.

48. $19\dfrac{3}{8} = 19 + \dfrac{3}{8} = 18 + \dfrac{8}{8} + \dfrac{3}{8} = 18\dfrac{11}{8}$

$$
\begin{array}{r}
18\dfrac{11}{8} \\[2mm]
-\ 5\dfrac{5}{8} \\[1mm]
\hline
13\dfrac{6}{8} = 13\dfrac{3}{4}
\end{array}
$$

50. $9\dfrac{2}{5} = 9 + \dfrac{2}{5} = 8 + \dfrac{5}{5} + \dfrac{2}{5} = 8\dfrac{7}{5}$

$$
\begin{array}{r}
8\dfrac{7}{5} \\[2mm]
-\ 1\dfrac{3}{5} \\[1mm]
\hline
7\dfrac{4}{5}
\end{array}
$$

52. $17\dfrac{2}{11} = 17 + \dfrac{2}{11} = 16 + \dfrac{11}{11} + \dfrac{2}{11} = 16\dfrac{13}{11}$

$16\dfrac{13}{11} - 5\dfrac{5}{11} = 11\dfrac{8}{11}$

54. $15\dfrac{9}{16} = 15 + \dfrac{9}{16} = 14 + \dfrac{16}{16} + \dfrac{9}{16} = 14\dfrac{25}{16}$

$14\dfrac{25}{16} - 14\dfrac{11}{16} = 0\dfrac{14}{16} = \dfrac{14}{16} = \dfrac{7}{8}$

Guide Problems

56. Subtract $8\dfrac{3}{4} - 2\dfrac{1}{3}$.

a. Find the LCD of the fraction parts.
Find the least common multiple of 3 and 4.

$$LCD = \underline{12}$$

b. Write the fractional part of each mixed number as an equivalent fraction with the LCD found in part a.

$$8\frac{3}{4} = 8\frac{3 \cdot \underline{3}}{4 \cdot \underline{3}} = 8\frac{9}{\underline{12}}$$

$$2\frac{1}{3} = 2\frac{1 \cdot \underline{4}}{3 \cdot \underline{4}} = 2\frac{4}{\underline{12}}$$

c. Subtract the fraction parts and then subtract the whole number parts. Simplify if possible.

$$8\frac{9}{12}$$
$$-\ 2\frac{4}{12}$$
$$\overline{\quad\quad}$$
$$6\frac{5}{12}$$

In problems 58 through 76, the approach is the same. The fraction parts have u like denominators. The mixed numbers are rewritten using the LCD as the common denominator. The subtraction is performed by subtracting the whole number parts and subtracting the fraction parts. The result is simplified, if possible. The subtraction may be written vertically or horizontally.

58. The LCD is 6.

$$25\frac{1}{2} = 25\frac{1 \cdot 3}{2 \cdot 3} = 25\frac{3}{6}$$

$$20\frac{1}{6} = 20\frac{1}{6}$$

$$25\frac{3}{6}$$
$$-\ 20\frac{1}{6}$$
$$\overline{\quad\quad}$$
$$5\frac{2}{6} = 5\frac{1}{3}$$

60. The LCD is 48.

$$2\frac{13}{16} = 2\frac{13 \cdot 3}{16 \cdot 3} = 2\frac{39}{48}$$

$$\frac{5}{12} = \frac{5 \cdot 4}{12 \cdot 4} = \frac{20}{48}$$

$$2\frac{39}{48}$$
$$-\ \frac{20}{48}$$
$$\overline{\quad\quad}$$
$$2\frac{19}{48}$$

62. The LCD is 36.

$$3\frac{13}{18} = 3\frac{13 \cdot 2}{18 \cdot 2} = 3\frac{26}{36}$$

$$\frac{7}{12} = \frac{7 \cdot 3}{12 \cdot 3} = \frac{21}{36}$$

$$3\frac{26}{36}$$
$$-\ \frac{21}{36}$$
$$\overline{\quad\quad}$$
$$3\frac{5}{36}$$

64. The LCD is 48.

$$2\frac{15}{16} = 2\frac{45}{48}, \quad \frac{5}{12} = \frac{20}{48}$$

$$2\frac{45}{48} - \frac{20}{48} = 2\frac{25}{48}$$

66. The LCD is 12.

$$18\frac{1}{2} = 18\frac{6}{12}, \quad 2\frac{5}{12} = 2\frac{5}{12}$$

$$18\frac{6}{12} - 2\frac{5}{12} = 16\frac{1}{12}$$

68. The LCD is 15.

$$3\frac{11}{15} = 3\frac{11}{15}, \quad \frac{2}{5} = \frac{6}{15}$$

$$3\frac{11}{15} - \frac{6}{15} = 3\frac{5}{15} = 3\frac{1}{3}$$

70. The LCD is 16.

$$5\frac{3}{8} = 5\frac{6}{16}, \quad 3\frac{5}{16} = 3\frac{5}{16}$$

$$5\frac{6}{16} - 3\frac{5}{16} = 2\frac{1}{16}$$

72. The LCD is 120.

$$5\frac{33}{40} = 5\frac{99}{120}, \quad \frac{7}{24} = \frac{35}{120}$$

$$5\frac{99}{120} - \frac{35}{120} = 5\frac{64}{120} = 5\frac{8}{15}$$

74. The LCD is 20.

$$18\frac{7}{10} = 18\frac{14}{20}, \quad 8\frac{1}{4} = 8\frac{5}{20}$$

$$18\frac{14}{20} - 8\frac{5}{20} = 10\frac{9}{20}$$

76. The LCD is 120.

$$4\frac{47}{60} = 4\frac{94}{120}, \quad 1\frac{17}{24} = 1\frac{85}{120}$$

$$4\frac{94}{120} - 1\frac{85}{120} = 3\frac{9}{120} = 3\frac{3}{40}$$

Guide Problems

78. Subtract $24\frac{1}{4} - 3\frac{4}{5}$

a. Find the LCD of the fraction parts. Find the least common multiple of the denominators 4 and 5.

$$LCD = \underline{20}$$

b. Write the fraction part of each mixed number as an equivalent fraction with the LCD found in part a.

$$24\frac{1}{4} = 24\frac{1 \cdot \underline{5}}{4 \cdot \underline{5}} = 24\frac{\underline{5}}{\underline{20}}$$

$$3\frac{4}{5} = 3\frac{4 \cdot \underline{4}}{5 \cdot \underline{4}} = 3\frac{\underline{16}}{\underline{20}}$$

c. Because the fraction part of the first mixed number is less than the fraction part of the second mixed number, borrow 1 from the whole number of the first mixed number in the form of $\dfrac{LCD}{LCD}$ and add it to the fraction part of the first mixed number.

$$24\frac{\underline{5}}{\underline{20}} = 24 + \frac{\underline{5}}{\underline{20}} = 23 + \frac{\underline{20}}{\underline{20}} + \frac{\underline{5}}{\underline{20}} = 23\frac{\underline{25}}{\underline{20}}$$

d. Subtract the fraction parts and then subtract the whole number parts. Simplify if possible.

$$\begin{aligned}23\frac{\underline{25}}{\underline{20}} \\ -\ 3\frac{\underline{16}}{\underline{20}} \\ \hline 20\frac{\underline{9}}{\underline{20}}\end{aligned}$$

In problems 78 through 94, the approach is the same. In each case, the fraction parts are unlike fractions. After equivalent mixed numbers are found with a common denominator, it is clear the fraction part of the first number is smaller than that of the second number so 1 must be borrowed from the whole number part of the first mixed number before subtraction can be performed. The subtraction is done either vertically or horizontally by subtracting the fraction parts and then the whole number parts.

80. The LCD is 6.

$$10\frac{1}{6} = 10 + \frac{1}{6} = 9 + \frac{6}{6} + \frac{1}{6}$$
$$= 9\frac{7}{6}$$

$$5\frac{1}{2} = 5\frac{1 \cdot 3}{2 \cdot 3} = 5\frac{3}{6}$$

$$9\frac{7}{6}$$
$$- \; 5\frac{3}{6}$$
$$\overline{\;\;4\frac{4}{6} = 4\frac{2}{3}}$$

82. The LCD is 6.

$$37\frac{1}{6} = 37 + \frac{1}{6} = 36 + \frac{6}{6} + \frac{1}{6}$$
$$= 36\frac{7}{6}$$

$$10\frac{1}{2} = 10\frac{1 \cdot 3}{2 \cdot 3} = 10\frac{3}{6}$$

$$36\frac{7}{6}$$
$$- \; 10\frac{3}{6}$$
$$\overline{\;\;26\frac{4}{6} = 26\frac{2}{3}}$$

84. The LCD is 15.

$$7\frac{1}{5} = 7\frac{3}{15} = 7 + \frac{3}{15} = 6 + \frac{15}{15} + \frac{3}{15}$$
$$= 6\frac{18}{15}$$

$$4\frac{11}{15} = 4\frac{11}{15}$$

$$6\frac{18}{15}$$
$$- \; 4\frac{11}{15}$$
$$\overline{\;\;2\frac{7}{15}}$$

86. The LCD is 6.

$$51\frac{1}{3} = 51\frac{2}{6} = 50\frac{8}{6}, \quad 26\frac{5}{6} = 26\frac{5}{6}$$

$$50\frac{8}{6} - 26\frac{5}{6} = 24\frac{3}{6} = 24\frac{1}{2}$$

88. The LCD is 4.

$$31 = 30\frac{4}{4}, \quad 9\frac{3}{4} = 9\frac{3}{4}$$

$$30\frac{4}{4} - 9\frac{3}{4} = 21\frac{1}{4}$$

90. The LCD is 24.

$$14\frac{1}{6} = 14\frac{4}{24} = 13\frac{28}{24}, \quad 4\frac{7}{8} = 4\frac{21}{24}$$

$$13\frac{28}{24} - 4\frac{21}{24} = 9\frac{7}{24}$$

92. The LCD is 9.

$$19 = 18\frac{9}{9}, \quad 5\frac{4}{9} = 5\frac{4}{9}$$

$$18\frac{9}{9} - 5\frac{4}{9} = 13\frac{5}{9}$$

94. The LCD is 10.

$$5 = 4\frac{10}{10}, \quad 2\frac{1}{10} = 2\frac{1}{10}$$

$$4\frac{10}{10} - 2\frac{1}{10} = 2\frac{9}{10}$$

96. Howard is $71\frac{3}{4} - 67\frac{1}{2} = 71\frac{3}{4} - 67\frac{2}{4} = 4\frac{1}{4}$ inches taller than Bob.

98. The number of acres remaining is $18\frac{1}{4} - 2\frac{3}{5} = 18\frac{5}{20} - 2\frac{12}{20} = 17\frac{25}{20} - 2\frac{12}{20} = 15\frac{13}{20}$ acres.

100. Since $\frac{7}{32}$ is removed, we are subtracting from the thickness. The new thickness is

$$\frac{3}{8} - \frac{7}{32} = \frac{12}{32} - \frac{7}{32} = \frac{5}{32} \text{ inch.}$$

102. The rate increased by $7\frac{5}{16} - 6\frac{3}{4} = 7\frac{5}{16} - 6\frac{12}{16} = 6\frac{21}{16} - 6\frac{12}{16} = \frac{9}{16}$ percent.

104. The whole of the business is represented by 1. The fraction representing Jill's portion is

$$1 - \frac{1}{4} - \frac{1}{3} = \frac{12}{12} - \frac{3}{12} - \frac{4}{12} = \frac{9}{12} - \frac{4}{12} = \frac{5}{12}.$$

106. a. The total time recorded so far is $1\frac{3}{10} + 3\frac{3}{5} = 1\frac{3}{10} + 3\frac{6}{10} = 4\frac{9}{10}$ hours.

   b. The time remaining is $6 - 4\frac{9}{10} = 5\frac{10}{10} - 4\frac{9}{10} = 1\frac{1}{10}$ hours.

108. If Lynn's total income is represented by 1, then the fraction representing the amount remaining after allowances for food and clothing, housing, and transportation is

$$1 - \frac{2}{5} - \frac{1}{4} - \frac{1}{8} = \frac{40}{40} - \frac{16}{40} - \frac{10}{40} - \frac{5}{40} = \frac{9}{40}.$$

110. You had $2\frac{1}{5}$ pounds but then George took half a pound so you have

$$2\frac{1}{5} - \frac{1}{2} = \frac{11}{5} - \frac{1}{2} = \frac{22}{10} - \frac{5}{10} = \frac{17}{10} = 1\frac{7}{10} \text{ pounds left.}$$

112. a. The combined weight of the boat hull and the motor is $1658\frac{1}{2} + 645\frac{1}{4} = 1658\frac{2}{4} + 645\frac{1}{4} = 2303\frac{3}{4}$ pounds. This weight is greater than the limit of 2170 pounds so the load is not safe and a heavy duty trailer is necessary.

   b. The load is over the limit by $2303\frac{3}{4} - 2170 = 133\frac{3}{4}$ pounds.

114. A full tank is represented by 1. By noon you had used $\frac{1}{4}$ leaving $1-\frac{1}{4}$. By late afternoon you used an additional $\frac{5}{16}$ leaving $1-\frac{1}{4}-\frac{5}{16}=\frac{16}{16}-\frac{4}{16}-\frac{5}{16}=\frac{7}{16}$. The fraction $\frac{7}{16}$ represents the remaining fuel.

Cumulative Skills Review

2. $\dfrac{4}{15}+\dfrac{2}{15}=\dfrac{4+2}{15}=\dfrac{6}{15}=\dfrac{\overset{2}{\cancel{6}}}{\underset{5}{\cancel{15}}}=\dfrac{2}{5}$

4. $18\dfrac{3}{7}+45\dfrac{1}{2}=18\dfrac{3\cdot2}{7\cdot2}+45\dfrac{1\cdot7}{2\cdot7}=18\dfrac{6}{14}+45\dfrac{7}{14}=63\dfrac{13}{14}$

6. The GCF of 8 and 144 is 8. Dividing out gives $\dfrac{8}{144}=\dfrac{\overset{1}{\cancel{8}}}{\underset{18}{\cancel{144}}}=\dfrac{1}{18}$.

8. $8\dfrac{1}{3}\cdot2\dfrac{2}{5}=\dfrac{25}{3}\cdot\dfrac{12}{5}=\dfrac{\overset{5}{\cancel{25}}}{\underset{1}{\cancel{3}}}\cdot\dfrac{\overset{4}{\cancel{12}}}{\underset{1}{\cancel{5}}}=\dfrac{5\cdot4}{1\cdot1}=20$

10. The total length is $34\dfrac{1}{2}+18\dfrac{3}{8}+12\dfrac{1}{4}=34\dfrac{1\cdot4}{2\cdot4}+18\dfrac{3}{8}+12\dfrac{1\cdot2}{4\cdot2}=34\dfrac{4}{8}+18\dfrac{3}{8}+12\dfrac{2}{8}=64\dfrac{9}{8}=65\dfrac{1}{8}$ inches.

Chapter 2 Numerical Facts of Life

The solutions to problems 2-6 are given in the table below. In each case the amount of the ingredient in the original recipe must be multiplied by 3 to arrive at the corresponding amount in the increased recipe.

Problem	Ingredient	Original recipe	Increased recipe
2.	butter	$\frac{1}{2}$ cup	$3\cdot\dfrac{1}{2}=\dfrac{3}{1}\cdot\dfrac{1}{2}=\dfrac{3}{2}$ or $1\dfrac{1}{2}$ cups
4.	flour	$2\dfrac{1}{4}$ cups	$3\cdot2\dfrac{1}{4}=\dfrac{3}{1}\cdot\dfrac{9}{4}=\dfrac{27}{4}$ or $6\dfrac{3}{4}$ cups
6.	salt	1 pinch $=\frac{1}{8}$ teaspoon	$3\cdot\dfrac{1}{8}=\dfrac{3}{1}\cdot\dfrac{1}{8}=\dfrac{3}{8}$ teaspoons

Chapter 2 Review Exercises

1. The following quotients with 10 as the dividend result in a natural number: $10\div1=10$, $10\div2=5$, before factors begin to repeat. The factors of 10 are 1, 2, 5, and 10.

2. The following quotients with 15 as the dividend result in a natural number: $15\div1=15$, $15\div3=5$, before factors begin to repeat. The factors of 15 are 1, 3, 5, and 15.

3. The following quotients with 44 as the dividend result in a natural number: $44 \div 1 = 44$, $44 \div 2 = 22$, $44 \div 4 = 11$, before factors begin to repeat. The factors of 44 are 1, 2, 4, 11, 22, and 44.

4. The following quotients with 48 as the dividend result in a natural number: $48 \div 1 = 48$, $48 \div 2 = 24$, $48 \div 3 = 16$, $48 \div 4 = 12$, $48 \div 6 = 8$. before factors begin to repeat. The factors of 44 are 1, 2, 3, 4, 6, 8, 12, 16, 24, and 48.

5. The following quotients with 46 as the dividend result in a natural number: $46 \div 1 = 46$, $46 \div 2 = 23$, before factors begin to repeat. The factors of 46 are 1, 2, 23, and 46.

6. The following quotients with 85 as the dividend result in a natural number: $85 \div 1 = 85$, $85 \div 5 = 17$, before factors begin to repeat. The factors of 85 are 1, 5, 17, and 85.

7. The factors of 89 are 1 and 89 as these are the only natural numbers that divide 89 evenly.

8. The factors of 61 are 1 and 61 as these are the only natural numbers that divide 61 evenly.

9. Find the factors of 24: $24 \div 1 = 24$, $24 \div 2 = 12$, $24 \div 3 = 8$, $24 \div 4 = 6$, $24 \div 6 = 4$ are the quotients that divide evenly. Note the factors begin to repeat with the last division. The factors of 24 are 1, 2, 3, 4, 6, 8, 12, and 24.

10. Find the factors of 63: $63 \div 1 = 63$, $63 \div 3 = 21$, $63 \div 7 = 9$, $63 \div 9 = 7$ are the quotients that divide evenly. Note the factors begin to repeat with the last division. The factors of 63 are 1, 3, 7, 9, 21, and 63.

11. Find the factors of 66: $66 \div 1 = 66$, $66 \div 2 = 33$, $66 \div 3 = 22$, $66 \div 6 = 11$, $66 \div 11 = 6$ are the quotients that divide evenly. Note the factors begin to repeat with the last division. The factors of 66 are 1, 2, 3, 6, 11, 22, 33 and 66.

12. Find the factors of 112: $112 \div 1 = 112$, $112 \div 2 = 56$, $112 \div 4 = 28$, $112 \div 7 = 16$, $112 \div 8 = 14$, $112 \div 14 = 8$ are the quotients that divide evenly. Note the factors begin to repeat with the last division. The factors of 112 are 1, 2, 4, 7, 8, 14, 16, 28, 56. and 112.

13. The only factors of 41 are 1 and 41, so 41 is a prime number.

14. Since 5 divides 50 evenly, $50 \div 5 = 10$, 5 is a factor of 50 different from 1 or 50 so the number 50 is composite.

15. By definition, prime and composite numbers are greater than one. Hence, 1 is neither prime nor composite.

16. Since 7 divides 91 evenly, $91 \div 7 = 13$, 7 is a factor of 91 different from 1 or 91 so the number 91 is composite.

17. The number 5 is a factor of 125 different from 1 or 125 because $125 \div 5 = 25$. Therefore 125 is composite.

18. By definition, prime and composite numbers are greater than one. Hence, 0 is neither prime nor composite.

19. The number 3 divides 57 evenly since $57 \div 3 = 19$. Thus 3 is a factor 57 not equal to 1 or 57 so 57 is composite.

20. The only factors of 97 are 1 and 97, so 97 is a prime number.

21. The number 2 divides 12 evenly since $12 \div 2 = 6$. Thus 2 is a factor 12 not equal to 1 or 12 so 12 is composite.

22. The only factors of 37 are 1 and 37, so 37 is a prime number.

23. Since $81 \div 9 = 9$, the number 9 is a factor of 81 that is not equal to 1 or 81. Thus 81 is composite.

24. The only factors of 13 are 1 and 13, so 13 is a prime number.

25.

$$75 = 3 \cdot 5 \cdot 5 = 3 \cdot 5^2$$

26.

$$40 = 2 \cdot 2 \cdot 2 \cdot 5 = 2^3 \cdot 5$$

27.

$$57 = 3 \cdot 19$$

28.

$$62 = 2 \cdot 31$$

29.

$$88 = 2 \cdot 2 \cdot 2 \cdot 11 = 2^3 \cdot 11$$

30.

$$105 = 3 \cdot 5 \cdot 7$$

31.

$$625 = 5 \cdot 5 \cdot 5 \cdot 5 = 5^4$$

32.

$$90 = 2 \cdot 3 \cdot 3 \cdot 5 = 2 \cdot 3^2 \cdot 5$$

33.

$$1000 = 2 \cdot 2 \cdot 2 \cdot 5 \cdot 5 \cdot 5 = 2^3 \cdot 5^3$$

34.

$$120 = 2 \cdot 2 \cdot 2 \cdot 3 \cdot 5 = 2^3 \cdot 3 \cdot 5$$

35.

$$50 = 2 \cdot 5 \cdot 5 = 2 \cdot 5^2$$

36.

$$504 = 2 \cdot 2 \cdot 2 \cdot 3 \cdot 3 \cdot 7 = 2^3 \cdot 3^2 \cdot 7$$

37. Prime factorizations:
    $3 = 3, \qquad 11 = 11$

    The LCM is $3 \cdot 11 = 33$

38. List multiples:
    13: 13, 26, 39, 52, …
    26: 26, 52, 78, 104,…
    The smallest value common to both
    lists is 26. The LCM of 13 and 26 is 26.

39. Prime factorizations:
    $2 = 2, \qquad 43 = 43$

    The LCM is $2 \cdot 43 = 86$.

40. Prime factorizations:
    $8 = 2 \cdot 2 \cdot 2, \qquad 20 = 2 \cdot 2 \cdot 5$

    Multiply each prime factor the maximum
    number of times it appears in any factorization.
    The LCM is $2 \cdot 2 \cdot 2 \cdot 5 = 40$.

41. Prime factorizations:
    $6 = 2 \cdot 3, \qquad 8 = 2 \cdot 2 \cdot 2$
    $9 = 3 \cdot 3, \qquad 12 = 2 \cdot 2 \cdot 3$

    Multiply each prime factor the
    maximum number of times it
    appears in any factorization.
    The LCM is $2 \cdot 2 \cdot 2 \cdot 3 \cdot 3 = 72$.

42. Prime factorizations:
    $8 = 2 \cdot 2 \cdot 2, \qquad 12 = 2 \cdot 2 \cdot 3$
    $14 = 2 \cdot 7, \qquad 18 = 2 \cdot 3 \cdot 3$

    Multiply each prime factor the
    maximum number of times it
    appears in any factorization.
    The LCM is $2 \cdot 2 \cdot 2 \cdot 3 \cdot 3 \cdot 7 = 504$.

43. Prime factorizations:
    $6 = 2 \cdot 3, \qquad 7 = 7$
    $12 = 2 \cdot 2 \cdot 3, \qquad 16 = 2 \cdot 2 \cdot 2 \cdot 2$

    The LCM is $2 \cdot 2 \cdot 2 \cdot 2 \cdot 3 \cdot 7 = 336$.

44. Prime factorizations:
    $8 = 2 \cdot 2 \cdot 2, \qquad 12 = 2 \cdot 2 \cdot 3$
    $16 = 2 \cdot 2 \cdot 2 \cdot 2, \qquad 18 = 2 \cdot 3 \cdot 3$

    The LCM is $2 \cdot 2 \cdot 2 \cdot 2 \cdot 3 \cdot 3 = 144$.

45. Prime factorizations:
    $6 = 2 \cdot 3, \qquad 8 = 2 \cdot 2 \cdot 2$
    $12 = 2 \cdot 2 \cdot 3, \qquad 14 = 2 \cdot 7$

    The LCM is $2 \cdot 2 \cdot 2 \cdot 3 \cdot 7 = 168$.

46. Prime factorizations:
    $6 = 2 \cdot 3, \qquad 9 = 3 \cdot 3$
    $12 = 2 \cdot 2 \cdot 3, \qquad 14 = 2 \cdot 7$

    The LCM is $2 \cdot 2 \cdot 3 \cdot 3 \cdot 7 = 252$.

47. Prime factorizations:
    $7 = 7, \qquad 8 = 2 \cdot 2 \cdot 2$
    $9 = 3 \cdot 3, \qquad 16 = 2 \cdot 2 \cdot 2 \cdot 2$

    The LCM is $2 \cdot 2 \cdot 2 \cdot 2 \cdot 3 \cdot 3 \cdot 7 = 1008$.

48. Prime factorizations:
    $3 = 3, \qquad 7 = 7$
    $13 = 13, \qquad 22 = 2 \cdot 11$

    The LCM is $2 \cdot 3 \cdot 7 \cdot 11 \cdot 13 = 6006$.

49. The numerator, 14, is greater than the denominator, 5, so $\dfrac{14}{5}$ is improper.

50. There is both a whole number part, 4, and a fraction part, $\dfrac{7}{9}$, so $4\dfrac{7}{9}$ is mixed.

51. The numerator, 8, is less than the denominator, 15, so $\dfrac{8}{15}$ is proper.

52. There is both a whole number part, 2, and a fraction part, $\frac{5}{8}$, so $2\frac{5}{8}$ is mixed.

53. The numerator, 9, is less than the denominator, 13, so $\frac{9}{13}$ is proper.

54. The numerator, 33, is greater than the denominator, 7, so $\frac{33}{7}$ is improper.

55. The rectangle is divided into 24 squares. Of these, 21 are shaded. The fraction represented is $\frac{21}{24}$.

56. There are nine disks in all with four shaded. The fraction represented is $\frac{4}{9}$.

57. There are three circles shaded wholly while the last circle has three of five sections shaded. The mixed number represented here is $3\frac{3}{5}$.

58. One of the figures is divided into three triangles. One whole figure is shaded while two of the three triangles are shaded in the other. The mixed number represented is $1\frac{2}{3}$.

59. a. There are 8 animals total, 3 of them dogs. The dogs represent $\frac{3}{8}$ of the total.

    b. There are 8 animals total, 5 of them cats. The cats represent $\frac{5}{8}$ of the total.

60. a. There are 7 vehicles total, 2 of them buses. The buses represent $\frac{2}{7}$ of the total.

    b. There are 7 vehicles total, 5 of them cars. The cars represent $\frac{5}{7}$ of the total.

61.
$$\begin{array}{r} 12 \\ 2\overline{)25} \\ \underline{24} \\ 1 \end{array}$$

$$\frac{25}{2} = 12\frac{1}{2}$$

62.
$$\begin{array}{r} 4 \\ 8\overline{)37} \\ \underline{32} \\ 5 \end{array}$$

$$\frac{37}{8} = 4\frac{5}{8}$$

63.
$$\begin{array}{r} 7 \\ 7\overline{)49} \\ \underline{49} \\ 0 \end{array}$$

$$\frac{49}{7} = 7$$

64.
$$6\overline{)107}$$ with quotient 17

$$\begin{array}{r} 17 \\ 6\overline{)107} \\ \underline{6} \\ 47 \\ \underline{42} \\ 5 \end{array}$$

$$\frac{107}{6} = 17\frac{5}{6}$$

65.
$$\begin{array}{r} 11 \\ 5\overline{)55} \\ \underline{5} \\ 5 \\ \underline{5} \\ 0 \end{array}$$

$$\frac{55}{5} = 11$$

66.
$$\begin{array}{r} 11 \\ 7\overline{)78} \\ \underline{7} \\ 8 \\ \underline{7} \\ 1 \end{array}$$

$$\frac{78}{7} = 11\frac{1}{7}$$

67. $2\frac{3}{5} = \frac{2 \cdot 5 + 3}{5} = \frac{13}{5}$

68. $14\frac{8}{9} = \frac{14 \cdot 9 + 8}{9} = \frac{134}{9}$

69. $7\frac{3}{8} = \frac{7 \cdot 8 + 3}{8} = \frac{59}{8}$

70. $22\frac{1}{5} = \frac{22 \cdot 5 + 1}{5} = \frac{111}{5}$

71. $45\frac{2}{15} = \frac{45 \cdot 15 + 2}{15} = \frac{677}{15}$

72. $10\frac{6}{17} = \frac{10 \cdot 17 + 6}{17} = \frac{176}{17}$

73. The GCF of 9 and 72 is 9.

$$\frac{9}{72} = \frac{\overset{1}{\cancel{9}}}{\underset{8}{\cancel{72}}} = \frac{1}{8}$$

74. The GCF of 25 and 125 is 25.

$$\frac{25}{125} = \frac{\overset{1}{\cancel{25}}}{\underset{5}{\cancel{125}}} = \frac{1}{5}$$

75. $15 = 3 \cdot 5$
$24 = 2 \cdot 2 \cdot 2 \cdot 3$

$$\frac{15}{24} = \frac{\overset{1}{\cancel{3}} \cdot 5}{2 \cdot 2 \cdot 2 \cdot \underset{1}{\cancel{3}}} = \frac{1 \cdot 5}{2 \cdot 2 \cdot 2 \cdot 1} = \frac{5}{8}$$

76. $20 = 2 \cdot 2 \cdot 5$
$32 = 2 \cdot 2 \cdot 2 \cdot 2 \cdot 2$

$$\frac{20}{32} = \frac{\overset{1}{\cancel{2}} \cdot \overset{1}{\cancel{2}} \cdot 5}{\underset{1}{\cancel{2}} \cdot \underset{1}{\cancel{2}} \cdot 2 \cdot 2 \cdot 2}$$
$$= \frac{1 \cdot 1 \cdot 5}{1 \cdot 1 \cdot 2 \cdot 2 \cdot 2} = \frac{5}{8}$$

77. The GCF of 12 and 36 is 12.

$$\frac{12}{36} = \frac{\overset{1}{\cancel{12}}}{\underset{3}{\cancel{36}}} = \frac{1}{3}$$

78. $18 = 2 \cdot 3 \cdot 3$
$60 = 2 \cdot 2 \cdot 3 \cdot 5$

$$\frac{18}{60} = \frac{\overset{1}{\cancel{2}} \cdot \overset{1}{\cancel{3}} \cdot 3}{\underset{1}{\cancel{2}} \cdot 2 \cdot \underset{1}{\cancel{3}} \cdot 5}$$
$$= \frac{1 \cdot 1 \cdot 3}{1 \cdot 2 \cdot 1 \cdot 5} = \frac{3}{10}$$

79. $25 = 5 \cdot 5$
$90 = 2 \cdot 3 \cdot 3 \cdot 5$

$$\frac{25}{90} = \frac{\overset{1}{\cancel{5}} \cdot 5}{2 \cdot 3 \cdot 3 \cdot \underset{1}{\cancel{5}}}$$
$$= \frac{1 \cdot 5}{2 \cdot 3 \cdot 3 \cdot 1} = \frac{5}{18}$$

80. $54 = 2 \cdot 3 \cdot 3 \cdot 3$
$90 = 2 \cdot 3 \cdot 3 \cdot 5$

$$\frac{54}{90} = \frac{\overset{1}{\cancel{2}} \cdot \overset{1}{\cancel{3}} \cdot \overset{1}{\cancel{3}} \cdot 3}{\underset{1}{\cancel{2}} \cdot \underset{1}{\cancel{3}} \cdot \underset{1}{\cancel{3}} \cdot 5}$$
$$= \frac{1 \cdot 1 \cdot 1 \cdot 3}{1 \cdot 1 \cdot 1 \cdot 5} = \frac{3}{5}$$

81. Since $14 \cdot 4 = 56$,

$$\frac{3}{14} = \frac{3 \cdot 4}{14 \cdot 4} = \frac{12}{56}$$

82. Since $10 \cdot 8 = 80$,

$$\frac{1}{10} = \frac{1 \cdot 8}{10 \cdot 8} = \frac{8}{80}$$

83. Since $11 \cdot 4 = 44$,

$$\frac{2}{11} = \frac{2 \cdot 4}{11 \cdot 4} = \frac{8}{44}$$

84. Since $8 \cdot 8 = 64$,

$$\frac{3}{8} = \frac{3 \cdot 8}{8 \cdot 8} = \frac{24}{64}$$

85. Rewrite using common denominator, then compare numerators.

$$\frac{11}{12} = \frac{11}{12}, \qquad \frac{5}{6} = \frac{5 \cdot 2}{6 \cdot 2} = \frac{10}{12}$$

Since $10 < 11$, we have

$$\frac{5}{6} < \frac{11}{12}.$$

86. Rewrite using common denominator, then compare numerators.

$$\frac{5}{6} = \frac{5 \cdot 3}{6 \cdot 3} = \frac{15}{18}, \qquad \frac{7}{9} = \frac{7 \cdot 2}{9 \cdot 2} = \frac{14}{18}$$

Since $14 < 15$, we have

$$\frac{7}{9} < \frac{5}{6}.$$

87. Rewrite using common denominator, then compare numerators.

$$\frac{5}{8} = \frac{5 \cdot 6}{8 \cdot 6} = \frac{30}{48}, \qquad \frac{11}{12} = \frac{11 \cdot 4}{12 \cdot 4} = \frac{44}{48}$$

$$\frac{13}{16} = \frac{13 \cdot 3}{16 \cdot 3} = \frac{39}{48}$$

Since $30 < 39 < 44$, we have

$$\frac{5}{8} < \frac{13}{16} < \frac{11}{12}.$$

88. Rewrite using common denominator, then compare numerators.

$$\frac{7}{9} = \frac{7 \cdot 8}{9 \cdot 8} = \frac{56}{72}, \qquad \frac{5}{6} = \frac{5 \cdot 12}{6 \cdot 12} = \frac{60}{72}$$

$$\frac{7}{8} = \frac{7 \cdot 9}{8 \cdot 9} = \frac{63}{72}$$

Since $56 < 60 < 63$, we have

$$\frac{7}{9} < \frac{5}{6} < \frac{7}{8}.$$

89. $\dfrac{7}{9} \cdot \dfrac{3}{9} = \dfrac{7}{9} \cdot \dfrac{\overset{1}{\cancel{3}}}{\underset{3}{\cancel{9}}} = \dfrac{7 \cdot 1}{9 \cdot 3} = \dfrac{7}{27}$

90. $\dfrac{2}{16} \cdot \dfrac{3}{6} = \dfrac{\overset{1}{\cancel{2}}}{\underset{8}{\cancel{16}}} \cdot \dfrac{\overset{1}{\cancel{3}}}{\underset{2}{\cancel{6}}} = \dfrac{1 \cdot 1}{8 \cdot 2} = \dfrac{1}{16}$

91. $\dfrac{2}{3} \cdot \dfrac{10}{11} = \dfrac{2 \cdot 10}{3 \cdot 11} = \dfrac{20}{33}$

92. $\dfrac{2}{5} \cdot \dfrac{1}{3} = \dfrac{2 \cdot 1}{5 \cdot 3} = \dfrac{2}{15}$

93. $\dfrac{4}{5} \cdot \dfrac{1}{4} = \dfrac{\overset{1}{\cancel{4}}}{5} \cdot \dfrac{1}{\underset{1}{\cancel{4}}} = \dfrac{1 \cdot 1}{5 \cdot 1} = \dfrac{1}{5}$

94. $\dfrac{12}{27} \cdot \dfrac{5}{19} = \dfrac{\overset{4}{\cancel{12}}}{\underset{9}{\cancel{27}}} \cdot \dfrac{5}{19} = \dfrac{4 \cdot 5}{9 \cdot 19} = \dfrac{20}{171}$

95. $\dfrac{9}{80} \cdot \dfrac{7}{72} = \dfrac{\overset{1}{\cancel{9}}}{80} \cdot \dfrac{7}{\underset{8}{\cancel{72}}} = \dfrac{1 \cdot 7}{80 \cdot 8} = \dfrac{7}{640}$

96. $\dfrac{7}{8} \cdot \dfrac{5}{7} = \dfrac{\overset{1}{\cancel{7}}}{8} \cdot \dfrac{5}{\underset{1}{\cancel{7}}} = \dfrac{1 \cdot 5}{8 \cdot 1} = \dfrac{5}{8}$

97. $3\dfrac{5}{7} \cdot 2\dfrac{7}{8} = \dfrac{26}{7} \cdot \dfrac{23}{8} = \dfrac{\overset{13}{\cancel{26}}}{7} \cdot \dfrac{23}{\underset{4}{\cancel{8}}}$

$\qquad = \dfrac{13}{7} \cdot \dfrac{23}{4} = \dfrac{299}{28}$

$\qquad = 10\dfrac{19}{28}$

98. $4\dfrac{1}{3} \cdot 7\dfrac{3}{4} = \dfrac{13}{3} \cdot \dfrac{31}{4} = \dfrac{403}{12}$

$\qquad = 33\dfrac{7}{12}$

99. $2\dfrac{1}{4} \cdot 19\dfrac{1}{2} = \dfrac{9}{4} \cdot \dfrac{39}{2} = \dfrac{351}{8}$

$= 43\dfrac{7}{8}$

100. $6\dfrac{3}{4} \cdot 5\dfrac{1}{2} = \dfrac{27}{4} \cdot \dfrac{11}{2} = \dfrac{297}{8}$

$= 37\dfrac{1}{8}$

101. $4\dfrac{8}{9} \cdot 1\dfrac{5}{6} = \dfrac{44}{9} \cdot \dfrac{11}{6} = \dfrac{\cancel{44}^{22}}{9} \cdot \dfrac{11}{\cancel{6}_{3}}$

$= \dfrac{22}{9} \cdot \dfrac{11}{3} = \dfrac{242}{27}$

$= 8\dfrac{26}{27}$

102. $3\dfrac{12}{15} \cdot 4\dfrac{7}{9} = \dfrac{57}{15} \cdot \dfrac{43}{9} = \dfrac{\cancel{57}^{19}}{15} \cdot \dfrac{43}{\cancel{9}_{3}}$

$= \dfrac{19}{15} \cdot \dfrac{43}{3} = \dfrac{817}{45}$

$= 18\dfrac{7}{45}$

103. $2\dfrac{1}{5} \cdot 12\dfrac{1}{6} = \dfrac{11}{5} \cdot \dfrac{73}{6} = \dfrac{803}{30}$

$= 26\dfrac{23}{30}$

104. $18\dfrac{2}{3} \cdot 5\dfrac{6}{7} = \dfrac{56}{3} \cdot \dfrac{41}{7} = \dfrac{\cancel{56}^{8}}{3} \cdot \dfrac{41}{\cancel{7}_{1}}$

$= \dfrac{8}{3} \cdot \dfrac{41}{1} = \dfrac{328}{3}$

$= 109\dfrac{1}{3}$

105. $\dfrac{2}{4} \div \dfrac{1}{8} = \dfrac{2}{4} \cdot \dfrac{8}{1} = \dfrac{2}{\cancel{4}_{1}} \cdot \dfrac{\cancel{8}^{2}}{1} = \dfrac{2 \cdot 2}{1 \cdot 1} = 4$

106. $\dfrac{5}{14} \div \dfrac{1}{2} = \dfrac{5}{14} \cdot \dfrac{2}{1} = \dfrac{5}{\cancel{14}_{7}} \cdot \dfrac{\cancel{2}^{1}}{1} = \dfrac{5 \cdot 1}{7 \cdot 1} = \dfrac{5}{7}$

107. $\dfrac{2}{6} \div \dfrac{5}{6} = \dfrac{2}{6} \cdot \dfrac{6}{5} = \dfrac{2}{\cancel{6}} \cdot \dfrac{\cancel{6}^{1}}{5} = \dfrac{2 \cdot 1}{1 \cdot 5} = \dfrac{2}{5}$

108. $\dfrac{1}{3} \div \dfrac{2}{13} = \dfrac{1}{3} \cdot \dfrac{13}{2} = \dfrac{1 \cdot 13}{3 \cdot 2} = \dfrac{13}{6} = 2\dfrac{1}{6}$

109. $\dfrac{6}{10} \div \dfrac{2}{5} = \dfrac{6}{10} \cdot \dfrac{5}{2} = \dfrac{\cancel{6}^{3}}{\cancel{10}_{2}} \cdot \dfrac{\cancel{5}^{1}}{\cancel{2}_{1}} = \dfrac{3 \cdot 1}{2 \cdot 1} = \dfrac{3}{2} = 1\dfrac{1}{2}$

110. $\dfrac{1}{3} \div \dfrac{7}{8} = \dfrac{1}{3} \cdot \dfrac{8}{7} = \dfrac{1 \cdot 8}{3 \cdot 7} = \dfrac{8}{21}$

111. $\dfrac{2}{3} \div \dfrac{5}{6} = \dfrac{2}{3} \cdot \dfrac{6}{5} = \dfrac{2}{\cancel{3}_{1}} \cdot \dfrac{\cancel{6}^{2}}{5} = \dfrac{2 \cdot 2}{1 \cdot 5} = \dfrac{4}{5}$

112. $\dfrac{3}{4} \div \dfrac{1}{2} = \dfrac{3}{4} \cdot \dfrac{2}{1} = \dfrac{3}{\cancel{4}_{2}} \cdot \dfrac{\cancel{2}^{1}}{1} = \dfrac{3 \cdot 1}{2 \cdot 1} = \dfrac{3}{2} = 1\dfrac{1}{2}$

113. $1\dfrac{3}{5} \div 2\dfrac{5}{6} = \dfrac{8}{5} \div \dfrac{17}{6} = \dfrac{8}{5} \cdot \dfrac{6}{17}$

$= \dfrac{8}{5} \cdot \dfrac{6}{17} = \dfrac{48}{85}$

114. $29\dfrac{1}{3} \div 2\dfrac{2}{3} = \dfrac{88}{3} \div \dfrac{8}{3} = \dfrac{88}{3} \cdot \dfrac{3}{8}$

$= \dfrac{\cancel{88}^{11}}{\cancel{3}_{1}} \cdot \dfrac{\cancel{3}^{1}}{\cancel{8}_{1}} = \dfrac{11 \cdot 1}{1 \cdot 1} = 11$

115. $20\dfrac{3}{4} \div 2\dfrac{1}{4} = \dfrac{83}{4} \div \dfrac{9}{4} = \dfrac{83}{4} \cdot \dfrac{4}{9}$

$= \dfrac{83}{\overset{}{\cancel{4}}} \cdot \dfrac{\overset{1}{\cancel{4}}}{9} = \dfrac{83}{9} = 9\dfrac{2}{9}$

116. $5\dfrac{3}{5} \div 6\dfrac{2}{3} = \dfrac{28}{5} \div \dfrac{20}{3} = \dfrac{28}{5} \cdot \dfrac{3}{20}$

$= \dfrac{\overset{7}{\cancel{28}}}{5} \cdot \dfrac{3}{\underset{5}{\cancel{20}}} = \dfrac{7 \cdot 3}{5 \cdot 5} = \dfrac{21}{25}$

117. $14\dfrac{2}{5} \div 1\dfrac{2}{7} = \dfrac{72}{5} \div \dfrac{9}{7} = \dfrac{72}{5} \cdot \dfrac{7}{9}$

$= \dfrac{\overset{8}{\cancel{72}}}{5} \cdot \dfrac{7}{\underset{1}{\cancel{9}}} = \dfrac{8 \cdot 7}{5 \cdot 1}$

$= \dfrac{56}{5} = 11\dfrac{1}{5}$

118. $10\dfrac{1}{3} \div 3\dfrac{1}{5} = \dfrac{31}{3} \div \dfrac{16}{5} = \dfrac{31}{3} \cdot \dfrac{5}{16}$

$= \dfrac{31 \cdot 5}{3 \cdot 16}$

$= \dfrac{155}{48} = 3\dfrac{11}{48}$

119. $24\dfrac{2}{9} \div 5\dfrac{1}{3} = \dfrac{218}{9} \div \dfrac{16}{3} = \dfrac{218}{9} \cdot \dfrac{3}{16}$

$= \dfrac{\overset{109}{\cancel{218}}}{\underset{3}{\cancel{9}}} \cdot \dfrac{\overset{1}{\cancel{3}}}{\underset{8}{\cancel{16}}} = \dfrac{109 \cdot 1}{3 \cdot 8}$

$= \dfrac{109}{24} = 4\dfrac{13}{24}$

120. $15\dfrac{13}{23} \div 6\dfrac{1}{2} = \dfrac{358}{23} \div \dfrac{13}{2} = \dfrac{358}{23} \cdot \dfrac{2}{13}$

$= \dfrac{358 \cdot 2}{23 \cdot 13} = \dfrac{716}{299}$

$= 2\dfrac{118}{299}$

121. $\dfrac{1}{4} + \dfrac{1}{5} = \dfrac{1 \cdot 5}{4 \cdot 5} + \dfrac{1 \cdot 4}{5 \cdot 4} = \dfrac{5}{20} + \dfrac{4}{20} = \dfrac{9}{20}$

122. $\dfrac{1}{4} + \dfrac{3}{4} = \dfrac{4}{4} = 1$

123. $\dfrac{2}{5} + \dfrac{1}{10} = \dfrac{2 \cdot 2}{5 \cdot 2} + \dfrac{1}{10} = \dfrac{4}{10} + \dfrac{1}{10} = \dfrac{5}{10} = \dfrac{\overset{1}{\cancel{5}}}{\underset{2}{\cancel{10}}} = \dfrac{1}{2}$

124. $\dfrac{5}{8} + \dfrac{7}{12} = \dfrac{5 \cdot 3}{8 \cdot 3} + \dfrac{7 \cdot 2}{12 \cdot 2} = \dfrac{15}{24} + \dfrac{14}{24} = \dfrac{29}{24} = 1\dfrac{5}{24}$

125. $\dfrac{6}{7} + \dfrac{1}{5} = \dfrac{6 \cdot 5}{7 \cdot 5} + \dfrac{1 \cdot 7}{5 \cdot 7} = \dfrac{30}{35} + \dfrac{7}{35} = \dfrac{37}{35} = 1\dfrac{2}{35}$

126. $\dfrac{8}{9} + \dfrac{2}{7} = \dfrac{8 \cdot 7}{9 \cdot 7} + \dfrac{2 \cdot 9}{7 \cdot 9} = \dfrac{56}{63} + \dfrac{18}{63} = \dfrac{74}{63} = 1\dfrac{11}{63}$

127. $\dfrac{5}{12} + \dfrac{1}{3} = \dfrac{5}{12} + \dfrac{1 \cdot 4}{3 \cdot 4} = \dfrac{5}{12} + \dfrac{4}{12} = \dfrac{9}{12} = \dfrac{\overset{3}{\cancel{9}}}{\underset{4}{\cancel{12}}} = \dfrac{3}{4}$

128. $\dfrac{7}{15} + \dfrac{5}{6} = \dfrac{7 \cdot 2}{15 \cdot 2} + \dfrac{5 \cdot 5}{6 \cdot 5} = \dfrac{14}{30} + \dfrac{25}{30} = \dfrac{39}{30} = \dfrac{\overset{13}{\cancel{39}}}{\underset{10}{\cancel{30}}} = 1\dfrac{3}{10}$

129. Convert fraction parts:

$$26\frac{1}{2} = 26\frac{1\cdot 3}{2\cdot 3} = 26\frac{3}{6},$$

$$28\frac{2}{3} = 28\frac{2\cdot 2}{3\cdot 2} = 28\frac{4}{6}$$

Add:

$$26\frac{3}{6}$$
$$+\ 28\frac{4}{6}$$
$$\overline{\ 54\frac{7}{6} = 55\frac{1}{6}}$$

130. Convert fraction parts:

$$1\frac{2}{3} = 1\frac{2\cdot 4}{3\cdot 4} = 1\frac{8}{12},$$

$$5\frac{5}{12} = 5\frac{5}{12}$$

Add:

$$1\frac{8}{12}$$
$$+\ 5\frac{5}{12}$$
$$\overline{\ 6\frac{13}{12} = 7\frac{1}{12}}$$

131. Convert fraction parts:

$$23\frac{1}{4} = 23\frac{1\cdot 5}{4\cdot 5} = 23\frac{5}{20},$$

$$20\frac{2}{5} = 20\frac{2\cdot 4}{5\cdot 4} = 20\frac{8}{20}$$

Add:

$$23\frac{5}{20}$$
$$+\ 20\frac{8}{20}$$
$$\overline{\ 43\frac{13}{20}}$$

132. Convert fraction parts:

$$37\frac{1}{5} = 37\frac{1\cdot 3}{5\cdot 3} = 37\frac{3}{15},$$

$$30\frac{2}{3} = 30\frac{2\cdot 5}{3\cdot 5} = 30\frac{10}{15}$$

Add:

$$37\frac{3}{15}$$
$$+\ 30\frac{10}{15}$$
$$\overline{\ 67\frac{13}{15}}$$

133. Convert fraction parts:

$$17\frac{1}{3} = 17\frac{1\cdot 4}{3\cdot 4} = 17\frac{4}{12},$$

$$2\frac{11}{12} = 2\frac{11}{12}$$

Add:

$$17\frac{4}{12}$$
$$+\ 2\frac{11}{12}$$
$$\overline{\ 19\frac{15}{12} = 20\frac{3}{12} = 20\frac{1}{4}}$$

134. Convert fraction parts:

$$1\frac{5}{8} = 1\frac{5\cdot 3}{8\cdot 3} = 1\frac{15}{24},$$

$$9\frac{13}{24} = 9\frac{13}{24}$$

Add:

$$1\frac{15}{24}$$
$$+\ 9\frac{13}{24}$$
$$\overline{\ 10\frac{28}{24} = 11\frac{4}{24} = 11\frac{1}{6}}$$

135. Convert fraction parts:

$$30\frac{1}{3} = 30\frac{1\cdot 2}{3\cdot 2} = 30\frac{2}{6},$$

$$24\frac{1}{2} = 24\frac{1\cdot 3}{2\cdot 3} = 24\frac{3}{6}$$

Add:

$$30\frac{2}{6}$$
$$+ \ 24\frac{3}{6}$$
$$\overline{54\frac{5}{6}}$$

136. Convert fraction parts:

$$12\frac{4}{7} = 12\frac{4\cdot 6}{7\cdot 6} = 12\frac{24}{42},$$

$$15\frac{5}{6} = 15\frac{5\cdot 7}{6\cdot 7} = 15\frac{35}{42}$$

Add:

$$12\frac{24}{42}$$
$$+ \ 15\frac{35}{42}$$
$$\overline{27\frac{59}{42} = 28\frac{17}{42}}$$

137. $\dfrac{4}{5} - \dfrac{3}{5} = \dfrac{4-3}{5} = \dfrac{1}{5}$

138. $\dfrac{14}{15} - \dfrac{4}{9} = \dfrac{14\cdot 3}{15\cdot 3} - \dfrac{4\cdot 5}{9\cdot 5} = \dfrac{42}{45} - \dfrac{20}{45} = \dfrac{42-20}{45} = \dfrac{22}{45}$

139. $\dfrac{7}{20} - \dfrac{4}{12} = \dfrac{7\cdot 3}{20\cdot 3} - \dfrac{4\cdot 5}{12\cdot 5} = \dfrac{21}{60} - \dfrac{20}{60} = \dfrac{1}{60}$

140. $\dfrac{2}{5} - \dfrac{1}{6} = \dfrac{2\cdot 6}{5\cdot 6} - \dfrac{1\cdot 5}{6\cdot 5} = \dfrac{12}{30} - \dfrac{5}{30} = \dfrac{12-5}{30} = \dfrac{7}{30}$

141. $\dfrac{5}{9} - \dfrac{7}{18} = \dfrac{5\cdot 2}{9\cdot 2} - \dfrac{7}{18} = \dfrac{10}{18} - \dfrac{7}{18} = \dfrac{3}{18} = \dfrac{\overset{1}{\cancel{3}}}{\underset{6}{\cancel{18}}} = \dfrac{1}{6}$

142. $\dfrac{3}{4} - \dfrac{1}{16} = \dfrac{3\cdot 4}{4\cdot 4} - \dfrac{1}{16} = \dfrac{12}{16} - \dfrac{1}{16} = \dfrac{11}{16}$

143. $\dfrac{3}{4} - \dfrac{1}{2} = \dfrac{3}{4} - \dfrac{1\cdot 2}{2\cdot 2} = \dfrac{3}{4} - \dfrac{2}{4} = \dfrac{1}{4}$

144. $\dfrac{5}{9} - \dfrac{5}{12} = \dfrac{5\cdot 4}{9\cdot 4} - \dfrac{5\cdot 3}{12\cdot 3} = \dfrac{20}{36} - \dfrac{15}{36} = \dfrac{5}{36}$

145. Convert the fraction parts to have a common denominator. If the fraction part of the minuend is smaller than that of the subtrahend, borrow 1 from the whole number part.

$$52\frac{1}{6} = 51\frac{7}{6}$$
$$14\frac{2}{3} = 14\frac{4}{6}$$

Subtract whole number parts and fraction parts.

$$51\frac{7}{6}$$
$$- \ 14\frac{4}{6}$$
$$\overline{37\frac{3}{6} = 37\frac{1}{2}}$$

146. Convert the fraction parts to have a common denominator. If the fraction part of the minuend is smaller than that of the subtrahend, borrow 1 from the whole number part.

$$50\frac{4}{7} = 50\frac{12}{21}$$
$$11\frac{5}{21} = 11\frac{5}{21}$$

Subtract whole number parts and fraction parts.

$$50\frac{12}{21}$$
$$- \ 11\frac{5}{21}$$
$$\overline{39\frac{7}{21} = 39\frac{1}{3}}$$

147. $35\dfrac{7}{16} = 34\dfrac{23}{16}$

$\quad 13\dfrac{5}{8} = 13\dfrac{10}{16}$

$$\begin{array}{r} 34\dfrac{23}{16} \\ -\ 13\dfrac{10}{16} \\ \hline 21\dfrac{13}{16} \end{array}$$

148. $49\dfrac{1}{3} = 49\dfrac{2}{6} = 48\dfrac{8}{6}$

$\quad 12\dfrac{4}{6} = 12\dfrac{4}{6}$

$$\begin{array}{r} 48\dfrac{8}{6} \\ -\ 12\dfrac{4}{6} \\ \hline 36\dfrac{4}{6} = 36\dfrac{2}{3} \end{array}$$

149. $32\dfrac{3}{4} = 32\dfrac{3}{4}$

$\quad 23\dfrac{1}{2} = 23\dfrac{2}{4}$

$$\begin{array}{r} 32\dfrac{3}{4} \\ -\ 23\dfrac{2}{4} \\ \hline 9\dfrac{1}{4} \end{array}$$

150. $57\dfrac{8}{13} = 57\dfrac{16}{26}$

$\quad 21\dfrac{15}{26} = 21\dfrac{15}{26}$

$$\begin{array}{r} 57\dfrac{16}{26} \\ -\ 21\dfrac{15}{26} \\ \hline 36\dfrac{1}{26} \end{array}$$

151. $35\dfrac{2}{3} = 35\dfrac{8}{12} = 34\dfrac{20}{12}$

$\quad 28\dfrac{11}{12} = 28\dfrac{11}{12}$

$$\begin{array}{r} 34\dfrac{20}{12} \\ -\ 28\dfrac{11}{12} \\ \hline 6\dfrac{9}{12} = 6\dfrac{3}{4} \end{array}$$

152. $56\dfrac{1}{6} = 55\dfrac{7}{6}$

$\quad 38\dfrac{2}{3} = 38\dfrac{4}{6}$

$$\begin{array}{r} 55\dfrac{7}{6} \\ -\ 38\dfrac{4}{6} \\ \hline 17\dfrac{3}{6} = 17\dfrac{1}{2} \end{array}$$

153. An hour is equal to 60 minutes. The fraction of an hour that is 18 minutes is $\dfrac{18}{60} = \dfrac{\overset{3}{\cancel{18}}}{\underset{10}{\cancel{60}}} = \dfrac{3}{10}$.

154. Since 20 out of 85 stocks went up, the fraction of stocks that went up is $\dfrac{20}{85} = \dfrac{\overset{4}{\cancel{20}}}{\underset{17}{\cancel{85}}} = \dfrac{4}{17}$.

155. Randy's total banana purchase weighs $2\dfrac{3}{4} + 3\dfrac{5}{7} = \dfrac{11}{4} + \dfrac{26}{7} = \dfrac{11 \cdot 7}{4 \cdot 7} + \dfrac{26 \cdot 4}{7 \cdot 4} = \dfrac{77}{28} + \dfrac{104}{28} = \dfrac{181}{28} = 6\dfrac{13}{28}$ pounds.

156. One half of $18\frac{3}{4}$ is $\frac{1}{2} \cdot 18\frac{3}{4} = \frac{1}{2} \cdot \frac{75}{4} = \frac{75}{8} = 9\frac{3}{8}$. The halved recipe requires $9\frac{3}{8}$ ounces of flour.

157. For 23 sweaters, 23 times the material is needed or $23 \cdot \frac{4}{7} = \frac{23}{1} \cdot \frac{4}{7} = \frac{92}{7} = 13\frac{1}{7}$ yards.

158. Victor has $3 \cdot 3\frac{4}{9} = \frac{3}{1} \cdot \frac{31}{9} = \frac{\cancel{3}^1}{1} \cdot \frac{31}{\cancel{9}_3} = \frac{31}{3} = 10\frac{1}{3}$ feet.

159. The number of jars Granny Nell can fill is given by $50 \div \frac{4}{5}$. Dividing gives

$$50 \div \frac{4}{5} = \frac{50}{1} \cdot \frac{5}{4} = \frac{250}{4} = 62\frac{2}{4} = 62\frac{1}{2}$$

so Granny Nell can fill $62\frac{1}{2}$ jars holding $\frac{4}{5}$ pints each.

160. Since $\frac{3}{8}$ of 4800 is $\frac{3}{8} \cdot 4800 = \frac{3}{8} \cdot \frac{4800}{1} = \frac{3}{\cancel{8}_1} \cdot \frac{\cancel{4800}^{600}}{1} = \frac{3 \cdot 600}{1 \cdot 1} = 1800$, the Lopez family spends $1800 of their monthly income on rent and utilities.

161. Area is equal to the length times the width. Compute $45\frac{1}{2} \cdot 15\frac{3}{4} = \frac{91}{2} \cdot \frac{63}{4} = \frac{5733}{8} = 716\frac{5}{8}$. Since the length and width were given in feet, the area is $716\frac{5}{8}$ square feet.

162. Since each gallon allows Guillermo to drive $24\frac{1}{6}$ miles, 9 gallons will allow him to travel

$$9 \cdot 24\frac{1}{6} = \frac{9}{1} \cdot \frac{145}{6} = \frac{\cancel{9}^3}{1} \cdot \frac{145}{\cancel{6}_2} = \frac{3 \cdot 145}{1 \cdot 2} = \frac{435}{2} = 217\frac{1}{2} \text{ miles.}$$

163. The difference in length is given by $5\frac{1}{4} - 3\frac{5}{16}$ inches. Subtracting gives

$$5\frac{1}{4} - 3\frac{5}{16} = \frac{21}{4} - \frac{53}{16} = \frac{84}{16} - \frac{53}{16} = \frac{31}{16} = 1\frac{15}{16} \text{ inches.}$$

164. If $12\frac{4}{5}$ inches of rain fell in total, the average per hour over the 7 hour period is

$$12\frac{4}{5} \div 7 = \frac{64}{5} \div 7 = \frac{64}{5} \cdot \frac{1}{7} = \frac{64}{35} = 1\frac{29}{35} \text{ inches.}$$

165. Since $3\frac{1}{4} \cdot 580 = \frac{13}{4} \cdot \frac{580}{1} = \frac{13}{\cancel{4}_1} \cdot \frac{\cancel{580}^{145}}{1} = \frac{13 \cdot 145}{1 \cdot 1} = 1885$, the dining room set cost $1885.

166. First find the total snowfall over the three month period:

$$15\frac{7}{8} + 9\frac{5}{8} + 18 = 24\frac{12}{8} + 18 = 42\frac{12}{8} = 43\frac{4}{8} = 43\frac{1}{2}$$ inches. The monthly average is then

$$43\frac{1}{2} \div 3 = \frac{87}{2} \cdot \frac{1}{3} = \frac{\overset{29}{\cancel{87}}}{2} \cdot \frac{1}{\underset{1}{\cancel{3}}} = \frac{29}{2} = 14\frac{1}{2}$$ inches per month.

Chapter 2 Assessment Test

1. The only whole numbers that divide 31 evenly are 1 and 31 so the factors of 31 are 1 and 31.

2. Since $64 \div 1 = 64$, $64 \div 2 = 32$, $64 \div 4 = 16$, $64 \div 8 = 8$ are the only quotients that yield whole numbers, before factors repeat, with 64 as the dividend, the factors of 64 are 1, 2, 4, 8, 16, 32, and 64.

3. The number 5 divides 75 evenly, $75 \div 5 = 15$, and is not equal to 1 or 75, therefore 75 is composite.

4. By trial and error 43 has no divisors other than itself or 1, so 43 is prime.

5.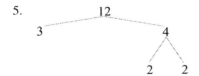

   $12 = 2 \cdot 2 \cdot 3 = 2^2 \cdot 3$

6.

   $81 = 3 \cdot 3 \cdot 3 \cdot 3 = 3^4$

7. List the multiples of each number:
   6: 6, 12, 18, 24, 30, 36,...
   9: 9, 18, 27, 36, 45, ...
   The smallest multiple common to both lists is 18. The LCM of 6 and 9 is 18.

8. Write the prime factorization of each number:
   $7 = 7$, $8 = 2 \cdot 2 \cdot 2$, $14 = 2 \cdot 7$
   The prime numbers involved are 2 and 7. The factor 2 appears at most three times in any factorization while 7 appears at most once. The LCM of 7, 8, and 14 is $2 \cdot 2 \cdot 2 \cdot 7 = 56$.

9. Since the numerator, 14, is greater than the denominator, 5, the fraction is improper.

10. The number contains both a whole number part and a fraction part, so $4\frac{7}{9}$ is a mixed number.

11. Since the numerator, 8, is less than the denominator, 15, the fraction is proper.

12. Two whole triangles are shaded and one out of two equal portions of another is shaded. The mixed number represented by the figure is $2\frac{1}{2}$.

13. Each circle is divided into eight sections so 8 sections represent a whole. There are a total of 11 sections shaded and so the figure represents the fraction $\frac{11}{8}$. Another way to view the figure is that one whole circle is shaded while 3 out of 8 sections of another are shaded. The figure represents the mixed number $1\frac{3}{8}$.

14.
$$6\overline{)23}$$
$$\underline{18}$$
$$5$$

$$\frac{23}{6} = 3\frac{5}{6}$$

15.
$$35\overline{)159}$$
$$\underline{140}$$
$$19$$

$$\frac{159}{35} = 4\frac{19}{35}$$

16.
$$27\overline{)81}$$
$$\underline{81}$$
$$0$$

$$\frac{81}{27} = 3$$

17. $7\frac{4}{5} = \frac{7 \cdot 5 + 4}{5} = \frac{39}{5}$

18. $2\frac{11}{16} = \frac{2 \cdot 16 + 11}{16} = \frac{43}{16}$

19. $21\frac{1}{3} = \frac{21 \cdot 3 + 1}{3} = \frac{64}{3}$

20. The GCF of 15 and 18 is 3.

$$\frac{15}{18} = \frac{\overset{5}{\cancel{15}}}{\underset{6}{\cancel{18}}} = \frac{5}{6}$$

21. $21 = 3 \cdot 7$
$49 = 7 \cdot 7$

$$\frac{21}{49} = \frac{3 \cdot \overset{1}{\cancel{7}}}{7 \cdot \underset{1}{\cancel{7}}} = \frac{3 \cdot 1}{7 \cdot 1} = \frac{3}{7}$$

22. The GCF of 36 and 81 is 9.

$$\frac{36}{81} = \frac{\overset{4}{\cancel{36}}}{\underset{9}{\cancel{81}}} = \frac{4}{9}$$

23. $16 = 2 \cdot 2 \cdot 2 \cdot 2$
$60 = 2 \cdot 2 \cdot 3 \cdot 5$

$$\frac{16}{60} = \frac{\overset{1}{\cancel{2}} \cdot \overset{1}{\cancel{2}} \cdot 2 \cdot 2}{\underset{1}{\cancel{2}} \cdot \underset{1}{\cancel{2}} \cdot 3 \cdot 5} = \frac{2 \cdot 2}{3 \cdot 5} = \frac{4}{15}$$

24. Since $8 \cdot 6 = 48$

$$\frac{5}{8} = \frac{5 \cdot 6}{8 \cdot 6} = \frac{30}{48}$$

25. Since $9 \cdot 9 = 81$

$$\frac{2}{9} = \frac{2 \cdot 9}{9 \cdot 9} = \frac{18}{81}$$

26. Since $6 \cdot 4 = 24$

$$\frac{15}{6} = \frac{15 \cdot 4}{6 \cdot 4} = \frac{60}{24}$$

27. Write the fractions with a common denominator.

$$\frac{4}{7} = \frac{4 \cdot 8}{7 \cdot 8} = \frac{32}{56}$$

$$\frac{1}{2} = \frac{1 \cdot 28}{2 \cdot 28} = \frac{28}{56}$$

$$\frac{5}{8} = \frac{5 \cdot 7}{8 \cdot 7} = \frac{35}{56}$$

Since $28 < 32 < 35$,

$$\frac{1}{2} < \frac{4}{7} < \frac{5}{8}$$

28. Write the fractions with a common denominator.

$$\frac{22}{35} = \frac{22 \cdot 2}{35 \cdot 2} = \frac{44}{70}$$

$$\frac{37}{70} = \frac{37}{70}$$

$$\frac{6}{10} = \frac{6 \cdot 7}{10 \cdot 7} = \frac{42}{70}$$

Since $37 < 42 < 44$,

$$\frac{37}{70} < \frac{6}{10} < \frac{22}{35}$$

29. $\dfrac{7}{9}\cdot\dfrac{3}{5}=\dfrac{7}{\cancel{9}_{3}}\cdot\dfrac{\cancel{3}^{1}}{5}=\dfrac{7\cdot1}{3\cdot5}=\dfrac{7}{15}$

30. $\dfrac{1}{5}\cdot\dfrac{5}{10}\cdot1\dfrac{2}{3}=\dfrac{1}{5}\cdot\dfrac{5}{10}\cdot\dfrac{5}{3}=\dfrac{1}{\cancel{5}_{1}}\cdot\dfrac{\cancel{5}^{1}}{\cancel{10}_{2}}\cdot\dfrac{\cancel{5}^{1}}{3}$

    $=\dfrac{1\cdot1\cdot1}{1\cdot2\cdot3}=\dfrac{1}{6}$

31. $3\dfrac{3}{4}\cdot8\dfrac{1}{2}\cdot2=\dfrac{15}{4}\cdot\dfrac{17}{2}\cdot\dfrac{2}{1}=\dfrac{15}{4}\cdot\dfrac{17}{\cancel{2}_{1}}\cdot\dfrac{\cancel{2}^{1}}{1}$

    $=\dfrac{15\cdot17\cdot1}{4\cdot1\cdot1}=\dfrac{255}{4}=63\dfrac{3}{4}$

32. $\dfrac{11}{18}\div\dfrac{5}{6}=\dfrac{11}{18}\cdot\dfrac{6}{5}=\dfrac{11}{\cancel{18}_{3}}\cdot\dfrac{\cancel{6}^{1}}{5}=\dfrac{11\cdot1}{3\cdot5}=\dfrac{11}{15}$

33. $4\dfrac{1}{3}\div2\dfrac{1}{5}=\dfrac{13}{3}\div\dfrac{11}{5}=\dfrac{13}{3}\cdot\dfrac{5}{11}=\dfrac{65}{33}=1\dfrac{32}{33}$

34. $120\div\dfrac{5}{6}=\dfrac{120}{1}\cdot\dfrac{6}{5}=\dfrac{\cancel{120}^{24}}{1}\cdot\dfrac{6}{\cancel{5}_{1}}=\dfrac{24\cdot6}{1\cdot1}=144$

35. $\dfrac{5}{9}+\dfrac{1}{2}=\dfrac{5\cdot2}{9\cdot2}+\dfrac{1\cdot9}{2\cdot9}=\dfrac{10}{18}+\dfrac{9}{18}=\dfrac{19}{18}=1\dfrac{1}{18}$

36. $\dfrac{4}{6}+3\dfrac{5}{8}+\dfrac{7}{12}=\dfrac{4}{6}+\dfrac{29}{8}+\dfrac{7}{12}=\dfrac{4\cdot4}{6\cdot4}+\dfrac{29\cdot3}{8\cdot3}+\dfrac{7\cdot2}{12\cdot2}$

    $=\dfrac{16}{24}+\dfrac{87}{24}+\dfrac{14}{24}=\dfrac{117}{24}$

    $=4\dfrac{21}{24}=4\dfrac{7}{8}$

37. $\dfrac{1}{10}+3\dfrac{2}{5}+1\dfrac{5}{6}+\dfrac{1}{15}=\dfrac{1}{10}+\dfrac{17}{5}+\dfrac{11}{6}+\dfrac{1}{15}$

    $=\dfrac{3}{30}+\dfrac{102}{30}+\dfrac{55}{30}+\dfrac{2}{30}$

    $=\dfrac{162}{30}=5\dfrac{12}{30}=5\dfrac{2}{5}$

38. $6\dfrac{3}{5}=6\dfrac{6}{10},\quad 4\dfrac{1}{2}=4\dfrac{5}{10}$

    $6\dfrac{6}{10}-4\dfrac{5}{10}=2\dfrac{1}{10}$

39. $12\dfrac{1}{3}=12\dfrac{4}{12}=11\dfrac{16}{12}$

    $5\dfrac{3}{4}=5\dfrac{9}{12}$

    $12\dfrac{1}{3}-5\dfrac{3}{4}=11\dfrac{16}{12}-5\dfrac{9}{12}=6\dfrac{7}{12}$

40. $15\dfrac{18}{25}=15\dfrac{54}{75}$

    $10\dfrac{7}{15}=10\dfrac{35}{75}$

    $15\dfrac{18}{25}-10\dfrac{7}{15}=15\dfrac{54}{75}-10\dfrac{35}{75}=5\dfrac{19}{75}$

41. a. The total number of students is $25+22+8=55$. There are 22 of these students from out-of-state.

    The fraction that represents the out-of-state students is $\dfrac{22}{55}=\dfrac{2\cdot\cancel{11}^{1}}{5\cdot\cancel{11}_{1}}=\dfrac{2}{5}$.

    b. There are 8 students out of 55 total that are from out of the country. The fraction represented by out-of-country students is $\dfrac{8}{55}$.

    c. The number of in-state and out-of-state students combined is $24+22=47$. The fraction representing these students is $\dfrac{47}{55}$.

42. The number of $\frac{5}{8}$ mile segments in a 75 mile stretch is $75 \div \frac{5}{8}$. Performing the division gives

$$75 \div \frac{5}{8} = \frac{75}{1} \cdot \frac{8}{5} = \frac{\overset{15}{\cancel{75}}}{1} \cdot \frac{8}{\underset{1}{\cancel{5}}} = \frac{15 \cdot 8}{1 \cdot 1} = 120 .$$ So 120 signs are on the 75-mile stretch.

43. If each lap is $3\frac{3}{5}$ miles long and 54 laps were run, the total number of miles covered is $3\frac{3}{5} \cdot 54$.

Multiplying we find this total is $3\frac{3}{5} \cdot 54 = \frac{18}{5} \cdot \frac{54}{1} = \frac{972}{5} = 194\frac{2}{5}$ miles.

44. The height of the plant is the sum of its original height and the growth over each of the last two months. Convert the different summands to equivalent mixed numbers with common denominators.

$$12\frac{3}{4} = 12\frac{9}{12}, \quad 2\frac{1}{6} = 2\frac{2}{12}, \quad 3\frac{1}{2} = 3\frac{6}{12}$$

The total height is $12\frac{9}{12} + 2\frac{2}{12} + 3\frac{6}{12} = 17\frac{17}{12} = 18\frac{5}{12}$ inches.

45. Two-thirds of the revenue is $\frac{2}{3} \cdot 54000 = \frac{2}{3} \cdot \frac{54000}{1} = \frac{2}{\underset{1}{\cancel{3}}} \cdot \frac{\overset{18000}{\cancel{54000}}}{1} = 36,000$. The company's expenses were

$36,000.

46. The thickness of the copper is $1\frac{13}{16} - \frac{35}{64}$. Computing this difference gives

$$1\frac{13}{16} - \frac{35}{64} = \frac{29}{16} - \frac{35}{64} = \frac{29 \cdot 4}{16 \cdot 4} - \frac{35}{64} = \frac{116}{64} - \frac{35}{64} = \frac{81}{64} = 1\frac{17}{64}$$ centimeters.

Chapter 3   Decimals

Section 3.1   Understanding Decimals

Concept Check

2. In decimal notation, the decimal fraction $\dfrac{31}{100}$ is written as __0.31__.

4. The place values to the left of the decimal point are powers of 10, while the place values to the right of the decimal point are fraction whose __denominators__ are powers of 10.

6. When writing a decimal in word form, write the word __and__ in place of the decimal point.

8. The symbol > means __greater__ __than__. The symbol < means __less__ __than__.

10. A decimal rounded to the nearest thousandth has __three__ decimal places.

Guide Problems

12. In the decimal 72.916, identify the name of each place value.

   the digit 7 is in the __tens__ place
   the digit 2 is in the __ones__ place
   the digit 9 is in the __tenths__ place
   the digit 1 is in the __hundredths__ place
   the digit 6 is in the __thousandths__ place

   The place values to the left of the decimal point are the ones place, the tens place, the hundreds place, and so on as you move to the right. The place values to the right of the decimal point all end in –ths and are the tenths place, the hundredths place, the thousandths place, and so on as you move to the right.

14. The digit 7 underlined in 327.41 is in the *ones* place, the first place to the left of the decimal.

16. The digit 7 underlined in 21.3_7_4 is in the *hundredths* place, the second place to the right of the decimal.

18. The digit 2 underlined in 6.0807_2_601 is in the third place of the thousandths group and so is in the *hundred-thousandths* place.

20. In 123.0870_7_63581, the digit 7 that is underlined is in the *hundred-thousandths* place.

Guide Problems

22. Write 134.029 in word form.

   a. Write the whole number portion in word form. The whole number portion here is 134 and the word form is "one hundred thirty-four"

   b. Write the word representing the decimal point. A decimal point is always represented by the word "and". Note this is the only time *and* is used in a number's word form.

c. How many decimal places are in the number? Three, since three digits: 0, 2, and 9 follow the decimal.

d. The number of decimal places in part c indicates the <u>thousandths</u> place. From part c. there are three places and the third is the thousandths place.

e. Write the decimal part of the number in word form. The digits after the decimal form 029 which are read *twenty-nine*. Add the word for the appropriate decimal place found in part d. to get "twenty-nine thousandths".

f. Write the entire number in word form. The word form for 134.029 is found by joining the answers to parts a, b, and e and is "one hundred thirty-four and twenty-nine thousandths". in part d. to get "twenty-nine thousandths".

24. 0.4 has one decimal place so the word form uses "tenths." The digits after the decimal point form "four" so 0.4 has word form "four tenths." Note that a whole number portion of 0 does not contribute to the word form and the word *and* is not used for the decimal point in this case.

26. 0.071 has decimal part 71 read "seventy-one." There are three decimal places indicating the thousandths place. The word form is "seventy-one thousandths."

28. For 3.8,
    whole number part of 3 is "three",
    decimal point is "and",
    decimal part of 8 is "eight",
    one decimal place means "tenths".
    The word form of 3.8 is
        "three and eight tenths."

30. For 99.4038,
    99 is read "ninety-nine"
    decimal point is read "and"
    4038 is read "four thousand thirty-eight"
    four decimal places means "ten-thousandths"
    The word form of 99.4038 is "ninety-nine and four thousand thirty-eight ten-thousandths."

32. Three decimal places in 0.089 indicate the thousandths place. The word form is "eighty-nine thousandths."

34. Two decimal places in 133.28 indicate hundredths. Decimal point is read as "and." The word form is "one hundred thirty-three and twenty-eight hundredths."

Guide Problems

36. Write the number two hundred thirty-six and eleven thousandths in decimal notation.

a. Write the whole number part of the number in decimal notation.
236
Note the whole number part "two hundred thirty-six" is *before* the "and."

b. Write the decimal part of the number in decimal notation.
.011
Note the decimal part, "eleven thousandths," comes *after* the "and." Further, "thousandths" indicates three decimal places.

c. Write the entire number in decimal notation.
236.011
Simply combine the whole number part from a. and the decimal part from b.

38. "two thousand six hundred forty-five ten-thousandths" There is no whole part so use 0. The phrase "ten-thousandths" indicates four decimal places so the decimal part is .2645 . The decimal notation is 0.2645 .

40. "twenty-nine thousandths" There is no whole number part so use 0. The word "thousandths" indicates three decimal places so decimal part is .029. The decimal notation is 0.029 .

42. "four thousand six hundred twenty-three and eleven hundredths"
    Whole number part: 4623
    Decimal part: .11
    Decimal notation: 4623.11

44. "twelve and four thousandths"
    Whole number part: 12
    Decimal part: .004
    Decimal notation: 12.004

46. "three hundred eighty-two thousandths"
    Whole number part: 0
    Decimal part: .382
    Decimal notation: 0.382

48. "six and twenty-three hundredths"
    Whole number part: 6
    Decimal part: .23
    Decimal notation: 6.23

Guide Problems

50. Consider the decimal 0.024

    a. To write 0.024 as a decimal fraction, what whole number do we write as the numerator? 24
    Use the digits that form the decimal part.

    b. What power of 10 do we write as the the numerator? 1000
    There are three decimal places in the given number so the denominator is that power of 10 having three zeros.

    c. Write 0.024 as a decimal fraction. Simplify if possible. Use the numerator and denominator from a. and b. above.

    $$0.024 = \frac{24}{1000} = \frac{3}{125}$$

52. Consider the decimal 7.0125.

    a. To write 7.0125 as a mixed number, what whole number do we write as the numerator of the fraction part?
     125   Use the digits after the decimal.

    b. What power of 10 do we write as the the numerator of the fraction part?
     10,000 There are four decimal places in the given number so the denominator is that power of 10 having four zeros.

    c. Write 7.0125 as a decimal fraction. Simplify, if possible.
    Use the whole number part of the decimal as the whole number part of the mixed number. Form the fraction part with the numerator and denominator from a. and b. above.

    $$7.0125 = 7\frac{125}{10000} = 7\frac{1}{800}$$

54. 0.13
    Numerator: 13
    Denominator: 100
    $$0.13 = \frac{13}{100}$$

56. 0.0009
    Numerator: 9
    Denominator: 10,000
    $$0.0009 = \frac{9}{10,000}$$

58. 0.425
    Numerator: 425
    Denominator: 1000
    $$0.425 = \frac{425}{1000} = \frac{17}{40}$$

60. 12.375
    Numerator: 375
    Denominator: 1000
    Whole number part: 12
    $$12.375 = 12\frac{375}{1000} = 12\frac{3}{8}$$

62. 7.268
    Numerator: 268
    Denominator: 1000
    Whole number part: 7
    $$7.268 = 7\frac{268}{1000} = 7\frac{67}{250}$$

64. 17.0041
    Numerator: 41
    Denominator: 10,000
    Whole number part: 17
    $$17.0041 = 17\frac{41}{10,000}$$

Guide Problems

66. Use the symbol < , >. or = to compare 0.0038 and 0.00387. Write 0.0038 and 0.00387 one above another so that the decimal points are aligned. (Insert zeros, as needed.)
    0.00380   (Add a zero.)
    0.00387

a. Compare the digits of each number. Which is the first place value where there is a difference? hundred-thousandths The top number has a 0 in the hundred-thousandths place while the bottom number has a 7.

b. Which number is larger? 0.00387 Comparing the digits in the hundred- thousandths places of each number (0 in 0.00380 is less than 7 in 0.00387) we see 0.00387 is the larger number.

c. Use the symbol <, >, or = to write a true statement for the numbers.   0.0038 < 0.00387 or 0.00387 > 0.0038 since 0.00387 is the larger number.

In problems 68 through 78, the procedure given in the Guide Problems is applied. The numbers are stacked with the decimal places aligned. Zeros are tacked on if necessary. The first place where the numbers disagree is given and the result of comparing the digits in that place is used to determine whether <, >, or = is appropriate.

68. 1.287 > 1.278

    1.287   Hundredths place: 8
    1.278   is greater than 7.

70. 0.694 > 0.685

    0.694 Hundredths place: 9
    0.685 is greater than 8.

72. 64.001 < 64.010

    64.001 Hundredths place:
    64.010 0 is less than 1.

74. 85.003 > 0.85003

    85.00300 Tens place: 8
    00.85003 is more than 0.

76. 0.920200 = 0.9202
    0.920200 Add zeros on
              bottom.
    0.920200 Numbers agree
              in every decimal
              place.

78. 2.05070 < 2.05700

    2.05070 Thousandths place:
    2.05700 0 is less than 7.

80. Since 12.0094 > 12.0 and 12.0094 > 12.0049 , the value 12.0094 is the largest. Since 12.0049 > 12.0 , the value 12.0 is the smallest. The numbers in descending order are 12.0094, 12.0049, 12.0.

82. Since 0.0026 < 0.00267 and 0.0026 < 0.2669 , the value 0.0026 is the smallest. Since 0.00267 < 0.2669 , the value 0.2669 is the largest. The numbers in ascending order are 0.0026, 0.00267, 0.2669.

84. Since 7.79 > 7.7681, 7.7681 > 7.6781, and 7.6781 > 7.678, the numbers in descending order are 7.79, 7.7681. 7.6781, 7.678.

Guide Problems

86. Round 22.1437 to the nearest hundredth.

a. What digit is in the hundredths place?
    4, as shown here: 22.1437

b. What number is to the right of the digit in the hundredths place?
    3, as shown here: 22.1437

c. Explain what to do next.
    The specified digit, 4, remains the same because the digit in the thousandths place is 4 or less. Change each digit to the right of the specified place value to zero.

d. Write the rounded number.
    22.14
    Note the digits that are changed to zero need not be written since they are at the end of the decimal part.

In problems 88 through 98, the procedure outlined in the Guide Problems is used. The digit in the specified place is indicated with a single underline. The digit to its right is doubly underlined. If the digit to the right is 5 or greater, increase the specified digit by one, otherwise leave the specified digit the same. In either case, change all digits to the right of the specified digits to zero. If the zeroed digits are on the right of the decimal point they are not written. However, if the digit in the specified place is a zero, as in problems 96 through 98, it is always written.

88. 907.2987 to the nearest tenth is 907.3.

90. 37.603 to the nearest one is 38.000.

92. 404.4838 to the nearest one is 404.

94. 48.9837 to the nearest thousandth is 48.984.

96. 31.8015 to the nearest hundredth is 31.80.

98. 685.992 to the nearest tenth is 686.0.

100. The three decimal places in 1.056 indicate a place value of thousandths. Reading the decimal point as "and" gives the word form of "1.056 quarts" as "one and fifty-six thousandths quarts."

102. In the word form "thirteen ten-thousandths" the word *ten-thousandths* indicates four decimal places. In decimal notation the number is 0.0013 so the thickness of the glass is 0.0013 inches.

104. First, note that $0.603 < 0.612$ and $0.603 < 0.6188$ since in both cases the two numbers first disagree in the hundredths place and 0 is less than 1. Thus, 0.603 is the smallest number. Further, $0.612 < 0.6188$, since the thousandths digit of 8 is greater than the thousandths digit of 2. The diameters in ascending order are 0.603 mm, 0.612 mm, 0.6188 mm.

106. In 433.57, the digit in the ones place is 3. The digit to the right is 5. The ones place is rounded up to 4 and so the rounded value is 434 rpm.

108. The digit in the ones place of 243.58 is 3. The digit to the right, in the tenths place, is 5. Since the tenths place value is 5 or more, increase the digit in the ones place and change the digits to its right to zeros to obtain the rounded distance of 244 miles.

110. a. Given the amount \$6744.03, the decimal part of .03 or 3 cents is written as $\dfrac{03}{100}$ on a check. Adding the word form of 6744 along with the word *and* for the decimal, the word form on the check is "six thousand seven hundred seventy-four and $\dfrac{03}{100}$ dollars."

   b. The word form "eleven dollars and fifteen cents" in decimal notation is \$11.15.

Cumulative Review Exercises

2. 5936
   Expanded form: $5000 + 900 + 30 + 6$
   Word form: five thousand nine hundred thirty-six

4. Subtract vertically:
$$\begin{array}{r} {}^{6}\ {}^{17} \\ 2\,\not{7}\,\not{7} \\ -\ 3\ 9 \\ \hline 2\ 3\ 8 \end{array}$$

6. The LCD of $\dfrac{5}{6}, \dfrac{5}{14},$ and $\dfrac{10}{21}$ is the LCM of 6, 14, and 21. Write each number as a product of primes $6 = 2 \cdot 3, 14 = 2 \cdot 7,$ and $21 = 3 \cdot 7$.

   Multiply each prime factor the maximum number of times it appears in one of the factorizations to find the LCD to be $2 \cdot 3 \cdot 7 = 42$.

8. $7 \cdot 7 \cdot 3 \cdot 3 \cdot 3 = 7^2 \cdot 3^3$

10. Amount paved:

$$1\frac{3}{5}+2\frac{2}{3}=\frac{8}{5}+\frac{8}{3}=\frac{24}{15}+\frac{40}{15}=\frac{64}{15} \text{ miles}$$

Amount remaining:

$$7-\frac{64}{15}=\frac{105}{15}-\frac{64}{15}=\frac{41}{15}=2\frac{11}{15} \text{ miles.}$$

Section 3.2   Adding and Subtracting Decimals

Concept Check

2.   When adding and subtracting decimals, it is sometimes necessary to insert extra zeros to the right of the last digit after the decimal point so that each decimal has the same number of decimal places.

4.   Explain where the decimal point should be placed in the answer of an addition or subtraction problem.
     Place the decimal so that it lines up vertically with the decimal points of the original numbers.

Guide Problems

6.   Add $43.5 + 21.29 + 16.31$.

a. Write the decimals so that the decimal points are vertically aligned. If necessary, insert extra zeros to the right of the last digit after the decimal point.

$$\begin{array}{r} 43.50 \\ 21.29 \\ + \ 16.31 \end{array}$$

Note a 0 was inserted in the first addend.

b. Add as with whole numbers. Place the decimal point in the sum.

$$\begin{array}{r} \overset{1\ 1\ 1}{43.50} \\ 21.29 \\ + \ 16.31 \\ \hline 81.10 \end{array}$$

The decimal point in the sum is aligned with the decimal points in the addends.

In problems 8 through 36, the procedure given in the Guide Problems is followed to add decimal numbers. First write the addends vertically with the decimal points aligned. Insert zeros after the decimal points so all addends have the same number of digits after the decimal. Add the numbers just as whole numbers were added in Chapter 1. Insert a decimal point in the sum so it is aligned with the decimal points in the addends.

| 8. | $\begin{array}{r}0.251\\+\ 5.208\\\hline 5.459\end{array}$ | 10. | $\begin{array}{r}\overset{1}{0.2}9\\+\ 0.82\\\hline 1.11\end{array}$ | 12. | $\begin{array}{r}\overset{1}{6.3}96\\+\ 1.452\\\hline 7.848\end{array}$ | 14. | $\begin{array}{r}94.08\\+\ 94.71\\\hline 188.79\end{array}$ |
| 16. | $\begin{array}{r}0.05\\+\ 0.63\\\hline 0.68\end{array}$ | 18. | $\begin{array}{r}\overset{1}{2.8}30\\+\ 0.903\\\hline 3.733\end{array}$ | 20. | $\begin{array}{r}\overset{1}{7.4}003\\+\ 3.4833\\\hline 10.8836\end{array}$ | 22. | $\begin{array}{r}\overset{1}{0.3}96\\+\ 0.452\\\hline 0.848\end{array}$ |

24.
$$\begin{array}{r} \overset{\text{\tiny 1}}{0.00}2\,762 \\ + \; 1.494\,500 \\ \hline 1.497\,262 \end{array}$$

26.
$$\begin{array}{r} \overset{\text{\tiny 1 \; 1}}{0}.38 \\ 4.55 \\ + \; 9.12 \\ \hline 14.05 \end{array}$$

28.
$$\begin{array}{r} \overset{\text{\tiny 1}}{1}6.11 \\ 44.10 \\ + \; 15.57 \\ \hline 75.78 \end{array}$$

30.
$$\begin{array}{r} \overset{\text{\tiny 1 1 2 \; 1}}{4}2.75 \\ 23.10 \\ 40.87 \\ + \; 143.50 \\ \hline 250.22 \end{array}$$

32.
$$\begin{array}{r} \overset{\text{\tiny 1 1}}{6}5.400 \\ 23.990 \\ 3.000 \\ 23.000 \\ + \; 0.003 \\ \hline 115.393 \end{array}$$

Problems 34 through 36 are all stated in word form. The keywords and phrases "add" and "the sum of" are indicators of an addition problem. The word forms of each number are first converted to decimal numbers and then the appropriate addition is performed.

34. Twenty-one and thirty-five hundredths is 21.35.One hundred forty-three and five thousandths is 143.005. Adding gives
$$\begin{array}{r} 21.350 \\ + \; 143.005 \\ \hline 164.355 \end{array}$$

36. Adding three and fourteen hundredths, 3.14, and twenty-six thousandths, 0.026, gives $3.14 + 0.026 = 3.166$.

Guide Problems

38. Subtract $8.96 - 6.17$.

a. Write the decimals so that the decimal points are vertically aligned. If necessary, insert extra zeros to the right of the last digit after the decimal point.
$$\begin{array}{r} 8.96 \\ - \; 6.17 \\ \hline \end{array}$$

b. Subtract as with whole numbers. Place the decimal point in the difference.
$$\begin{array}{r} \overset{\text{\tiny 8 \; 16}}{8}.\cancel{9}\,\cancel{6} \\ - \; 6.17 \\ \hline 2.79 \end{array}$$

The decimal point in the difference is aligned with the other decimal points.

In problems 40 through 68, the procedure given in the Guide Problems is followed to subtract decimal numbers. First write the numbers vertically with the decimal points aligned. Insert zeros after the decimal points so all numbers have the same number of digits after the decimal. Subtract the numbers just as whole numbers were subtracted in Chapter 1. Insert a decimal point in the difference so it is aligned with the decimal points in the other numbers.

40.
$$\begin{array}{r} 1.5 \\ - \; 1.2 \\ \hline 0.3 \end{array}$$

42.
$$\begin{array}{r} 6.56 \\ - \; 3.42 \\ \hline 3.14 \end{array}$$

44.
$$\begin{array}{r} \overset{\text{\tiny 3 \; 10}}{\cancel{4}\,\cancel{0}}.79 \\ - \; 36.48 \\ \hline 4.31 \end{array}$$

46.
$$\begin{array}{r} \overset{\text{\tiny 2 11 \; 5 10}}{\cancel{3}\,\cancel{1}}.8\,\cancel{6}\,\cancel{0} \\ - \; 23.737 \\ \hline 8.123 \end{array}$$

48.   3.8

    − 1.5

    ‾‾‾‾‾
    2.3

50.   44.8

    − 3.6

    ‾‾‾‾‾
    41.2

52. $8\overset{6}{\cancel{7}}.\overset{13}{\cancel{3}}8$

    − 1 4 . 4 4

    ‾‾‾‾‾‾‾
    7 2 . 9 4

54. $16.3\overset{5}{\cancel{6}}\overset{10}{\cancel{0}}$

    − 1 5 . 2 3 1

    ‾‾‾‾‾‾‾
    1 . 1 2 9

56. $\overset{3}{\cancel{4}}\overset{11}{\cancel{2}}.\overset{15}{\cancel{6}}\overset{10}{\cancel{1}}\overset{10}{\cancel{0}}$

    − 2 3 . 7 9 6

    ‾‾‾‾‾‾‾
    1 8 . 8 1 4

58. $\overset{4}{\cancel{5}}\overset{10}{\cancel{0}}\overset{11}{\cancel{1}}.\overset{12}{\cancel{2}}$

    − 1 1 7 . 9

    ‾‾‾‾‾‾‾
    3 9 4 . 3

60. $9\overset{1}{\cancel{2}}\overset{14}{\cancel{4}}.\overset{7}{\cancel{8}}\overset{11}{\cancel{1}}4$

    −   7 . 1 8 0

    ‾‾‾‾‾‾‾
    9 1 7 . 6 3 4

62. $65.0\overset{6}{\cancel{7}}\overset{10}{\cancel{0}}$

    − 6 5 . 0 0 1

    ‾‾‾‾‾‾‾
    0 . 0 6 9

Problems 64 through 68 are all stated in word form. The keywords and phrases "minus," "subtracted from," and "difference" are all indicators of a subtraction problem. The word forms of each number are first converted to decimal numbers and then the appropriate subtraction is performed.

64. Thirty-seven and eleven hundredths is 37.11. Twenty-nine and fifteen thousandths is 29.015. The first minus the second is

$\overset{2}{\cancel{3}}\overset{17}{\cancel{7}}.\overset{0}{\cancel{1}}\overset{10}{\cancel{1}}\overset{10}{\cancel{0}}$

2 9 . 0 1 5

‾‾‾‾‾‾‾
8 . 0 9 5

66. Eleven dollars and sixteen cents is \$11.16. Subtracting this amount from \$20 gives \$20 − \$11.16 = \$8.84.

68. The difference between ninety-six and seven hundredths, 96.07, and eighty-two and one tenth, 82.1, is 96.07 − 82.1 = 13.97.

Guide Problems

70. Estimate 509.96 − 432.48 by rounding the minuend and subtrahend to the nearest ten. The arrow indicates rounding to the specified digit.

    509.96 →   510

    − 432.48 → − 430

    ‾‾‾‾‾‾‾‾‾
                  80

72. Rounding to the nearest ten:

    159.25 →   160

    + 18.98 → + 20

    ‾‾‾‾‾‾‾‾‾
                  180

74. Rounding to the nearest ten:

    339.20 →   340

    − 23.19 → − 20

    ‾‾‾‾‾‾‾‾‾
                  320

76. Rounding to the nearest hundredth:

    33.569 →   33.57

    3.289 →   3.29

    + 0.344 → + 0.34

    ‾‾‾‾‾‾‾‾‾
                  37.20

78. Rounding to the nearest tenth:

    13.665 →   13.7

    − 4.814 → − 4.8

    ‾‾‾‾‾‾‾‾‾
                  8.9

80.   46.2

        42.8

    + 50.9

    ‾‾‾‾‾‾‾
        139.9

    Bob worked 139.9 hours.

82. The perimeter is the sum of the lengths of all the sides or
$$10.4 + 8.08 + 11.21 + 10.35 + 7.05 + 4.15 + 6.1 + 3.5 = 60.84 \text{ inches.}$$

84. The acreage remaining is the difference

$$\begin{array}{r} 127.9 \\ -43.6 \\ \hline 84.3 \end{array}$$

so Miguel has 84.3 acres left.

86. The difference in mileage is

$$\begin{array}{r} 15.77 \\ -12.65 \\ \hline 3.12 \end{array}$$

so Ken ran 3.12 miles more than Anita.

88. Adding the decimal numbers

$$\begin{array}{r} \overset{1}{1}12.5 \\ +256.8 \\ \hline 369.3 \end{array}$$

gives a total of 369.3 miles Larry has traveled.

90. a. Adding the sale price and the savings

$$\begin{array}{r} \overset{1}{3}\overset{1}{4}\overset{1}{2}2.99 \\ +590.50 \\ \hline 40\,13.49 \end{array}$$

gives the original price of $4013.49.

b. Add the sale price, sales tax, the delivery and setup charges.

$$\begin{array}{r} \overset{2}{3}\overset{2}{4}\overset{1}{2}\overset{2}{2}.99 \\ 194.39 \\ 125.00 \\ 88.25 \\ \hline 3830.63 \end{array}$$

for a total cost of $3830.63.

92.

Number or Code	Date	Transaction Description	Payment, Fee, Withdrawal (–)		✓	Deposit, Credit (+)		$ Balance	
	7/1							1438	01
	7/8	deposit				193	40	1631	41
260	7/15	Union Oil	89	22				1542	19
	7/25	ATM withdrawal	300	00				1242	19

Calculations:

$$\begin{array}{r} \overset{1}{1}\overset{1}{4}38.01 \\ +193.40 \\ \hline 1631.41 \end{array}$$

$$\begin{array}{r} 1\,6\,3\,1\,.\,4\,1 \\ -8\,9\,.\,2\,2 \\ \hline 1\,5\,4\,2\,.\,1\,9 \end{array}$$

$$\begin{array}{r} 1542.19 \\ -300.00 \\ \hline 1242.19 \end{array}$$

Cumulative Skills Review

2. $\dfrac{5}{8} + 1\dfrac{3}{4} = \dfrac{5}{8} + \dfrac{7}{4} = \dfrac{5}{8} + \dfrac{14}{8} = \dfrac{19}{8} = 2\dfrac{3}{8}$

4. Applying the order of operations:
$$59 \cdot 8 - 12 \cdot 3 \cdot 1$$
$$472 - 12 \cdot 3 \cdot 1$$
$$472 - 36 \cdot 1$$
$$472 - 36$$
$$436$$

6. Since $7\overline{)13}$ $\overset{1}{} R\,6$, $\dfrac{13}{7} = 1\dfrac{6}{7}$.

8. $4^3 = 4 \cdot 4 \cdot 4 = 16 \cdot 4 = 64$

10. The number of wedges is given by

$$35 \div 1\frac{3}{4} = \frac{35}{1} \div \frac{7}{4} = \frac{35}{1} \cdot \frac{4}{7} = \frac{\overset{5}{\cancel{35}}}{1} \cdot \frac{4}{\underset{1}{\cancel{7}}} = 20.$$

Section 3.3   Multiplying Decimals

Concept Check

2. When multiplying decimals, insert __zeros__ as placeholders to get the correct number of decimal places.

4. When multiplying a number by a power of 10 less than one (such as 0.1, 0.01, 0.001, and so on), move the decimal point to the __left__ the same number of places as there are place values in the power of 10.

Guide Problems

6. Multiply 0.0007 · 4.2.

a. How many decimal places are
   in the factor 0.0007. __four__

b. How many decimal places are
   in the factor 4.2. __one__

c. How many decimal places will
   the product have?
   Add the answers to a. and b. The
   product will have $4 + 1 = 5$ places.

d. Determine the product.
   Multiply as with whole numbers,
   ignoring the decimal points. Place
   the decimal point in the result so
   the product has the number of
   decimal places determined in part c.

$$
\begin{array}{r}
0.0007 \\
\times \quad 4.2 \\
\hline
14 \\
28 \quad \\
\hline
0.00294
\end{array}
$$

   Note multiplication without decimal
   points resulted in 294. For the result to
   have five decimal places, zeros were
   appended on the left to yield 0.00294.

In Problems 8 through 34, the followed steps are carried out to perform the indicated multiplication. First, if the problem is written horizontally, rewrite the multiplication in a vertical format. Next, count the number of decimal places in the first factor and the second factor and add the two numbers. This is the number of decimal places in the answer. Multiply the numbers as if they were whole numbers. Lastly, position the decimal point in the answer so that the result has the pre-determined number of decimal places. This may require adding zeros to the left of the multiplication result.

8.
$$
\begin{array}{r}
3.7 \\
\times\ 0.2 \\
\hline
0.74
\end{array}
$$
The result must have
$1 + 1 = 2$ decimal places.

10.
$$
\begin{array}{r}
155 \\
\times\ 3.1 \\
\hline
155 \\
465 \\
\hline
480.5
\end{array}
$$
The result must have
$0 + 1 = 1$ decimal place.

12.
$$
\begin{array}{r}
23.1 \\
\times\ 12.4 \\
\hline
924 \\
462 \\
231 \\
\hline
286.44
\end{array}
$$

14.
$$
\begin{array}{r}
0.0075 \\
\times\ 5.8 \\
\hline
600 \\
375 \\
\hline
0.04350
\end{array}
$$
Note a zero was needed to achieve five decimal places. The final answer can be written as 0.0435.

16.
$$
\begin{array}{r}
0.374 \\
\times\ 20 \\
\hline
7.480
\end{array}
$$
or 7.48

18.
$$
\begin{array}{r}
11.2 \\
\times\ 4.8 \\
\hline
896 \\
448 \\
\hline
53.76
\end{array}
$$

20.
$$
\begin{array}{r}
0.123 \\
\times\ 0.84 \\
\hline
492 \\
984 \\
\hline
0.10332
\end{array}
$$

22.
$$
\begin{array}{r}
62.2 \\
\times\ 0.005 \\
\hline
0.3110
\end{array}
$$
or 0.311

24.
$$
\begin{array}{r}
216 \\
\times\ 89.32 \\
\hline
432 \\
648 \\
1944 \\
1728 \\
\hline
19293.12
\end{array}
$$

26.
$$
\begin{array}{r}
9.75 \\
\times\ 2.4 \\
\hline
3900 \\
1950 \\
\hline
23.400
\end{array}
$$
or $23.40

28.
$$
\begin{array}{r}
19.375 \\
\times\ 14.2 \\
\hline
38750 \\
77500 \\
19375 \\
\hline
275.1250
\end{array}
$$
or 275.125

30.
$$
\begin{array}{r}
1.00062 \\
\times\ 3.2 \\
\hline
200124 \\
3\ 00186 \\
\hline
3.201984
\end{array}
$$

Problems 32 through 34 are stated in word form. The words "times" and "product" indicate these are multiplication problems. In each case, the factors are converted, if necessary, from word form to decimal notation and then the multiplications are carried out as in the previous problems.

32. Five and two hundredths: 5.02
Eighteen: 18

$$
\begin{array}{r}
5.02 \\
\times\ 18 \\
\hline
40\ 16 \\
50\ 2 \\
\hline
90.36
\end{array}
$$

34.
$$
\begin{array}{r}
35.25 \\
\times\ 33.78 \\
\hline
2\ 8200 \\
24\ 675 \\
105\ 75 \\
1057 5 \\
\hline
1190.7450
\end{array}
$$
or 1190.745

Guide Problems

36. Multiply $(5.1)(0.0001)$.

Because there are __four__ place values in 0.0001, move the decimal point __four__ places to the __left__.
$(5.1)(0.0001) = 0.00051$ The decimal point is moved to the *left* since 0.0001 is a power of ten less than 1.

Problems 38 through 48 are all multiplication problems where one factor is a power of ten. If the power of ten is greater than 1, count the number of zeros in the power of ten. Move the decimal point in the other factor to the right that number of times to find the product. If necessary, add zeros on the right as you move the decimal *point. If the power of ten is smaller than 1, count the number of place values in the power of ten. Move the decimal point in the other factor to the left that number of times to find the product. If necessary, add zeros on the left as you move the decimal point.*

38. $(8.93)(10,000) = 89,300$
four zeros mean
move the decimal to
the right four places.

40. $(0.16)(100,000) = 16,000$

42. $(3.5)(10^3) = (3.5)(1000)$
$= 3500$

44. $(21.3)(0.0001) = 0.00213$
Four place values mean
move the decimal to
the left four places.

46. $(0.006302)(0.1) = 0.0006302$

48. $(45.69)(0.00001) = 0.0004569$

50. 100 billion is
$(100)(1,000,000,000)$
or $100,000,000,000$.

52. 312.26 million is
$(312.26)(1,000,000)$
or $312,260,000$.

Guide Problems

54. Estimate $(24.66)(1.499)$ by rounding each factor to two nonzero digits. The arrow indicates rounding to the specified number of digits.

$$
\begin{array}{rcr}
24.66 & \rightarrow & 25 \\
\times \quad 1.499 & \rightarrow & \times\ 1.5 \\
\hline
& & 37.5
\end{array}
$$

56. Rounding to one nonzero digit:

$$
\begin{array}{rcr}
7.9 & \rightarrow & 8 \\
\times\ 0.95 & \rightarrow & \times\ 1 \\
\hline
& & 8
\end{array}
$$

58. Rounding to one nonzero digit:

$$
\begin{array}{rcr}
2.5 & \rightarrow & 3 \\
\times\ 0.49 & \rightarrow & \times\ 0.5 \\
\hline
& & 1.5
\end{array}
$$

60. Rounding to two nonzero digits:

$$
\begin{array}{rcr}
16.99 & \rightarrow & 17 \\
\times\ 10.721 & \rightarrow & \times\ 11 \\
\hline
& & 187
\end{array}
$$

62. Rounding to two nonzero digits:

$$
\begin{array}{rcr}
43.218 & \rightarrow & 43 \\
\times \quad 21.3 & \rightarrow & \times\ 21 \\
\hline
& & 903
\end{array}
$$

64. At 0.88 grams per ounce, 2.5 ounces contains

$$
\begin{array}{r}
0.88 \\
\times \quad 2.5 \\
\hline
4\ 40 \\
1\ 76 \\
\hline
2.200
\end{array}
$$

or 2.2 grams.

66. Twelve books, each 1.6 inches thick will have a total thickness of

$$
\begin{array}{r}
12 \\
\times\ 1.6 \\
\hline
72 \\
12 \\
\hline
19.2
\end{array}
$$

or 19.2 inches.

68. Three years is a total of 36 months. At $725.40 per month, Patrice will pay a total of
$36 \times \$725.40 = \$26,114.40$ In three years. her balance will then be $\$65,000 - \$26,114.40 = \$38,885.60$.

70. The first 3 minutes of the 10 minute call cost $2.27. The remaining $10 - 3 = 7$ cost $0.38 apiece for a total of $7 \times \$0.38 = \$2.66$. The total cost of the call is then $\$2.27 + \$2.66 = \$4.93$.

72. a. In standard notation, $2.48 million dollars is
2.48 times $1,000,000$ or $\$2,480,000$.

b. Using part a., the total cost of 15 floors is
$\$2,480,000 \times 15 = \$37,200,000$.

74. Martinez' gross pay total is
    $(38.12)(\$9.18) = \$349.9416$ or $\$349.94$.
    Deducting $102.29 leaves a net pay of
    $\$349.94 - \$102.29 = \$247.65$.

76. Dinkowitz' gross pay total is
    $(25.1)(\$12.65) = \$317.515$ or $\$317.52$.
    If Dinkowitz' net pay was $248.01 his
    deductions must have totaled
    $\$317.52 - \$248.01 = \$69.51$.

78. a. At four doses a day, the patient will take
       $(4)(5.8) = 23.2$ mg of the drug each day.

    b. At 23.2 mg per day for 15 days, a total
       of $(15)(23.2) = 348$ mg are needed.

80. From the table, the monthly premium
    for a $250,000 policy on a 35-year-old
    male is $12.18. Over 12 months the
    annual premium will total

$$
\begin{array}{r}
12.18 \\
\times \quad 12 \\
\hline
2436 \\
1218 \quad \\
\hline
146.16
\end{array}
$$

    or $146.16.

82. For a $500,000 policy, the difference in
    the monthly payment for a 35-year-old
    male and a 35-year-old female is
    $\$20.01 - \$18.71 = \$1.30$. Over 12 months
    this difference amounts to

$$
\begin{array}{r}
1.30 \\
\times \quad 12 \\
\hline
260 \\
130 \quad \\
\hline
15.60
\end{array}
$$

    or $15.60.

84. Cost of one P205/70R14: $89.99
    Cost of four P205/70R14: $4 \times \$89.99 = \$359.96$
    Cost of one P235/75R15: $74.99
    Cost of four P205/70R14: $4 \times \$74.99 = \$299.96$
    Merchandise total: $\$359.96 + \$299.96 = \$659.92$
    Total with sales tax: $\$659.92 + \$37.50 = \$697.42$

Cumulative Review Exercises

2. In "fifty-two and thirty-six hundredths"
   the "and" represents the decimal point
   and "hundredths" tells us there are two
   decimal places. The decimal notation
   for this number is 52.36.

4. The LCD is the LCM of 7, 8, and 14.
$$
7 = 7
$$
$$
8 = 2^3
$$
$$
14 = 2 \cdot 7
$$
$$
\text{LCM} = 2^3 \cdot 7 = 56
$$

6. Subtract vertically:

$$
\begin{array}{r}
10 \;\; 4 \;\; \overset{14}{\cancel{5}} \;\; 12 \\
\cancel{1}\;\cancel{0}\;\cancel{5}\;\cancel{5}\;\cancel{2} \\
- \quad 5\;3\;8\;9 \\
\hline
5\;1\;6\;3
\end{array}
$$

8. $18 = 2 \cdot 9 = 2 \cdot 3 \cdot 3 = 2 \cdot 3^2$

10. The average of 136, 122, 170, and 144 is
$$
\frac{136 + 122 + 170 + 144}{4} = \frac{572}{4} = 143
$$

Section 3.4   Dividing Decimals

Concept Check

2. The number by which the dividend is divided is called the _divisor_ .

4. When dividing a decimal by a whole number, place the decimal point in the quotient directly _above_ the decimal point in the dividend.

6. Explain how to write an equivalent division problem when the divisor contains a decimal point.
    <u>Write an equivalent division problem with a whole number divisor. In particular, move the decimal point in the divisor to the right as many places as necessary until the divisor is a whole number. Also, move the decimal point in the dividend the same number of places to the right.</u>

8. When dividing a decimal by a power of 10 less than one (such as 0.1, 0.01, 0.001, and so on), move the decimal point in the dividend to the _right_ the same number of places as there are _place_   _values_   in the decimal power of 10.

Guide Problems

10. Divide $57.23 \div 2$.

    Dividing decimals by whole numbers is just like dividing whole numbers. Divide as usual, then place the decimal point in the quotient directly above its position in the dividend. Zeros may be added after the decimal places in order to continue dividing.

    $$
    \begin{array}{r}
    28.615 \\
    2\overline{)57.230} \\
    -\,4 \\
    \hline
    17 \\
    -\,16 \\
    \hline
    12 \\
    -\,12 \\
    \hline
    03 \\
    2 \\
    \hline
    10 \\
    -\,10 \\
    \hline
    0
    \end{array}
    $$

12. $\begin{array}{r} 0.005 \\ 3\overline{)0.015} \\ -\,15 \\ \hline 0 \end{array}$

14. $\begin{array}{r} 3.85 \\ 7\overline{)26.95} \\ -\,21 \\ \hline 59 \\ -\,56 \\ \hline 35 \\ -\,35 \\ \hline 0 \end{array}$

16.
$$
\begin{array}{r}
16.52 \\
12\overline{)198.24} \\
-12 \\
\hline
78 \\
-72 \\
\hline
62 \\
-60 \\
\hline
24 \\
-24 \\
\hline
0
\end{array}
$$

18.
$$
\begin{array}{r}
6.1 \\
8\overline{)48.8} \\
-48 \\
\hline
8 \\
-8 \\
\hline
0
\end{array}
$$

20.
$$
\begin{array}{r}
6.25 \\
8\overline{)50.00} \\
-48 \\
\hline
20 \\
-16 \\
\hline
40 \\
-40 \\
\hline
0
\end{array}
$$

22.
$$
\begin{array}{r}
11.5 \\
5\overline{)57.5} \\
-5 \\
\hline
7 \\
-5 \\
\hline
25 \\
-25 \\
\hline
0
\end{array}
$$

24.
$$
\begin{array}{r}
8.18 \\
3\overline{)24.54} \\
-24 \\
\hline
05 \\
-3 \\
\hline
24 \\
-24 \\
\hline
0
\end{array}
$$

26.
$$
\begin{array}{r}
0.38 \\
18\overline{)6.84} \\
-54 \\
\hline
144 \\
-144 \\
\hline
0
\end{array}
$$

Guide Problems

28. Divide $9.2 \div 0.00001$.

Because there are ___five___ decimal places in 0.00001, move the decimal point ___five___ places to the ___right___ .

$$9.2 \div 0.00001 = 920,000.$$

The rules for dividing by powers of 10 are applied in problems 30 through 36. If dividing by a power of 10 that is greater than one, such as 10, 100, etc., count the number of zeros in the divisor and move the decimal place in the dividend that many places to the left. If dividing by a power of 10 less than one, such as 0.1, 0.01, etc. ,count the total number of decimal places in the divisor and move the decimal point in the dividend that many places to the right.

30. $\dfrac{0.85}{0.0001}$

Divisor is less than one.
Decimal places in divisor: four.
Move decimal point to the right.
$$\frac{0.85}{0.0001} = 8500$$

32. $\dfrac{954.58}{10}$

Divisor is greater than one.
Zeros in divisor: one.
Move decimal point to the left.
$$\frac{954.58}{10} = 95.458$$

34. $\dfrac{13.1}{10,000}$

Divisor is greater than one.
Zeros in divisor: four.
Move decimal point to the left.
$$\frac{13.1}{10,000} = 0.00131$$

36. $\dfrac{9.04}{0.01}$

Divisor is less than one.
Decimal places in divisor: two.
Move decimal point to the right.
$$\frac{9.04}{0.01} = 904$$

Guide Problems

38. Consider $5.23\overline{)0.039748}$

a. Write an equivalent division problem in which the divisor is a whole number. Since the divisor has two decimal places, move the decimal two places to the right in both the dividend and divisor.

$5.23\overline{)0.039748}$ is equivalent to $523\overline{)3.9748}$

b. Divide.

$$
\begin{array}{r}
0.0076 \\
523\overline{)3.9748} \\
-3661 \\
\hline
3138 \\
-3138 \\
\hline
0
\end{array}
$$

In problems 40 through 50, if the divisor is a decimal number, the division is rewritten with a whole number divisor by moving the decimal point in both the divisor and dividend the same number of places to the right until the divisor is a whole number. Once the problem is rewritten the division is carried as usual when dividing a decimal number by a whole number.

40. $0.54\overline{)2.7} \rightarrow 54\overline{)270}$

$$
\begin{array}{r}
5 \\
54\overline{)270} \\
-270 \\
\hline
0
\end{array}
$$

42. $4.9\overline{)102.9} \rightarrow 49\overline{)1029}$

$$
\begin{array}{r}
21 \\
49\overline{)1029} \\
-98 \\
\hline
49 \\
-49 \\
\hline
0
\end{array}
$$

44. $6.5\overline{)50.7} \rightarrow 65\overline{)507}$

$$
\begin{array}{r}
7.8 \\
65\overline{)507.0} \\
-455 \\
\hline
520 \\
-520 \\
\hline
0
\end{array}
$$

46. The divisor is not a decimal number so no rewriting is required.

$$
\begin{array}{r}
0.006 \\
63\overline{)0.378} \\
-0.378 \\
\hline
0
\end{array}
$$

48. $15.18 \div 0.69 \rightarrow 1518 \div 69$

$$
\begin{array}{r}
22 \\
69\overline{)1518} \\
-138 \\
\hline
138 \\
-138 \\
\hline
0
\end{array}
$$

50. $0.7 \div 0.28 \rightarrow 70 \div 28$

$$
\begin{array}{r}
2.5 \\
28\overline{)70.0} \\
-56 \\
\hline
140 \\
-140 \\
\hline
0
\end{array}
$$

Problems 52 through 62 require the answer to be rounded to a specified place. Division is carried out as usual, however the division is stopped one place past the specified place value since that is all that is needed for rounding. For example, in 51 through 54 the answer is rounded to the nearest whole number so division stops when the value in the tenths place of the quotient is determined.

52. $11.4\overline{)2000} \rightarrow 114\overline{)20000}$

$$
\begin{array}{r}
175.4 \\
114\overline{)20000.0} \\
-114 \\
\hline
860 \\
-798 \\
\hline
620 \\
-570 \\
\hline
500 \\
456 \\
\hline
44
\end{array}
$$

Rounded to the nearest whole number the quotient is 175.

54. $\dfrac{66.7}{3.4} \rightarrow \dfrac{667}{34}$

$$
\begin{array}{r}
19.6 \\
34\overline{)667.0} \\
-34 \\
\hline
327 \\
-306 \\
\hline
210 \\
-204 \\
\hline
6
\end{array}
$$

Rounded to the nearest whole number the quotient is 20.

56. $18\overline{)5.70}$

$$
\begin{array}{r}
.31 \\
18\overline{)5.70} \\
-54 \\
\hline
30 \\
-18 \\
\hline
12
\end{array}
$$

Rounded to the nearest tenth the quotient is 0.3.

58. $0.0096 \div 0.0011 \rightarrow 96 \div 11$

$$
\begin{array}{r}
8.72 \\
11\overline{)96.00} \\
-88 \\
\hline
80 \\
-77 \\
\hline
30 \\
-22 \\
\hline
8
\end{array}
$$

Rounded to the nearest tenth the quotient is 8.7.

60.

$$
\begin{array}{r}
0.935 \\
7\overline{)6.550} \\
-63 \\
\hline
25 \\
-21 \\
\hline
40 \\
-35 \\
\hline
5
\end{array}
$$

Rounded to the nearest hundredth the quotient is 0.94.

62. $148.267 \div 10 = 14.8267$
Rounded to the nearest hundredth the quotient is 14.83.

Guide Problems

64. Estimate $0.061 \div 0.52$ by rounding the dividend and divisor to one nonzero digit.

a. Round the dividend and divisor to one nonzero digit.

$0.061 \rightarrow \underline{0.06}$

$0.52 \rightarrow 0.5$

b. Divide the rounded numbers.

$$0.5\overline{)0.06} \rightarrow 5\overline{)0.60} \quad \dfrac{0.12}{}$$

An estimate of $0.061 \div 0.52$ is 0.12.

66. $5.842 \rightarrow 6$

$1.91 \rightarrow 2$

$$2\overline{)6}\;\dfrac{3}{}$$

$5.842 \div 1.91$ is about 3.

68. $85.7 \rightarrow 90$

$0.118 \rightarrow 0.1$

$$0.1\overline{)90} \rightarrow 1\overline{)900}\;\dfrac{900}{}$$

$85.7 \div 0.118$ is about 900.

70. At \$12.68 per share, Ted can buy $3200 \div 12.68$ shares. This division is equivalent to $320000 \div 1268 = 252.36...$ To the nearest tenth of a share, Ted can buy 252.4 shares.

72. If 6 plays cost \$167.52 then the cost per play is $\$167.52 \div 6 = \$27.92$.

74. Mickey bought $22.08 \div 0.48 = 2208 \div 48 = 46$ pounds of finishing nails.

76. a. A total of $26.4 + 19.7 + 23.1 = 69.2$ gallons of fuel were put in the tank. Since there were 6.4 gallons remaining after the race, $69.2 - 6.4 = 62.8$ were used in the race.

   b. To find miles per gallon, divide total mileage by total gallons used. Using the answer to a. the car averaged $350 \div 62.8 = 3500 \div 628 = 5.573...$ or 5.6 miles per gallon to the nearest tenth.

78. Given the cost for five plants, one plant will cost $\$12.45 \div 5 = \$2.49$. At \$2.49 apiece, 18 plants will cost $18 \times \$2.49 = \$44.82$.

80. The number of 2.2 megabyte photos that will fit in 512 megabytes is $512 \div 2.2 = 5120 \div 22 = 232.72...$ or about 233 photos.

82. First find the sum of the heights of Karen's three vaults: $12.6 + 11.8 + 12.4 = 36.8$ feet. To find the average, divide the total by three: $36.8 \div 3 = 12.2666...$ or 12.3 feet to the nearest tenth.

84. a. We need to know how many times 154.8 goes into 23,220. The answer is
   $23,220 \div 154.8 = 232,200 \div 1548 = 150$ so the ship can hold 150 containers.

   b. Computing the cost per cubic foot requires dividing the cost by the volume or computing
   $\$890.10 \div 154.8 = \$5.75$. The shipping cost is \$5.75 per cubic foot.

Cumulative Skills Review

2. $(10^2 + 9^2) + 10$

   $(100 + 81) + 10$

   $181 + 10$

   191

6. $\overset{1\ 1}{8\,5\,6}$

   $\underline{+\ \ 45}$

   $9\,0\,1$

4. The numbers 0.266, 0.2787, and 0.2345 all agree in the first decimal place and disagree in the second. In ascending order the second digits are 3, 6 and 7 so in increasing order we have 0.2345, 0.266, 0.2787.

8. The perimeter is the sum of the lengths of the sides or
   $$11\frac{1}{2} + 14\frac{3}{8} + 9\frac{7}{12} = \frac{23}{2} + \frac{115}{8} + \frac{115}{12} = \frac{276}{24} + \frac{345}{24} + \frac{230}{24} = \frac{851}{24} = 35\frac{11}{24} \text{ feet.}$$

10. Since one billion is equivalent to 10^9, standard notation for 4.62 billion is found by moving the decimal point nine places to the right or 4,620,000,000.

Section 3.5   Working with Fractions and Decimals

Concept Check

2. A decimal whose expansion ends is known as a terminating decimal. A decimal whose expansion continues indefinitely with one or more repeating digits is called repeating decimal.

4. When an expression contains a mix of fractions and decimals, we can either convert all fractions to decimals , or alternatively, we can convert all decimals to fractions .

Guide Problems

6.   Convert $\dfrac{7}{15}$ to a decimal.

To convert a fraction to a decimal, divide the denominator into the numerator. Continue the division until a zero remainder is obtained or until the digits in the quotient repeat in an obvious pattern.

$$
15\overline{)\begin{array}{l}0.4666... \\ 7.000000\end{array}} \qquad \dfrac{7}{15} = 0.4\overline{6}
$$

$$
\begin{array}{r}
-\ 60 \\ \hline
100 \\
-\ 90 \\ \hline
100 \\
-\ 90 \\ \hline
100 \\
-\ 90 \\ \hline
0
\end{array}
$$

In problems 8 through 26, fractions and mixed numbers are converted to decimal numbers as in the Guide problems. Divide the denominator into the numerator using long division. Continue the division until the decimal quotient terminates or begins to repeat. If the decimal form repeats, indicate the portion that repeats with a bar over the repeating set of digits. When converting a mixed number, there are two approaches. One way is to convert the fraction part and then place the integer part on the left side of the decimal point. The other is convert the mixed number to an improper fraction and then convert to a decimal in the usual fashion.

8. $4\overline{)\begin{array}{l}0.25\\1.00\end{array}}$ $\qquad \dfrac{1}{4} = 0.25$

$$
\begin{array}{r}
-\ 8 \\ \hline
20 \\
-\ 20 \\ \hline
0
\end{array}
$$

10. $25\overline{)\begin{array}{l}0.72\\18.00\end{array}}$ $\qquad \dfrac{18}{25} = 0.72$

$$
\begin{array}{r}
-\ 17\ 5 \\ \hline
50 \\
-\ 50 \\ \hline
0
\end{array}
$$

12. $4\overline{)\begin{array}{l}1.25\\5.00\end{array}}$ $\qquad \dfrac{5}{4} = 1.25$

$$
\begin{array}{r}
-\ 4 \\ \hline
10 \\
-\ 8 \\ \hline
20 \\
-\ 20 \\ \hline
0
\end{array}
$$

14. $3\overline{)\begin{array}{l}0.333...\\1.000000\end{array}}$ $\qquad \dfrac{1}{3} = 0.\overline{3}$

$$
\begin{array}{r}
-\ 9 \\ \hline
10 \\
-\ 9 \\ \hline
10 \\
-\ 9 \\ \hline
1
\end{array}
$$

16. $12\dfrac{7}{8} = 12 + \dfrac{7}{8}$

$$\begin{array}{r} 0.875 \\ 8\overline{)7.000} \end{array} \qquad 12\dfrac{7}{8} = 12.875$$

$$\begin{array}{r} -\ 64 \\ \hline 60 \\ -\ 56 \\ \hline 40 \\ -\ 40 \\ \hline 0 \end{array}$$

18. $\begin{array}{r} 0.6875 \\ 16\overline{)11.0000} \end{array} \qquad \dfrac{11}{16} = 0.6875$

$$\begin{array}{r} -\ 96 \\ \hline 140 \\ -\ 128 \\ \hline 120 \\ -\ 112 \\ \hline 80 \\ -\ 80 \\ \hline 0 \end{array}$$

20. $\begin{array}{r} 0.266... \\ 15\overline{)4.000} \end{array} \qquad \dfrac{4}{15} = 0.2\overline{6}$

$$\begin{array}{r} -\ 30 \\ \hline 100 \\ -\ 90 \\ \hline 100 \\ -\ 90 \\ \hline 10 \end{array}$$

22. $\begin{array}{r} 0.775 \\ 40\overline{)31.000} \end{array} \qquad \dfrac{31}{40} = 0.775$

$$\begin{array}{r} -\ 280 \\ \hline 300 \\ -\ 280 \\ \hline 200 \\ -\ 200 \\ \hline 0 \end{array}$$

24. $2\dfrac{5}{12} = \dfrac{29}{12}$

$$\begin{array}{r} 2.4166... \\ 12\overline{)29.0000} \end{array} \qquad 2\dfrac{5}{12} = 2.41\overline{6}$$

$$\begin{array}{r} -\ 24 \\ \hline 50 \\ -\ 48 \\ \hline 20 \\ -\ 12 \\ \hline 80 \\ -\ 72 \\ \hline 80 \\ -\ 72 \\ \hline 8 \end{array}$$

26. $1\dfrac{3}{32} = 1 + \dfrac{3}{32}$

$$\begin{array}{r} 0.09375 \\ 32\overline{)3.00000} \end{array} \qquad 1\dfrac{3}{32} = 1.09375$$

$$\begin{array}{r} -\ 288 \\ \hline 120 \\ -\ 96 \\ \hline 240 \\ -\ 224 \\ \hline 160 \\ -\ 160 \\ \hline 0 \end{array}$$

In Problems 28 through 34, fractions are converted to decimals rounded to a specified place. Division only needs to be carried out to one place beyond the specified place in order to round. In Problems 28 through 30, the division stops once the hundredths digit is determined so we can round to tenths. Similarly, in Problems 32 through 34, where rounding to hundredths is required, division stops at the thousandths place.

28. $\begin{array}{r} 0.68... \\ 16\overline{)11.00} \end{array}$ so $\dfrac{11}{16} = 0.68...$ or 0.7 to the nearest tenth.

30. $5\dfrac{19}{32} = \dfrac{179}{32}$ and $\begin{array}{r} 5.59... \\ 32\overline{)179.00} \end{array}$ so $5\dfrac{19}{32}$ is 5.59... or 5.6 to the nearest tenth.

32. $24\overline{)11.000}^{\,0.458...}$ so $\dfrac{11}{24} = 0.458...$ or 0.46 to the nearest hundredth.

34. $9\overline{)19.00}^{\,2.111...}$ so $\dfrac{19}{9} = 2.111...$ or 2.11 to the nearest hundredth.

Guide Problems

36. Calculate $\left(2\dfrac{2}{5} + 19\right) \div 1\dfrac{13}{25}.$
   Round to the nearest tenth.

   a. Convert each fraction to a decimal.
   $$\left(2\dfrac{2}{5} + 19\right) \div 1\dfrac{13}{25}. = (2.\underline{4} + 19) \div 1.\underline{52}$$

   b. Simplify the expression. Round to the nearest tenth.
   $(2.\underline{4} + 19) \div 1.\underline{52}$
   $\underline{21.4} \div 1.\underline{52}$
   $14.078...$ or $\underline{14.1}$

In Problems 38 through 54, the following steps are applied. First convert any fraction or mixed numbers to decimals. Second, simplify the expression by applying the order of operations: 1. Simplify within parentheses and other grouping symbols including numerators and denominators of fractions, 2. Evaluate exponents, 3. Evaluate multiplications and divisions from left to right, and 4. Evaluate additions and subtractions from left to right.

38. $82.7 + 6 \cdot 2.3$
   $82.7 + 13.8$
   96.5

40. $10.7 - 4\dfrac{3}{10} + 3.2$
   $10.7 - 4.3 + 3.2$
   $6.4 + 3.2$
   9.6

42. $\dfrac{2}{5} + \dfrac{3.5^2}{2}$
   $0.4 + \dfrac{12.25}{2}$
   $0.4 + 6.125$
   6.525

44. $18.3 + 2\dfrac{4}{5}\left(3\dfrac{1}{10}\right)$
   $18.3 + 2.8 \cdot 3.1$
   $18.3 + 8.68$
   26.98

46. $2 \cdot 6.2 + 5.2 \div 2.6 - 4\dfrac{3}{4}$
   $2 \cdot 6.2 + 5.2 \div 2.6 - 4.75$
   $12.4 + 5.2 \div 2.6 - 4.75$
   $12.4 + 2 - 4.75$
   $14.4 - 4.75$
   9.65

48. $3\dfrac{1}{5} \cdot 4 - 5.3(6.8 \div 3.4)$
   $3.2 \cdot 4 - 5.3(6.8 \div 3.4)$
   $3.2 \cdot 4 - 5.3 \cdot 2$
   $12.8 - 5.3 \cdot 2$
   $12.8 - 10.6$
   2.2

50. $2.03 + \left(5\dfrac{2}{5} + 7.8\right) + 5^2 - 3\dfrac{4}{5}$
   $2.03 + (5.4 + 7.8) + 5^2 - 3.8$
   $2.03 + 13.2 + 5^2 - 3.8$
   $2.03 + 13.2 + 25 - 3.8$
   $15.23 + 25 - 3.8$
   $40.23 - 3.8$
   36.43

52. $3\left(2.5 + 3\dfrac{1}{2}\right) \div 1.5^2$
   $3(2.5 + 3.5) \div 1.5^2$
   $3 \cdot 6 \div 1.5^2$
   $3 \cdot 6 \div 2.25$
   $18 \div 2.25$
   8

54. $2\dfrac{1}{8} + \dfrac{\left(\dfrac{1}{2}\right)^2}{100} \div 0.1$
   $2.125 + \dfrac{0.5^2}{100} \div 0.1$
   $2.125 + \dfrac{0.25}{100} \div 0.1$
   $2.125 + 0.0025 \div 0.1$
   $2.125 + 0.025$
   2.15

56. One-third of $2068.20 is $2068.20 ÷ 3.

$$
\begin{array}{r}
689.40 \\
3\overline{)2068.20} \\
-18 \\
\hline
26 \\
-24 \\
\hline
28 \\
-27 \\
\hline
12 \\
-12 \\
\hline
0
\end{array}
$$

The company pays $689.40

58. $A = \dfrac{1}{2}bh = \dfrac{1}{2}\cdot 12.42\cdot 5.05$

$= 0.5\cdot 12.42\cdot 5.05$

$= 6.21\cdot 5.05$

$= 31.3605$

or 31.4 square inches rounded.

60. a. Finishing nails: $3\dfrac{1}{2}\cdot\$3.25 = 3.5\cdot\$3.25 = \$11.375$ or $11.38. Crown molding:

$8\dfrac{3}{8}\cdot\$10.15 = 8.375\cdot\$10.15 = \$85.00625$ or $85.01. Rope: $2\dfrac{1}{4}\cdot\$2.17 = 2.25\cdot\$2.17 = \$4.8825$ or $4.88.

b. The total cost to Elliot was $\$11.38 + \$85.01 + \$4.88 = \$101.27.62$.   The thickness of the aluminum

is $2\dfrac{1}{8}$ inches decreased by 0.5 inches or $2\dfrac{1}{8} - 0.5 = 2.125 - 0.5 = 1.625$ inches.

Cumulative Skills Review

2. Over the course of a day the patient will take $24 \div 4 = 6$ doses. At 8.6 mg per dose, the total will be $8.6 \times 6 = 51.6$ milligrams.

4. $\dfrac{5}{7} = \dfrac{5}{7}\cdot\dfrac{5}{5} = \dfrac{5\cdot 5}{7\cdot 5} = \dfrac{25}{35}$

6. $40 \div 2^3 + 3(15-6) =$

$40 \div 2^3 + 3\cdot 9 =$

$40 \div 8 + 3\cdot 9 =$

$5 + 3\cdot 9 =$

$5 + 27 = 32$

8. Add vertically:

$$
\begin{array}{r}
\overset{1\ 1}{2.7\,58} \\
1.290 \\
+\ \ 3.000 \\
\hline
7.048
\end{array}
$$

10.

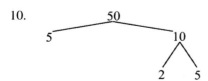

$50 = 2\cdot 5\cdot 5 = 2\cdot 5^2$

Chapter 3 Numerical Facts Of Life

2. For each figure in the Rounded 2006 Payroll column, the corresponding average payroll per game is found by diving the rounded payroll by 162, the number of games each team plays in a season. In each case, the division is carried to three decimal places since the answer has to be rounded to the nearest cent. For example, $\dfrac{\$195,000,000}{162} = \$1,203,703.703...$ is $\$1,203,703.70$ to the nearest cent.

Team	Rounded 2006 Payroll	Average Payroll Per Game
New York Yankees	$195,000,000	$1,203,703.70
Boston Red Sox	$120,000,000	$740,740.74
Los Angeles Angels	$103,000,000	$635,802.47
Colorado Rockies	$41,000,000	$253,086.42
Tampa Bay Devil Rays	$35,000,000	$216,049.38
Florida Marlins	$15,000,000	$92,592.59

Chapter 3 Review Exercises

1. The indicated digit in 13.3512 is in the first place to the right of the decimal point and so is in the *tenths* place.

2. The indicated digit in 0.1457919 is in the fourth place to the right of the decimal point and so is in the *ten-thousandths* place.

3. The indicated digit in 314.09245 is in the third place to the right of the decimal point and so is in the *thousandths* place.

4. The indicated digit in 89.25901 is in the second place to the right of the decimal point and so is in the *hundredths* place.

5. The indicated digit in 0.350218 is in the sixth place to the right of the decimal point and so is in the *millionths* place.

6. The indicated digit in 1476.00215962 is in the seventh place to the right of the decimal point and so is in the *ten-millionths* place.

7. Given 28.355 the three decimal places indicate thousandths. The decimal point is written as *and*. The word form is "twenty-eight and three hundred fifty-five thousandths."

8. Given 0.00211 the five decimal places indicate hundred-thousandths. The word form is "two hundred eleven hundred-thousandths."

9. Given 0.158 the three decimal places indicate thousandths. The word form is "one hundred fifty-eight thousandths."

10. Given 142.12 the two decimal places indicate hundredths. The decimal point is written as *and*. The word form is "one hundred forty-two and twelve hundredths."

11. Given 59.625 the three decimal places indicate thousandths. The decimal point is written as *and*. The word form is "fifty-nine and six hundred twenty-five thousandths."

12. Given 0.39 the two decimal places indicate hundredths. The word form is "thirty-nine hundredths."

13. The phrase *ten-thousandths* tells us there are four decimal places while the absence of and tells us there is a zero to the left of the decimal point. The number is 0.0298.

14. The word *thousandths* indicates three decimal places, while *and* indicates the decimal point. The number is 22.324.

15. *Hundredths* indicates two decimal places. The number is 178.13.

16. *Ten-thousandths* indicates four decimal places. The number is 0.0735.

17. *Hundredths* indicates two decimal places. The number is 912.25.

18. *Hundred-thousandths* indicates five decimal places. The number is 0.00016.

19. $9.57 = 9\dfrac{57}{100}$

Two decimal places indicate a denominator of 100.

20. $0.315 = \dfrac{315}{1000} = \dfrac{63}{200}$

Three decimal places indicate a denominator of 1000.

21. $5.006 = 5\dfrac{6}{1000} = 5\dfrac{3}{500}$

22. $1.19 = 1\dfrac{19}{100}$

In problems 23 through 28, the first place where the numbers disagree is underlined. Compare these digits to determine if a less than symbol, greater than symbol, or equal sign should be inserted. If that digit is smaller in the number on the left, then a less than symbol, <, is inserted. If it is greater on the left then a greater than symbol, >, is inserted. If there is no place where the digits disagree the numbers are equal.

23. $23.51\underline{2} < 23.51\underline{9}$

24. $0.81\underline{2}4 < 0.81\underline{3}3$

25. $3.458\underline{8}7 > 3.458\underline{7}7$

26. $12\underline{5}.6127 > 12\underline{4}.78$

27. $0.02324 = 0.02324$

28. $55.3\underline{9}8 > 55.3\underline{8}9$

In problems 29 through 34, the specified place to which to round the number is underlined. The digit to its right determines whether we round up or down in the usual fashion.

29. 1.8$\underline{5}$3 rounded to the nearest hundredth is 1.85.

30. 2.14$\underline{8}$7 rounded to the nearest thousandth is 2.149.

31. 3.$\underline{3}$96 rounded to the nearest tenth is 3.4.

32. 4.114$\underline{5}$8 rounded to the nearest ten-thousandth is 4.1146.

33. 1.588$\underline{5}$56 rounded to the nearest hundred-thousandth is 1.58856.

34. 7.45$\underline{1}$2 rounded to the nearest thousandth is 7.451.

35.
$$\begin{array}{r} \overset{1}{}2.13\,5 \\ +\ 3.447 \\ \hline 5.582 \end{array}$$

36.
$$\begin{array}{r} \overset{1}{}6.0\,98 \\ +\ 1.211 \\ \hline 7.309 \end{array}$$

37.
$$\begin{array}{r} \overset{2}{}5.51\,73 \\ 0.0991 \\ +\ 6.0070 \\ \hline 11.6234 \end{array}$$

38.
$$\begin{array}{r} \overset{1\ \ 1}{}1.2\,3\,4 \\ 0.022 \\ +\ 8.455 \\ \hline 9.71\,1 \end{array}$$

39.
$$\begin{array}{r} \overset{1}{}15.4\,4\,50 \\ +\ 0.3369 \\ \hline 15.7819 \end{array}$$

40.
$$\begin{array}{r} \overset{1\ \ 1\ 1}{}12.6\,4\,5 \\ +\ 0.856 \\ \hline 13.501 \end{array}$$

41.
$$\begin{array}{r} \overset{1\ \ 1}{}0.0\,8\,9 \\ +\ 9.6\,52 \\ \hline 9.741 \end{array}$$

42.
$$\begin{array}{r} \overset{1}{}6.2\,4\,4 \\ +\ 0.048 \\ \hline 6.292 \end{array}$$

43.
$$\begin{array}{r} \overset{1}{}22.123 \\ 9.003 \\ +\ 0.450 \\ \hline 31.576 \end{array}$$

44.
$$\begin{array}{r} {}^{1\ 1}\\ 0.033\\ 11.920\\ +\ 18.200\\ \hline 30.153 \end{array}$$

45.
$$\begin{array}{r} {}^{5\ \ 15}\\ 24.\cancel{6}\,\cancel{6}\,5\\ -\ \ 2.3\,6\,2\\ \hline 22.2\,9\,3 \end{array}$$

46.
$$\begin{array}{r} {}^{2\ \ 12}\\ 18.\cancel{3}\,\cancel{2}\,9\\ -\ \ 6.1\,5\,4\\ \hline 12.1\,7\,5 \end{array}$$

47.
$$\begin{array}{r} 12.127\\ -\ \ 6.015\\ \hline 6.112 \end{array}$$

48.
$$\begin{array}{r} {}^{1\ \ 17}\\ 10.5\,\cancel{2}\,\cancel{7}\\ -\ \ 8.5\,1\,9\\ \hline 2.0\,0\,8 \end{array}$$

49.
$$\begin{array}{r} {}^{6\ \ 13\ \ 10}_{\ \ \cancel{3}\ \cancel{0}\ 10}\\ 0.0\,\cancel{7}\,\cancel{4}\,\cancel{1}\,\cancel{0}\\ -\ 0.0\,0\,5\,6\,2\\ \hline 0.0\,6\,8\,4\,8 \end{array}$$

50.
$$\begin{array}{r} {}^{0\ \ 14\ 14}_{\ \cancel{1}\ \cancel{1}\ 10}\\ 11.\cancel{1}\,\cancel{5}\,\cancel{5}\,\cancel{0}\\ -\ 0.0\,8\,7\,7\\ \hline 11.0\,6\,7\,3 \end{array}$$

51.
$$\begin{array}{r} {}^{7\ \ 15}_{\ \cancel{8}\ 14}\\ 0.0\,\cancel{8}\,\cancel{6}\,\cancel{4}\\ -\ 0.0\,5\,9\,6\\ \hline 0.0\,2\,6\,8 \end{array}$$

52.
$$\begin{array}{r} {}^{3\ \ 14}_{\ \cancel{4}\ 10}\\ 6.3\,\cancel{4}\,\cancel{5}\,\cancel{0}\\ -\ 2.0\,0\,8\,9\\ \hline 4.3\,3\,6\,1 \end{array}$$

53.
$$\begin{array}{r} 15.629\\ -\ \ 0.609\\ \hline 15.020 \end{array}$$
or 15.02

54.
$$\begin{array}{r} 0.988\\ -\ 0.036\\ \hline 0.952 \end{array}$$

55.
$$\begin{array}{r} 5.025\\ \times\ \ 1.25\\ \hline 25125\\ 1\,0050\\ 5\,025\\ \hline 6.28125 \end{array}$$

56.
$$\begin{array}{r} 3.972\\ \times\ \ 0.035\\ \hline 19860\\ 11916\\ \hline 0.139020 \end{array}$$
or 0.13902

57.
$$\begin{array}{r} 9.041\\ \times\ \ 1.44\\ \hline 36164\\ 3\,6164\\ 9\,041\\ \hline 13.01904 \end{array}$$

58.
$$\begin{array}{r} {}^{1}\\ 7.2\,21\\ \times\ \ 0.009\\ \hline 0.064989 \end{array}$$

59. $(0.0945)(100) = 9.45$
Move the decimal point two places to the right.

60. $(11.33)(10) = 113.3$
Move the decimal point one place to the right.

61.
$$\begin{array}{r} 1.46\\ \times\ \ 8.1\\ \hline 146\\ 1168\\ \hline 11.826 \end{array}$$

62.
$$\begin{array}{r} 15.66\\ \times\ \ 1.75\\ \hline 7830\\ 10962\\ 1566\\ \hline 27.4050 \end{array}$$
or 27.405

63.
$$\begin{array}{r} 19.02\\ \times\ \ 0.92\\ \hline 3804\\ 17\,118\\ \hline 17.4984 \end{array}$$

64.
$$\begin{array}{r} 21.14\\ \times\ \ 0.005\\ \hline 0.10570 \end{array}$$
or 0.1057

65. 145.9 million is 145.9 times 1,000,000.
Move the decimal six places to the right
to get the standard notation 145,900,000.

66. 1.25 trillion is 1.25 times 1,000,000,000,000.
Move the decimal twelve places to the right
to get the standard notation 1,250,000,000,000.

67. 455.2 billion is 455.2 times 1,000,000,000.
Move the decimal nine places to the right
to get the standard notation 455,200,000,000.

68. $16.78 million is $16.78 times 1,000,000.
Move the decimal six places to the right
to get the standard notation $16,780,000.

69. $100\overline{)8.9}$

100 has two zeros so move the
decimal in the dividend two
places to the left.

$$100\overline{)8.9}^{\,0.089}$$

70.
$$
\begin{array}{r}
1.409 \\
13\overline{)18.317} \\
-13 \\
\hline
53 \\
-52 \\
\hline
117 \\
-117 \\
\hline
0
\end{array}
$$

71.
$$
\begin{array}{r}
1.79 \\
20\overline{)35.80} \\
-20 \\
\hline
158 \\
-140 \\
\hline
180 \\
-180 \\
\hline
0
\end{array}
$$

72. $\dfrac{15.95}{10} = 1.595$

10 has one zeros so move the
decimal in the dividend one
place to the left.

73.
$$
\begin{array}{r}
8.275 \\
12\overline{)99.300} \\
-96 \\
\hline
33 \\
-24 \\
\hline
90 \\
-84 \\
\hline
60 \\
60 \\
\hline
0
\end{array}
$$

74.
$$
\begin{array}{r}
36.352 \\
15\overline{)545.280} \\
-45 \\
\hline
95 \\
-90 \\
\hline
52 \\
-45 \\
\hline
78 \\
75 \\
\hline
30 \\
30 \\
\hline
0
\end{array}
$$

75. $0.1\overline{)49.88} \to 1\overline{)498.8}$

$$\to 1\overline{)498.8}^{\,498.8}$$

76. $2.6\overline{)32.76} \to 26\overline{)327.6}$

$$
\begin{array}{r}
12.6 \\
26\overline{)327.6} \\
-26 \\
\hline
67 \\
-52 \\
\hline
156 \\
-156 \\
\hline
0
\end{array}
$$

77. $\dfrac{21.8}{4.5} \to \dfrac{218}{45}$

$$
\begin{array}{r}
4.844... \\
45\overline{)218.000} \\
-180 \\
\hline
380 \\
-360 \\
\hline
200 \\
-180 \\
\hline
200 \\
180 \\
\hline
20
\end{array}
$$

or 4.8 rounded

78. $\dfrac{92.6}{2.3} \rightarrow \dfrac{926}{23}$

$$\begin{array}{r} 40.260... \\ 23\overline{)926.000} \\ -\underline{92} \\ 60 \\ -\underline{46} \\ 140 \\ -\underline{138} \\ 20 \end{array}$$

or 40.3 rounded.

79. $5 \div 0.82 \rightarrow 500 \div 82$

$$\begin{array}{r} 6.097... \\ 82\overline{)500.000} \\ -\underline{492} \\ 800 \\ -\underline{738} \\ 620 \\ -\underline{574} \\ 46 \end{array}$$

or 6.1 rounded.

80. $55 \div 1.6 \rightarrow 550 \div 16$

$$\begin{array}{r} 34.375 \\ 16\overline{)550.000} \\ -\underline{48} \\ 70 \\ -\underline{64} \\ 60 \\ -\underline{48} \\ 120 \\ \underline{112} \\ 80 \\ \underline{80} \\ 0 \end{array}$$

or 34.4 rounded.

81. $$\begin{array}{r} 0.2 \\ 60\overline{)12.0} \\ -\underline{12\ 0} \\ 0 \end{array}$$

$\dfrac{12}{60} = 0.2$

82. $$\begin{array}{r} 0.04 \\ 25\overline{)1.00} \\ -\underline{1\ 00} \\ 0 \end{array}$$

$\dfrac{1}{25} = 0.04$

83. $$\begin{array}{r} 0.9166... \\ 12\overline{)11.0000} \\ -\underline{108} \\ 20 \\ -\underline{12} \\ 80 \\ -\underline{72} \\ 80 \\ \underline{72} \\ 8 \end{array}$$

$\dfrac{11}{12} = 0.9166... = 0.91\overline{6}$

84. $3\dfrac{7}{11} = \dfrac{40}{11}$

$$\begin{array}{r} 3.6363... \\ 11\overline{)40.0000} \\ -\underline{33} \\ 70 \\ -\underline{66} \\ 40 \\ -\underline{33} \\ 70 \\ \underline{66} \\ 40 \\ \underline{33} \\ 7 \end{array}$$

$3\dfrac{7}{11} = 3.6363... = 3.\overline{63}$

85.
$$\begin{array}{r} 0.856... \\ 7\overline{)6.000} \\ -\underline{5\,6} \\ 40 \\ -\underline{35} \\ 50 \\ -\underline{42} \\ 8 \end{array}$$

$\dfrac{6}{7}$ rounded to hundredths is 0.86.

86. $4\dfrac{3}{16} = \dfrac{67}{16}$

$$\begin{array}{r} 4.187... \\ 16\overline{)67.000} \\ -\underline{64} \\ 30 \\ -\underline{16} \\ 140 \\ -\underline{128} \\ 120 \\ \underline{112} \\ 8 \end{array}$$

$4\dfrac{3}{16}$ rounded to hundredths is 4.19.

87. $25 + (130.99 - 5.3^2)$
$25 + (130.99 - 28.09)$
$25 + 102.9$
127.9

88. $1000 \div 125 + 9.2^2$
$1000 \div 125 + 84.64$
$8 + 84.64$
92.64

89. $\dfrac{1.5^3}{5}(96.6 \div 12) \cdot 10^2$

$\dfrac{3.375}{5}(96.6 \div 12) \cdot 10^2$

$\dfrac{3.375}{5} \cdot 8.05 \cdot 10^2$

$\dfrac{3.375}{5} \cdot 8.05 \cdot 100$

$0.675 \cdot 8.05 \cdot 100$

$5.43375 \cdot 100$

543.375

90. $85.3 - 4^3 - \left(1\dfrac{1}{5} \cdot 5\right)$
$85.3 - 4^3 - (1.2 \cdot 5)$
$85.3 - 4^3 - 6$
$85.3 - 64 - 6$
$21.3 - 6$
15.3

91. $\dfrac{(45.3 \div 9.06)^2}{10} + 12.1$

$\dfrac{5^2}{10} + 12.1$

$\dfrac{25}{10} + 12.1$

$2.5 + 12.1$

14.6

92. $30 \div 0.1 \cdot \dfrac{2.6 + 7^2}{10}$

$30 \div 0.1 \cdot \dfrac{2.6 + 49}{10}$

$30 \div 0.1 \cdot \dfrac{51.6}{10}$

$30 \div 0.1 \cdot 5.16$

$300 \cdot 5.16$

1548

93. The numbers 12.65, 12.18, and 12.27 agree until the tenths place where the digits are 6, 1, and 2 respectively. Order the original values as you would order these digits: 12.18 feet, 12.27 feet, 12.65 feet.

94. The four weights agree in the hundreds place but all disagree in the tens place where the digits are 2, 5, 1, 8. Order the weights in descending order by ordering these digits in descending order: 189.44 pounds, 155.65 pounds, 126.32 pounds, 114.18 pounds.

95. Mike and Morley climbed a total of $1265.38 + 1389.12 = 2654.50$ or 2654.5 feet.

96. The new bill is the old bill plus the additional fee or $\$46.95 + \$5.75 = \$52.70$.

97. First, find the total of Trish's bills. Rent, food, and the car payment total
    $1975.12 + $322.45 + $655.24 = $2952.81. Subtract this amount from her paycheck amount
    $4789.25 − $2952.81 = $1836.44. Trish has $1836.44 remaining.

98. The first tree was 145.54 − 103.92 = 41.62 feet taller.

99. Twelve reams at $5.81 cost a total of 12·$5.81 = $69.72.

100. If Greg earns $825.45 dollars per week, then in one year Greg earns 52·$825.45 = $42,923.40.

101. The number 161.27 million is 161.27 times 1,000,000. To find standard notation for 161.27 million move
    the decimal point six places to the right. In standard notation the distance is 161,270,000 kilometers.

102. The number 778.1 million is 778.1 times 1,000,000. To find standard notation for 778.1 million move the
    decimal point six places to the right. In standard notation the distance is 778,100,000 kilometers.

103. With 14.5 gallons of gasoline at 55 miles per gallon, the car will travel 14.5·55 = 797.5 miles.

104. First, determine the cost Kool-Beanz paid per cap. There were 12 caps at a total of $134.40 so each
    cap cost
    $134.40 ÷ 12 = $11.20. For a profit of $8.75 on each cap, they should charge $11.20 + $8.75 = $19.95.

105. a. In currency, you have 54·$1 + 18·$5 + 11·$10 + 27·$20 + 2·$50 = $54 + $90 + $110 + $540 + $100
    or $894.00.

    b. In coins, you have 28·$0.01 + 24·$0.05 + 16·$0.10 + 13·$0.25 = $0.28 + $1.20 + $1.60 + $3.25 = $6.33.

    c. The total deposit is $894.00 + $6.33 = $900.33.

    d. In words, you are depositing nine hundred dollars and thirty-three cents.

106. a. In currency, you have 26·$1 + 15·$5 + 19·$10 + 32·$20 + 4·$50 = $26 + $75 + $190 + $640 + $200
    or $1131.00.

    b. In coins, you have
    16·$0.01 + 42·$0.05 + 36·$0.10 + 28·$0.25 = $0.16 + $2.10 + $3.60 + $7.00 = $12.86.

    c. The total deposit is $1131.00 + $12.86 = $1143.86.

    d. In words, you are depositing one thousand, one hundred forty-three dollars and eighty-six cents.

107.

Number or Code	Date	Transaction Description	Payment, Fee, Withdrawal (−)		✓	Deposit, Credit (+)		$ Balance	
	7/1							1694	20
228	7/12	Wal-Mart	183	40				1510	80
	7/16	deposit				325.50		1836	30
	7/24	ATM withdrawal	200	00				1636	30

Calculations:

$$
\begin{array}{ccc}
\overset{3\ \ \ 12}{169\cancel{4}.\cancel{2}0} & \overset{1}{1510.80} & 1836.30 \\
-\ 18\,3\ .4\,0 & +\ 325.50 & -\ 200.00 \\
\hline
1510\ .8\,0 & 1836.30 & 1636.30
\end{array}
$$

108.

Number or Code	Date	Transaction Description	Payment, Fee, Withdrawal (–)		✓	Deposit, Credit (+)		$ Balance	
	3/1							2336	40
	3/11	deposit				1550	35	3886	75
357	3/19	Visa	253	70				3633	05
358	3/23	FedEx	45	10				3587	95

Calculations:

$$
\begin{array}{r} 2336.40 \\ +\ 1550.35 \\ \hline 3886.75 \end{array}
\qquad
\begin{array}{r} 3886.75 \\ -\ 253.70 \\ \hline 3633.05 \end{array}
\qquad
\begin{array}{r} 3\,6\,3\,3\,.\,0\,5 \\ -\ \ \ 4\,5\,.1\,0 \\ \hline 3\,5\,8\,7\,.9\,5 \end{array}
$$

109. a. Three shirts at \$56.75 each will cost $3 \cdot \$56.75 = \$170.25$.

b. If a \$75.00 shirt is on sale for \$56.75, you save $\$75.00 - \$56.75 = \$18.25$ for each shirt you buy. If you buy three shirts, your total savings will be $3 \cdot \$18.25 = \$54.75$.

110. a. Vickie's new job will pay her $\$60,000 - \$56,000 = \$4000$ more per year. This is $\$4000 \div 52 = \$76.9230...$ more per week or about \$76.92.

b. From part a., Vickie's extra income is \$76.92 per week. If she saves this amount every week, it will take her $\$2307.60 \div \$76.92 = 30$ weeks to save the down payment.

111. First, add the three temperatures: $52.6 + 42.8 + 40.9 = 136.3$ degrees. Next, divide by three: $136.3 \div 3 = 45.4333...$ degrees. To the nearest tenth, the average temperature was $45.4^{\circ}F$.

112. Find the total of the four GPAs: $3.56 + 3.48 + 3.72 + 3.88 = 14.64$. The average is $14.64 \div 4 = 3.66$.

113. a. First, find the total cost of the pizza. With tip and delivery the total cost is $\$18.80 + \$1.14 + \$3.50$ or \$23.44. George's share of the cost is three-fourths of \$23.44 or $\frac{3}{4} \cdot \$23.44 = 0.75 \cdot \$23.44 = \$17.58$.

b. Clarissa's share can be found by subtracting George's share from the total. Clarissa' share is $\$23.44 - \$17.58 = \$5.86$.

114. a. The charity received $\frac{7}{8}$ of \$158,700 or $\frac{7}{8} \cdot \$158,700 = 0.875 \cdot \$158,700 = \$138,862.50$.

b. Using part a., the balance was $\$158,700 - \$138,862.50 = \$19,837.50$ so \$19,837.50 went to printing costs and administrative expenses.

115. The total weight of the purchase is $6.7 + 3.9 + 4\frac{1}{2} = 6.7 + 3.9 + 4.5 = 15.1$ pounds. In fraction notation, this is $15.1 = 15\frac{1}{10}$ pounds.

116. The total weight of the purchase is $2.1 + 1\frac{4}{5} + 3\frac{3}{4} = 2.1 + 1.8 + 3.75 = 7.65$ pounds. In fraction notation, this is $7.65 = 7\frac{65}{100} = 7\frac{13}{20}$ pounds.

117. First, round the cost of the amplifier to two nonzero digits: $567.68 rounds to $570.00. Next, estimate the required monthly savings by dividing this number by twelve: $570 ÷ 12 = $47.50. Toby should save roughly $47.50 each month.

118. First, round the yearly average to two nonzero digits: 653.6 rounds to 650. To estimate the weekly average, divide this amount by the number of weeks in a year. Since $650 ÷ 52 = 12.5$, each household recycles roughly 12.5 pounds of glass and aluminum per week.

Chapter 3 Assessment Test

1. The 7 in 23.0719 is in the second place to the right of the decimal point which is the *hundredths* place.

2. The 9 in 0.360914 is in the fourth place to the right of the decimal point which is the *ten-thousandths* place.

3. The three decimal places in 42.949 indicate *thousandths* while the decimal point is read as *and*. The word form is "forty-two and nine hundred forty-nine thousandths."

4. The four decimal places in 0.0365 indicate *ten-thousandths*. The word form is "three hundred sixty-five ten-thousandths."

5. In "twenty-one hundred-thousandths" the phrase *hundred-thousandths* tells us there are five decimal places. The decimal notation is 0.00021.

6. In "sixty-one and two hundred eleven thousandths" the word *thousandths* tells us there are three decimal places. The word *and* locates the decimal point and sixty-one is to the left of and so the decimal notation is 61.211.

7. $8.85 = 8\dfrac{85}{100} = 8\dfrac{17}{20}$

8. $0.125 = \dfrac{125}{1000} = \dfrac{1}{8}$

9. The thousandths place is the first place where 0.6643 and 0.66349 disagree. Since 4 is larger than 3, then 0.6643 > 0.66349.

10. The hundredths place is the first place where 12.118 and 12.181 disagree. Since 1 is smaller than 8, we have 12.118 < 12.181.

11. 2.14530 = 2.145300 since adding a zero to 2.14530 does not change its value.

12. The digit in the tenths place in 1.597 is 5. The digit to its right is 9 which is more than five so change the 5 to 6 and delete the digits to the right to get 1.6.

13. The digit in the hundredths place in 4.11089 is 1. The digit to its right is 0 which is less than five so leave the 1 unchanged but delete the digits to the right to get 4.11.

14.
$$
\begin{array}{r}
\overset{1}{}3.490\\
0.006\\
+\;5.800\\
\hline
9.296
\end{array}
$$

15. Add vertically, tacking on zeros so all values have the same number of decimal places.

$$
\begin{array}{r}
\overset{1}{1}3.4400\\
10.9370\\
+\;0.1009\\
\hline
24.4779
\end{array}
$$

16.
$$
\begin{array}{r}
\overset{2\;\overset{13}{\cancel{3}}\;10}{\cancel{3}\,\cancel{4}.\,\cancel{0}\,29}\\
-\;6.\,5\,12\\
\hline
2\,7.\,5\,17
\end{array}
$$

17. Subtract vertically.

$$
\begin{array}{r}
\overset{8\;13}{0.0\,\cancel{9}\,\cancel{3}\,8}\\
-\;0.0\,0\,4\,5\\
\hline
0.0\,8\,9\,3
\end{array}
$$

18.
$$
\begin{array}{r}
7.228\quad\leftarrow 3\text{ decimal places}\\
\times\quad 1.3\quad\leftarrow 1\text{ decimal place}\\
\hline
2\,1684\\
7\,228\quad\\
\hline
9.3964\quad\leftarrow 3+1=4\text{ decimal places}
\end{array}
$$

19. Reverse the order for easier multiplication.

$$
\begin{array}{r}
15.42\quad\leftarrow 2\text{ decimal places}\\
\times\quad 0.008\quad\leftarrow 3\text{ decimal place}\\
\hline
0.12336\quad\leftarrow 2+3=5\text{ decimal places}
\end{array}
$$

20. Standard notation for 218.6 million is found by moving the decimal six places to the right giving 218,600,000.

21. Standard notation for 3.37 billion is found by moving the decimal nine places to the right giving 3,370,000,000.

22. To divide by 1000 move the decimal point three places to the left.

$$\frac{92.8}{1000}=0.0928$$

23. To divide $1.6\overline{)40.96}$, first move the decimal point one place in the divisor and dividend, then use long division.

$$
\begin{array}{r}
25.6\\
16\overline{)409.6}\\
\underline{32}\quad\\
89\\
\underline{80}\\
96\\
\underline{96}
\end{array}
$$

24. $\dfrac{4.2^2}{8}\cdot(12.5-3.6)-10.6045=$

$\dfrac{4.2^2}{8}\cdot 8.9-10.6045=$

$\dfrac{17.64}{8}\cdot 8.9-10.6045=$

$2.205\cdot 8.9-10.6045=$

$19.6245-10.6045=9.02$

25. $36.3\div 6.6+(3.34-2.64)^3=$

$36.3\div 6.6+0.7^3=$

$36.3\div 6.6+0.343=$

$5.5+0.343=5.843$

26. a. Emerson earned $\$14 \times 19.25$ or $\$269.50$.

    b. A total of $\$20.62 + \$64.20 = \$84.82$ was deducted from her check. Using the answer in a., her take-home pay was $\$269.50 - \$84.82 = \$184.68$.

27. a. Sam spent a total of $3 \cdot \$12.69 + 2 \cdot \$16.50 + \$3.70 = \$38.07 + \$33.00 + \$3.70 = \$74.77$.

    b. Sam pays with four twenties or $\$80$. From part a., his change is $\$80 - \$74.77 = \$5.23$.

28. First write $465\dfrac{6}{10}$ as the decimal number 465.6. The average miles per gallon are given by $23.1\overline{)465.6} = 231\overline{)4656}$. Dividing out to two decimal places gives 20.15…. After rounding to the nearest tenth, the average miles per gallon was 20.2 mpg.

29. The average temperature was $(62.3 + 39.6 + 43.4) \div 3 = 145.3 \div 3 = 48.433...$ or 48.4 degrees.

30. Total cost of the Power Play Advance ($99.99), the carrying case ($7.99), and two games ($26.99 each) is $\$99.99 + \$7.99 + 2 \cdot \$26.99 = \$99.99 + \$7.99 + \$53.98 = \$161.96$.

31. Rounded to the nearest dollar, the magnifier costs $\$8.00$ while each game costs $\$27.00$, so the magnifier and four games cost approximately $\$8.00 + 4 \cdot \$27.00 = \$8.00 + \$108.00 = \$116.00$.

32. The total cost of the Power Play Advance and three games would be $\$99.99 + 3 \cdot \$26.99 = \$99.99 + \$80.97 = \$180.96$. If twelve equal payments are made, with no other charges, each payment will be $\$180.96 \div 12 = \$15.08$.

Chapter 4   Ratio and Proportion

Section 4.1   Understanding Ratios

Concept Check

2. The quantities being compared in a ratio are called the _terms_ of the ratio.

4. Write the ratio of *a* to *b*, where $b \neq 0$, in three different ways.
      Using the word *to*:   _a to b_
      With a colon: _a : b_
      As a fraction: $\dfrac{a}{b}$

6. A ratio can be simplified by dividing out _common_ factors.

8. To write a ratio containing different units in the same "measurement category," such as feet and inches, it is generally easier to use values in terms of the _smaller_ measurement unit.

Guide Problems

10. Write the ratio of 2.9 to 1.42.

     a. Use the word *to*.
        _2.9 to 1.42_
        Insert the word *to* between the values being compared.

     b. Use the word *to*.   _2.9 : 1.42_
        Insert a colon between the values being compared.

     c. Write in fraction notation
        $\dfrac{2.9}{1.42}$
        Create a fraction using the first term of the ratio as the numerator and the second term as denominator.

12. The ratio of 11 to 7 may be written
     using the word *to*, 11 to 7
     using a colon, 11 : 7
     as a fraction, $\dfrac{11}{7}$.

14. The ratio of $6\frac{1}{2}$ to $9\frac{1}{3}$ may be written

     using the word *to*, $6\frac{1}{2}$ to $9\frac{1}{3}$

     using a colon, $6\frac{1}{2} : 9\frac{1}{3}$

     as a fraction, $\dfrac{6\frac{1}{2}}{9\frac{1}{3}}$.

16. The ratio of 5.8 to 2 may be written

     5.8 to 9   5.8 : 2 $\dfrac{5.8}{2}$

18. The ratio of 1 to 10 may be written

     1 to 10   1 : 10 $\dfrac{1}{10}$

20. The ratio of 15 to 32 may be written

     15 to 32   15 : 32 $\dfrac{15}{32}$

22. The ratio of 10 to 10.3 may be written

     10 to 10.3   10 : 10.3 $\dfrac{10}{10.3}$

Guide Problems

24. Consider the ratio 40 to 16.

   a. Write the ratio in fraction notation.

   $$\frac{40}{16}$$

   Create a fraction using the first term of the ratio as the numerator and the second term as denominator.

   b. Simplify.
   Divide out the common factor of 8.

   $$\frac{40}{16} = \frac{\overset{5}{\cancel{40}}}{\underset{2}{\cancel{16}}} = \frac{5}{2}$$

26. Consider the ratio $1\frac{5}{8}$ to $2\frac{1}{4}$.

   a. Write the ratio in fraction notation.

   $$\frac{1\frac{5}{8}}{2\frac{1}{4}}$$

   Create a fraction using the first term of the ratio as the numerator and the second term as denominator.

   b. Convert each mixed number to an improper fraction.

   $$1\frac{5}{8} = \frac{13}{8} \ , \quad 2\frac{1}{4} = \frac{9}{4}$$

   $$\frac{\frac{13}{8}}{\frac{9}{4}}$$

   c. Divide.

   $$\frac{\frac{13}{8}}{\frac{9}{4}} = \frac{13}{8} \div \frac{9}{4} = \frac{13}{8} \cdot \frac{4}{9} = \frac{13}{\underset{2}{\cancel{8}}} \cdot \frac{\overset{1}{\cancel{4}}}{9} = \frac{13}{18}$$

In problems 28-46, a ratio must be simplified. The following strategy is used. The ratio is first written as a fraction. If decimals appear in the numerator or denominator, we multiply by the appropriate form of 1 to clear all decimals. If mixed numbers are involved, each mixed number is converted to an improper fraction and then division is performed. In all cases, the resulting fraction is simplified, if possible.

28. 18 to 96

   Convert to fraction: $\frac{18}{96}$
   Simplify by dividing out 6.

   $$\frac{18}{96} = \frac{\overset{3}{\cancel{18}}}{\underset{16}{\cancel{96}}} = \frac{3}{16}$$

30. 25 to 45

   $$\frac{25}{45} = \frac{\overset{5}{\cancel{25}}}{\underset{9}{\cancel{45}}} = \frac{5}{9}$$

32. 42 to 56

$$\frac{42}{56} = \frac{\overset{3}{\cancel{42}}}{\underset{4}{\cancel{56}}} = \frac{3}{4}$$

34. 81 to 18

$$\frac{81}{18} = \frac{\overset{9}{\cancel{81}}}{\underset{2}{\cancel{18}}} = \frac{9}{2}$$

36. 2.4 to 4.6

Convert to fraction: $\dfrac{2.4}{4.6}$

Multiplying each term by 10 would clear the decimal so multiply the ratio by 1 in the form 10/10.

$$\frac{2.4}{4.6} = \frac{2.4}{4.6} \cdot \frac{10}{10} = \frac{2.4(10)}{4.6(10)} = \frac{24}{46}$$

Simplify by dividing out a factor of 2.

$$\frac{24}{46} = \frac{\overset{12}{\cancel{24}}}{\underset{23}{\cancel{46}}} = \frac{12}{23}$$

38. 5.2 to 5.6

$$\frac{5.2}{5.6} = \frac{5.2}{5.6} \cdot \frac{10}{10} = \frac{52}{56}$$

$$\frac{52}{56} = \frac{\overset{13}{\cancel{52}}}{\underset{14}{\cancel{56}}} = \frac{13}{14}$$

40. 0.95 to 0.05

$$\frac{0.95}{0.05} = \frac{0.95}{0.05} \cdot \frac{100}{100} = \frac{95}{5}$$

$$\frac{95}{5} = \frac{\overset{19}{\cancel{95}}}{\underset{1}{\cancel{5}}} = \frac{19}{1}$$

42. $\dfrac{3}{8}$ to $\dfrac{1}{8}$

Convert to fraction: $\dfrac{\dfrac{3}{8}}{\dfrac{1}{8}}$

Perform the division of fractions as usual.

$$\frac{\frac{3}{8}}{\frac{1}{8}} = \frac{3}{8} \div \frac{1}{8} = \frac{3}{8} \cdot \frac{8}{1} = \frac{3}{\cancel{8}} \cdot \frac{\overset{1}{\cancel{8}}}{1} = \frac{3}{1}$$

No further simplification is possible.

44. $2\dfrac{4}{9}$ to $3\dfrac{2}{3}$

$$\frac{2\frac{4}{9}}{3\frac{2}{3}} = \frac{\frac{22}{9}}{\frac{11}{3}} = \frac{22}{9} \div \frac{11}{3} = \frac{22}{9} \cdot \frac{3}{11} = \frac{\overset{2}{\cancel{22}}}{\underset{3}{\cancel{9}}} \cdot \frac{\overset{1}{\cancel{3}}}{\underset{1}{\cancel{11}}} = \frac{2}{3}$$

46. $2\dfrac{3}{7}$ to $\dfrac{5}{14}$

$$\frac{2\frac{3}{7}}{\frac{5}{14}} = \frac{\frac{17}{7}}{\frac{5}{14}} = \frac{17}{7} \div \frac{5}{14} = \frac{17}{7} \cdot \frac{14}{5} = \frac{17}{\cancel{7}} \cdot \frac{\overset{2}{\cancel{14}}}{5} = \frac{34}{5}$$

Guide Problems

48. Consider the ratio 18 minutes to 1.5 hours.
  a. Identify the smaller units.
     minutes

  b. Convert hours to minutes.
     Express the quantity using the larger unit in terms of the smaller unit.

     Since 1 hour = 60 minutes ,
     1.5 hours = 1.5 · 60 minutes = 90 minutes

c. Write the ratio.

$$\frac{18}{90} \left(\frac{18 \text{ minutes}}{1.5 \text{ hours}} = \frac{18 \text{ minutes}}{90 \text{ minutes}} = \frac{18}{90} \right)$$

d. Simplify.

$$\frac{18}{90} = \frac{1}{5}$$

In problems 50-60, the steps outlined above are applied. First, identify the smaller of the two units involved. Second, write the quantity having the larger unit in terms of the smaller unit. Write the desired ratio in terms of the smaller unit. The unit will cancel out. Lastly, simplify the resulting fraction, if possible. Remember, when a fraction represents a ratio and the denominator simplifies to one, you always write the one in the denominator.

50. 2200 pounds to 2 tons
Smaller unit: pounds
2 tons = $2 \cdot 2000$ pounds
$\qquad = 4000$ pounds

$$\frac{2200 \text{ pounds}}{2 \text{ tons}} = \frac{2200}{4000} = \frac{11}{20}$$

52. 5 weeks to 18 days
Smaller unit: days
5 weeks = $5 \cdot 7$ days = 35 days

$$\frac{5 \text{ weeks}}{18 \text{ days}} = \frac{35}{18}$$

54. 15 quarts to 3 pints
Smaller unit: pints
15 quarts = $15 \cdot 2$ pints
$\qquad = 30$ pints

$$\frac{15 \text{ quarts}}{3 \text{ pints}} = \frac{30}{3} = \frac{10}{1}$$

56. 65 seconds to 2 minutes
Smaller unit: seconds
2 minutes = $2 \cdot 60$ seconds
$\qquad = 120$ seconds

$$\frac{65 \text{ seconds}}{2 \text{ minutes}} = \frac{65}{120} = \frac{13}{24}$$

58. 4 gallons to 17 quarts
Smaller unit: quarts
4 gallons = $4 \cdot 4$ quarts
$\qquad = 16$ quarts

$$\frac{4 \text{ gallons}}{17 \text{ quarts}} = \frac{16}{17}$$

60. 240 seconds to 5 minutes
Smaller unit: seconds
5 minutes = $5 \cdot 60$ seconds
$\qquad = 300$ seconds

$$\frac{240 \text{ seconds}}{5 \text{ minutes}} = \frac{240}{300} = \frac{4}{5}$$

62. a. The ratio of 5 minutes of charge time to 45 minutes of talk time can be written as $\frac{5}{45}$ which simplifies to $\frac{1}{9}$. The three ways to write this ratio are

$$\frac{1}{9}, 1 \text{ to } 9, 1 : 9$$

b. The ratio of 45 minutes of talk time to 5 minutes charge time can be written by reversing the ratios in part a. as shown below

$$\frac{9}{1}, 9 \text{ to } 1, 9 : 1$$

64. We have 1850 passengers and 540 crew members.

a. The ratio of passengers to crew members is
$$\frac{1850}{540} = \frac{185}{54}$$

b. The total people on board is
$1850 + 540 = 2390$.
If 30 crew members are chefs, the ratio of chefs to people on board is
$$\frac{30}{2390} = \frac{3}{239}.$$

66. Using feet, the smaller measurement unit, the ratio of the fence's length to its width is

$$\frac{25 \text{ yards}}{80 \text{ feet}} = \frac{25 \cdot 3 \text{ feet}}{80 \text{ feet}} = \frac{75}{80} = \frac{15}{16}$$

68. Using minutes, the smaller measurement unit, the ratio of the movie's length to that of its sequel is

$$\frac{88 \text{ minutes}}{2 \text{ hours}} = \frac{88 \text{ minutes}}{2 \cdot 60 \text{ minutes}} = \frac{88}{120} = \frac{11}{15}$$

70. The perimeter of the triangle is $6 + 8 + 10 = 24$. The ratio of the shortest side, length 6, to the perimeter is $\frac{6}{24} = \frac{1}{4}$.

72. The perimeter of the rectangle is $2 \cdot 12 + 2 \cdot 7 = 38$. The ratio of the shortest side, length 7, to the perimeter is $\frac{7}{38}$.

74. The total number of restaurants in Japan, China/Hong Kong, Canada and the UK is $1156 + 1000 + 741 + 578 = 3475$. The number in the US is 5447. The ratio of the two values can be expressed as

$$3475 \text{ to } 5447, \quad 3475:5447, \quad \frac{3475}{5447}$$

76. The total restaurants in the top five markets is $5447 + 1156 + 1000 + 741 + 578 = 8922$. The ratio of China/Hong Kong's restaurants to the total is $\dfrac{1000}{8922} = \dfrac{500}{4461}$.

78. From the table there are 6700 Wendy's to 11,200 Burger Kings. As a fraction, this ratio is $\dfrac{6700}{11,200} = \dfrac{67}{112}$.

80. The three chains combined total $31,100 + 11,200 + 6700 = 49,000$ restaurants. The ratio of McDonald's to the total is $\dfrac{31,100}{49,000} = \dfrac{311}{490}$.

82. The online purchase of food totaled $17.4 billion. The online purchase of office supplies totaled $14.1 billion. The corresponding ratio can be expressed in three ways. First, determine and simplify the fraction form to use whole numbers. Then write the other two forms. The three forms are

$$\frac{17.4}{14.1} = \frac{174}{141} = \frac{58}{47}, \quad 58 \text{ to } 47, \quad 58:47$$

84. Food and flowers purchases totaled $17.4 + \$3.7 = \$21.1$ billion while tool and office supply purchases totaled $7.0 + \$14.1 = \$21.1$ billion. The ratio of these totals can be written as

$$\frac{2.1}{2.1} = \frac{21}{21} = \frac{1}{1}, \quad 1 \text{ to } 1, \quad 1:1$$

Cumulative Skills Review

2. $8\dfrac{1}{4}$ acres divided into $\dfrac{1}{4}$ acre lots yields

$$8\frac{1}{4} \div \frac{1}{4} = \frac{33}{4} \div \frac{1}{4} = \frac{33}{4} \cdot \frac{4}{1} = 33 \text{ lots. At}$$

$55,000 per lot, the investment corporation could make $33 \cdot \$55,000 = \$1,815,000$.

4. The LCD is the LCM of the denominators 3, 8 and 9. Write the prime factorizations:

$$3 = 3, \, 8 = 2^3, \, 9 = 3^2$$

Multiply each different prime factor, the largest number of times it appears in the factorizations above to find the LCM is $2^3 \cdot 3^2 = 72$. The LCD is 72.

6. $\begin{aligned} 40 &= 8 \cdot 5 \\ &= 2 \cdot 4 \cdot 5 \\ &= 2 \cdot 2 \cdot 2 \cdot 5 \\ &= 2^3 \cdot 5 \end{aligned}$

8. The total cost of 50 pounds of clay at $6.25 per pound is found by multiplying

$$\begin{array}{r} 6.25 \\ \times \quad 50 \\ \hline 312.50 \end{array}$$

so the total was $312.50.

10. Add vertically.

$$\begin{array}{r} {\scriptstyle 1\,\,2\,2} \\ 10,879 \\ 599 \\ 19 \\ + \quad 5\,050 \\ \hline 16,547 \end{array}$$

Section 4.2   Working with Rates and Units

Concept Check

2. Rates are written in fraction notation with the units included.

4. A unit rate is a special type of rate in which the denominator is 1 .

6. A common application of unit rate is unit   price .

8. When comparing shopping choices, everything else being equal, the best buy is the choice with the lowest price per unit.

Guide Problems

10. a. Write the rate $55 for 80 pounds of
     fertilizer in fraction notation.

     b. Simplify.
        Divide out the common factor of 5.

$$\frac{\$55}{80 \text{ pounds of fertilizer}}$$

$$\frac{\$55}{80 \text{ pounds of fertilizer}} = \frac{\overset{11}{\cancel{\$55}}}{\underset{16}{\cancel{80}} \text{ pounds of fertilizer}}$$

$$= \frac{\$11}{16 \text{ pounds of fertilizer}}$$

c. Write the rate in word form.

$\underline{\$11 \text{ pages for every 16 pounds of fertilizer}}$

Problems 12 through 28 are solved exactly as above. The given rate is first written in fraction form. The numerical fraction is simplified in the usual manner. Lastly, the simplified rate is written in word form.

12. $58 for 6 tickets
$$\frac{\$58}{6 \text{ tickets}} = \frac{\$29}{3 \text{ tickets}}$$
Word form: $29 for every 3 tickets

14. 500 gifts for 200 children
$$\frac{500 \text{ gifts}}{200 \text{ children}} = \frac{5 \text{ gifts}}{2 \text{ children}}$$
Word form: 5 gifts for every 2 children

16. 4 pizzas for 18 children
$$\frac{4 \text{ pizzas}}{18 \text{ children}} = \frac{2 \text{ pizzas}}{9 \text{ children}}$$
Word form: 2 pizzas for every 9 children

18. 1798 pounds for 12 packages
$$\frac{1798 \text{ pounds}}{12 \text{ packages}} = \frac{899 \text{ pounds}}{6 \text{ packages}}$$
Word form: 899 pounds for every 6 packages

20. $26 for 500 photos
$$\frac{\$26}{500 \text{ photos}} \frac{\$13}{250 \text{ photos}}$$
Word form: $13 for every 250 photos

22. 22,568 pixels for 30 square inches
$$\frac{22,568 \text{ pixels}}{30 \text{ square inches}}$$
$$= \frac{11,284 \text{ pixels}}{15 \text{ square inches}}$$
Word form: 11,284 pixels for every 15 square inches

24. 65 swing sets for 15 playgrounds

$$\frac{65 \text{ swing sets}}{15 \text{ playgrounds}} = \frac{13 \text{ swing sets}}{3 \text{ playgrounds}}$$

Word form: 13 swing sets for every 3 playgrounds

26. 49 aces for 14 tennis matches

$$\frac{49 \text{ aces}}{14 \text{ tennis matches}}$$

$$= \frac{7 \text{ aces}}{2 \text{ tennis matches}}$$

Word form: 7 aces for every 2 tennis matches

28. 90 flowers for 8 bouquets

$$\frac{90 \text{ flowers}}{8 \text{ bouquets}} = \frac{45 \text{ flowers}}{4 \text{ bouquets}}$$

Word form: 45 flowers for every 4 bouquets

Guide Problems

30. a. Write the rate 15 pounds in 3 months in fraction notation.

$$\frac{15 \text{ pounds}}{3 \text{ months}}$$

b. Divide the numerator by the denominator and write the unit rate as a fraction.

$$\frac{15 \text{ pounds}}{3 \text{ months}} = \frac{15 \div 3 \text{ pounds}}{3 \div 3 \text{ months}} = \frac{5 \text{ pounds}}{1 \text{ month}}$$

c. Write the unit rate in word form.
    5 pounds per month

The solutions to Problems 32 through 48 all follow the strategy as above. The given rate is written in fraction form by placing the first quantity over the second. Next divide both the numerator and denominator by the value in the denominator so the denominator is now 1 and the fraction represents a unit rate. Lastly, write the unit rate in word form. This typically involves writing the numerator and the unit of the denominator separated by the word per. If the division of the numerator resulted in a decimal number, round the numerator to the nearest tenth.

32. 72 interns in 18 summers

$$\frac{72 \text{ interns}}{18 \text{ summers}} = \frac{72 \div 18 \text{ interns}}{18 \div 18 \text{ summers}} = \frac{4 \text{ interns}}{1 \text{ summer}}$$

4 interns per summer

34. 55 calories for 4 ounces

$$\frac{55 \text{ calories}}{4 \text{ ounces}} = \frac{55 \div 4 \text{ calories}}{4 \div 4 \text{ ounces}} = \frac{13.75 \text{ calories}}{1 \text{ ounce}}$$

13.8 calories per ounce

36. 60 gallons in 10 hours

$$\frac{60 \text{ gallons}}{10 \text{ hours}} = \frac{60 \div 10 \text{ gallons}}{10 \div 10 \text{ hours}} = \frac{6 \text{ gallons}}{1 \text{ hour}}$$

6 gallons per hour

38. 14 events in 6 years

$$\frac{14 \text{ events}}{6 \text{ years}} = \frac{14 \div 6 \text{ events}}{6 \div 6 \text{ years}}$$

$$= \frac{2.333... \text{ events}}{1 \text{ year}}$$

2.3 events per year

40. 25 bushels for 5 acres

$$\frac{25 \text{ bushels}}{5 \text{ acres}} = \frac{25 \div 5 \text{ bushels}}{5 \div 5 \text{ acres}} = \frac{5 \text{ bushels}}{1 \text{ acre}}$$

5 bushels per acre

42. 180 cinemas in 12 cities

$$\frac{180 \text{ cinemas}}{12 \text{ cities}} = \frac{180 \div 12 \text{ cinemas}}{12 \div 12 \text{ cities}} = \frac{15 \text{ cinemas}}{1 \text{ city}}$$

15 cinemas per city

44. 65 golf shots in 16 holes

$$\frac{65 \text{ shots}}{16 \text{ holes}} = \frac{65 \div 16 \text{ shots}}{16 \div 16 \text{ holes}} = \frac{4.0625 \text{ shots}}{1 \text{ hole}}$$

4.1 golf shots per hole

46. 395 miles in 5 hours

$$\frac{395 \text{ miles}}{5 \text{ hours}} = \frac{395 \div 5 \text{ miles}}{5 \div 5 \text{ hours}} = \frac{79 \text{ miles}}{1 \text{ hour}}$$

79 miles per hour

48. 18 children for 9 families

$$\frac{18 \text{ children}}{9 \text{ familes}} = \frac{18 \div 9 \text{ children}}{9 \div 9 \text{ familes}} = \frac{2 \text{ children}}{1 \text{ family}}$$

2 children per family

Guide Problems

50. a. Set up the ratio, a 16-ounce can of corn for $2.79, as a rate in fraction notation with price as the numerator and the quantity (number of items or units) as the denominator.

$$\frac{\$2.79}{16 \text{ ounces}}$$

b. Divide the numerator by the denominator and write the unit price in fraction notation.

$$\frac{\$2.79 \div 16}{16 \div 16 \text{ ounces}} = \frac{\$0.174375}{1 \text{ ounce}}$$

c. Write the unit price in word form. Round to the nearest cent.

$0.17 per ounce of corn
($0.174375 rounds to $0.17)

In Problems 52 through 66 a unit price is found using the steps outlined above. Write the given rate in fraction notation. Always put the price or cost in the numerator and the quantity in the denominator. Next divide both the numerator and denominator by the value in the denominator so the denominator is now 1 and the fraction represents a unit price. Lastly, write the unit price in word form. If necessary, round the dollar amount in the numerator to the nearest cent.

52. $675 for 18 passengers

$$\frac{\$675}{18 \text{ passengers}} = \frac{\$675 \div 18}{18 \div 18 \text{ passengers}} = \frac{\$37.50}{1 \text{ passenger}}$$

The unit price is $37.50 per passenger.

54. 18 hours of work for $522

$$\frac{\$522}{18 \text{ hours}} = \frac{\$522 \div 18}{18 \div 18 \text{ hours}} = \frac{\$29}{1 \text{ hours}}$$

The unit price is $29 per hour of work.

56. 19 dresses for $910.10

$$\frac{\$910.10}{19 \text{ dress}} = \frac{\$910.10 \div 19}{19 \div 19 \text{ dress}} = \frac{\$47.90}{1 \text{ dress}}$$

The unit price is $47.90 per dress.

58. $17.60 for 55 party invitations

$$\frac{\$17.60}{55 \text{ invitations}} = \frac{\$17.60 \div 55}{55 \div 55 \text{ invitations}}$$
$$= \frac{\$0.32}{1 \text{ invitation}}$$

The unit price is $0.32 per invitation.

60. 25 plants for $15.95

$$\frac{\$15.95}{25 \text{ plant}} = \frac{\$15.95 \div 25}{25 \div 25 \text{ plant}} = \frac{\$0.638}{1 \text{ plant}}$$

The unit price is $0.64 per plant.

62. $18.75 for 75 jukebox songs

$$\frac{\$18.75}{75 \text{ songs}} = \frac{\$18.75 \div 75}{75 \div 75 \text{ songs}} = \frac{\$0.25}{1 \text{ song}}$$

The unit price is $0.25 per jukebox song.

64. 5 shirts laundered for $22.65

$$\frac{\$22.65}{5 \text{ shirt}} = \frac{\$22.65 \div 5}{5 \div 5 \text{ shirt}} = \frac{\$4.53}{1 \text{ shirt}}$$

The unit price is $4.53 per laundered shirt.

66. $17.25 for 30 candy bars

$$\frac{\$17.25}{30 \text{ bars}} = \frac{\$17.25 \div 30}{30 \div 30 \text{ bars}} = \frac{\$0.575}{1 \text{ bar}}$$

The unit price is $0.58 per candy bar.

68. 75 plates on 10 shelves can be written as $\dfrac{75 \text{ plates}}{10 \text{ shelves}} = \dfrac{15 \text{ plates}}{2 \text{ shelves}}$ or in word form as 15 plates for every 2 shelves.

70. If Norm gives 27 tennis lessons in 12 days, this rate may be expressed as $\dfrac{27 \text{ lessons}}{12 \text{ days}} = \dfrac{9 \text{ lessons}}{4 \text{ days}}$ or in word form as 9 tennis lessons every 4 days.

72. a. Ben's unit rate:
$$\frac{30 \text{ minutes}}{2 \text{ miles}} = \frac{30 \div 2 \text{ minutes}}{2 \div 2 \text{ miles}} = \frac{15 \text{ minutes}}{1 \text{ miles}}$$

or 15 minutes per mile.

b. Mal's unit rate:
$$\frac{36 \text{ minutes}}{3 \text{ miles}} = \frac{36 \div 3 \text{ minutes}}{3 \div 3 \text{ miles}} = \frac{12 \text{ minutes}}{1 \text{ miles}}$$

or 12 minutes per mile.

c. Since Mal has the smaller unit rate, Mal is the faster walker. Note that the rates are in terms of minutes per mile so a smaller rate means it takes Mal less time to walk a mile than it takes Ben, so Mal must be the faster walker.

76. From the table, there are 612,274 total pilots and 5026 public airports. The simplified fraction for the ratio of pilots to airports is
$$\frac{612,274 \text{ pilots}}{5026 \text{ airports}} = \frac{306,137 \text{ pilots}}{2513 \text{ airports}}$$
Note, 2 is the only common factor.
In word form, this ratio is
306,137 pilots to 2513 general aviation aircraft.

80. 10 visits for $350 dollars is
$$\frac{\$350}{10 \text{ visits}} = \frac{\$350 \div 10}{10 \div 10 \text{ visits}} = \frac{\$35}{1 \text{ visit}}$$
or $35 per visit.
16 visits for $540 dollars is
$$\frac{\$540}{16 \text{ visits}} = \frac{\$540 \div 16}{16 \div 16 \text{ visits}} = \frac{\$33.75}{1 \text{ visit}}$$
or $33.75 per visit. This is the smaller unit rate so 16 visits at $33.75 is the better deal.

74. a. Ed's unit rate:
$$\frac{1500 \text{ square feet}}{12 \text{ hours}} = \frac{1500 \div 12 \text{ square feet}}{12 \div 12 \text{ hours}}$$
$$= \frac{125 \text{ square feet}}{1 \text{ hour}}$$
or 125 square feet of tile per hour.

b. Jim's unit rate:
$$\frac{1200 \text{ square feet}}{10 \text{ hours}} = \frac{1200 \div 10 \text{ square feet}}{10 \div 10 \text{ hours}}$$
$$= \frac{120 \text{ square feet}}{1 \text{ hour}}$$
or 120 square feet of tile per hour.

c. Ed has the higher unit rate so Ed is the quicker installer.

78. From the table, there are 211,446 general aviation aircraft and 8497 commercial aircraft. The corresponding unit rate is
$$\frac{211,446 \text{ aircraft}}{8497 \text{ aircraft}}$$
$$= \frac{211,446 \div 8497 \text{ aircraft}}{8497 \div 8497 \text{ aircraft}}$$
$$= \frac{24.88... \text{ aircraft}}{1 \text{ aircraft}}$$
In word form, this unit rate is
25 general aviation aircraft for every commercial aircraft.

82. $2.65 for 12 ounces gives a unit price of
$$\frac{\$2.65}{12 \text{ ounces}} = \frac{\$2.65 \div 12}{12 \div 12 \text{ ounces}} = \frac{\$0.22083...}{1 \text{ ounce}}$$
or $0.22 per ounce.
$3.20 for 16 ounces gives a unit price of
$$\frac{\$3.20}{16 \text{ ounces}} = \frac{\$3.20 \div 16}{16 \div 16 \text{ ounces}} = \frac{\$0.20}{1 \text{ ounce}}$$
or $0.20 per ounce.
The 16 ounce can at $0.20 an ounce is the best buy.

84. The unit prices for each size are summarized in the table below.

Size	Price	Unit price
24 exposures	$6.00	$6.00 ÷ 24 = $0.25
36 exposures	$9.36	$9.36 ÷ 36 = $0.26
48 exposures	$11.04	$11.04 ÷ 48 = $0.23

48 exposures at $0.23 per exposure is the best buy.

86. The unit prices for each size are summarized in the table below.

Size	Price	Unit price
200 yards	$8.00	$8.00 ÷ 200 = $0.04
370 yards	$11.10	$11.10 ÷ 370 = $0.03
450 yards	$18.00	$18.00 ÷ 450 = $0.04

370 yards at $0.03 per yard is the best buy.

88. a. The Hearty twist Tie bags come in a box of 36 bags for $3.99. The unit price is $3.99 ÷ 36 = $0.11083... per bag. To the nearest cent, the unit price is $0.11 per bag.

   c. The unit price for the larger box of Cinch Saks is $7.50 ÷ 65 = $0.11538... per bag, or $0.12 per bag to the nearest cent. This is less than the unit price for the box of 30 bags of $0.13 found in part b. so the larger box is the better buy.

   b. There are 30 bags in a box of Hearty Cinch Sak bags costing $3.99. The unit price is $3.99 ÷ 30 = $0.133 per bag or $0.13 per bag, to the nearest cent.

Cumulative Skills Review

2. There are $2 + 1 = 3$ total decimal places in the factors so the product will have 3 decimal places.

$$\begin{array}{r} 3.95 \\ \times\ 8.3 \\ \hline 1185 \\ 3160 \\ \hline 32.785 \end{array}$$

4. Divide 83 by the prime numbers less than 83. None of these primes divide 83 evenly so 83 is a prime number.

6. $$\begin{array}{r} 23,695 \\ -\ 12,014 \\ \hline 11,681 \end{array}$$

8. You can make
$$3\frac{3}{4} \div \frac{1}{2} = \frac{15}{4} \div \frac{1}{2} = \frac{15}{4} \cdot \frac{2}{1}$$
$$= \frac{15}{2} = 7\frac{1}{2}$$
batches of cookies.

10. a. There are 12 yellow pages and 15 blue pages. The ratio of yellow pages to blue pages is $\frac{12}{15} = \frac{4}{5}$. Two other forms of the ratio are 4 to 5 and 4:5.

   c. There are 8 orange pages and $12 + 10 + 15 + 8 + 45 = 90$ total pages. The ratio of orange pages to total pages is $\frac{8}{90} = \frac{4}{45}$. Two other forms of the ratio are 4 to 45 and 4:45.

   b. There are 10 red pages and 45 white pages. The ratio of red pages to white pages is $\frac{10}{45} = \frac{2}{9}$. Two other forms of the ratio are 2 to 9 and 2:9.

Section 4.3   Understanding and Solving Proportions

Concept Check

2. Because they express an "equality" relationship, proportions are written with one ratio on each side of an <u>equal sign</u> .

4. The proportion $\dfrac{a}{b} = \dfrac{c}{d}$ is read as <u>*a* is to *b* as *c* is to *d*</u> .

6. As a general rule for proportions, for $b \neq 0$ and $d \neq 0$, if $\dfrac{a}{b} = \dfrac{c}{d}$, then <u>*bc*</u> = <u>*ad*</u> .

8. List the steps to solve a proportion.

    <u>Step 1. Assign a letter to represent the *unknown* quantity.</u>
    <u>Step 2. Cross multiply to find the cross products.</u>
    <u>Step 3. Separate the cross products by an equal sign to form an equation.</u>
    <u>Step 4. Divide both sides of the equation by the *number* on the side with the *unknown*.</u>
    <u>Step 5. Simplify, if possible.</u>
    <u>Step 6. Verify the answer by replacing the unknown in the original proportion with</u>
    <u>   the answer, and check that the cross products are equal.</u>

10. Similar geometric figures have the same shape and the ratios of the lengths of their corresponding sides are <u>equal</u> .

Guide Problems

12. Write 25 miles is to 5 hours as 15 miles is to 3 hours as a proportion.

    a. Write 25 miles to 5 hours as a rate.   b. Write 15 miles to 3 hours as a rate.

    $$\frac{25 \text{ miles}}{10 \text{ hours}}$$ $$\frac{15 \text{ miles}}{3 \text{ hours}}$$

    c. Write a proportion by separating the two rates with an equal sign

    $$\frac{25 \text{ miles}}{5 \text{ hours}} = \frac{15 \text{ miles}}{3 \text{ hours}}$$

Problems 14 through 24 are solved in the same manner. A proportion is stated as a sentence and consists of two ratios separated by the word "as." Write each ratio as a fraction, then separate the two fractions with an equal sign to convert the sentence to a proportion.

14. 4 is to 7 as 60 is to 105.

    $$4 \text{ to } 7: \frac{4}{7}$$

    $$60 \text{ to } 105: \frac{60}{105}$$

    $$\frac{4}{7} = \frac{60}{105}$$

16. 3 ice cream cones is to 2 children as 60 ice cream cones is to 40 children.

    3 ice cream cones to 2 children:

    $$\frac{3 \text{ ice cream cones}}{2 \text{ children}}$$

    60 ice cream cones to 40 children:

    $$\frac{60 \text{ ice cream cones}}{40 \text{ children}}$$

    $$\frac{3 \text{ ice cream cones}}{2 \text{ children}} = \frac{60 \text{ ice cream cones}}{40 \text{ children}}$$

18. 9.9 is to 1.2 as 19.8 is to 2.4.

$$\frac{9.9}{1.2} = \frac{19.8}{2.4}$$

20. 13 employees is to 5 departments as 52 employees is to 20 departments.

$$\frac{13 \text{ employees}}{5 \text{ departments}} = \frac{52 \text{ employees}}{20 \text{ departments}}$$

22. 1.5 is to 4.7 as 7.5 is to 23.5.

$$\frac{1.5}{4.7} = \frac{7.5}{23.5}$$

24. 5 gallons is to 2 square feet as 25 gallons is to 10 square feet.

$$\frac{5 \text{ gallons}}{2 \text{ square feet}} = \frac{25 \text{ gallons}}{10 \text{ square feet}}$$

Problems 26 through 36 reverse the process of Problems 14 through 24, turning a proportion into sentence form. Given a proportion, write the fraction on the left in word form, do the same with the fraction on the right. Separate the two with "as" to write the proportion in word form. Remember that a ratio such as "5 to 2" is written as "5 is to 2" when part of a proportion.

26. $\dfrac{25}{4} = \dfrac{100}{16}$

left hand side: 25 to 4
right hand side: 100 to 16
Sentence form:
25 is to 4 as 100 is to 16.

28. $\dfrac{2 \text{ showrooms}}{9 \text{ cars}} = \dfrac{6 \text{ showrooms}}{27 \text{ cars}}$

left hand side:
   2 showrooms to 9 cars
right hand side:
   6 showrooms to 27 cars
Sentence form:
2 showrooms is to 9 cars as 6 showrooms is to 27 cars.

30. $\dfrac{4 \text{ fish}}{60 \text{ gallons}} = \dfrac{20 \text{ fish}}{300 \text{ gallons}}$

Sentence form:
4 fish is to 60 gallons as 20 fish is to 300 gallons.

32. $\dfrac{14}{33} = \dfrac{56}{132}$

Sentence form:
14 is to 33 as 56 is to 132.

34. $\dfrac{13.2}{17.7} = \dfrac{52.8}{70.8}$

Sentence form:
13.2 is to 17.7 as 52.8 is to 70.8.

36. $\dfrac{19 \text{ nurses}}{2 \text{ doctors}} = \dfrac{57 \text{ nurses}}{6 \text{ doctors}}$

Sentence form:
19 nurses is to 2 doctors as 57 nurses is to 6 doctors.

Guide Problems

38. Determine whether the ratios $\dfrac{2}{18}$ and $\dfrac{8}{74}$ are proportional.

   a. Multiply the denominator of the first ratio by the numerator of the second ratio.
   $18 \cdot 8 = 144$

   b. Multiply the numerator of the first ratio by the denominator of the second ratio.
   $2 \cdot 74 = 148$

   c. Are the cross products equal?
   No. 144 does not equal 148

   d. Are the ratios proportional?
   No. The cross products are not equal.

   e. If the ratios are proportional, write a proportion.
   Because the ratios are not proportional, no proportion can be written.

In Problems 40 through 52, determine if two ratios are proportional by computing the cross products. If the cross products are equal, the ratios are proportional and are written as a proportion. If the cross products are not equal, the rations are not proportional.

40. $\dfrac{24}{3} \overset{?}{=} \dfrac{56}{7}$

$3 \cdot 56 = 168, \quad 24 \cdot 7 = 168$

The cross products are equal.
The ratios are proportional.

$$\dfrac{24}{3} = \dfrac{56}{7}$$

42. $\dfrac{65}{12} \overset{?}{=} \dfrac{100}{28}$

$12 \cdot 100 = 1200, \quad 65 \cdot 28 = 1820$

The cross products are not equal. The ratios are not proportional.

44. $\dfrac{18}{93} \overset{?}{=} \dfrac{25}{129}$

$93 \cdot 25 = 2325, \quad 18 \cdot 129 = 2322$

The cross products are not equal. The ratios are not proportional.

46. $\dfrac{6}{45} \overset{?}{=} \dfrac{12}{90}$

$45 \cdot 12 = 540, \quad 6 \cdot 90 = 540$

The cross products are equal.
The ratios are proportional.

$$\dfrac{6}{45} = \dfrac{12}{90}$$

48. $\dfrac{93}{39} \overset{?}{=} \dfrac{31}{12}$

$39 \cdot 31 = 1209, \quad 93 \cdot 12 = 1116$

The cross products are not equal. The ratios are not proportional.

50. $\dfrac{100}{36} \overset{?}{=} \dfrac{50}{18}$

$36 \cdot 50 = 1800, \quad 100 \cdot 18 = 1800$

The cross products are equal.
The ratios are proportional.

$$\dfrac{100}{36} = \dfrac{50}{18}$$

52. $\dfrac{76}{22} \overset{?}{=} \dfrac{38}{11}$

$22 \cdot 38 = 836, \quad 76 \cdot 11 = 836$

The cross products are equal. The ratios are proportional.

$$\dfrac{76}{22} = \dfrac{38}{11}$$

Guide Problems

54. Solve for the unknown quantity in the proportion
$\dfrac{7}{49} = \dfrac{b}{91}$.

a. Cross multiply to find the cross products.

$49 \cdot b = 49b$

$7 \cdot 91 = 637$

b. Separate the cross products by an equal sign to form an equation.

$49b = 637$

c. Divide both sides of the equation by the number on the side with the unknown. In this case, the number on the side with the unknown is 56.

$$\dfrac{49b}{49} = \dfrac{637}{49}$$

d. Simplify.

$$\dfrac{49b}{49} = \dfrac{\cancel{49}b}{\cancel{49}} = b = \dfrac{\overset{13}{\cancel{637}}}{\underset{1}{\cancel{49}}} = 13$$

or $b = 13$.

e. To verify, replace the unknown in the original proportion with the answer, and check that the cross products are equal.

$$\dfrac{7}{49} = \dfrac{13}{91} \qquad 49 \cdot 13 = 637$$
$$7 \cdot 91 = 637$$

The cross products are equal.

Problems 56 through 72 are solved using the same steps outlined above. Compute the cross products from the given proportion. Then form an equation by separating the cross products with an equal sign. Divide both sides by the number on the side with the unknown. This guarantees the unknown will be by itself on one side of the equation and the solution to the proportion problem will be on the other. As a last step, check your answer by writing the proportion with the unknown replaced by the value you found and verify the cross products are equal.

56. $\dfrac{11}{12} = \dfrac{r}{84}$

$12 \cdot r = 12r$

$11 \cdot 84 = 924$

$12r = 924$

$\dfrac{12r}{12} = \dfrac{924}{12}$

$r = 77$

Verify:

$\dfrac{11}{12} = \dfrac{77}{84}$ $\quad 12 \cdot 77 = 924$

$\quad\quad\quad\quad\quad 11 \cdot 84 = 924$

58. $\dfrac{24}{5} = \dfrac{48}{s}$

$5 \cdot 48 = 240$

$24 \cdot s = 24s$

$24s = 240$

$\dfrac{24s}{24} = \dfrac{240}{24}$

$s = 10$

Verify:

$\dfrac{24}{5} = \dfrac{48}{10}$ $\quad 5 \cdot 48 = 240$

$\quad\quad\quad\quad\quad 24 \cdot 10 = 240$

60. $\dfrac{3.5}{k} = \dfrac{1.5}{21}$

$k \cdot 1.5 = 1.5k$

$3.5 \cdot 21 = 73.5$

$1.5k = 73.5$

$\dfrac{1.5k}{1.5} = \dfrac{73.5}{1.5}$

$k = 49$

Verify:

$\dfrac{3.5}{49} = \dfrac{1.5}{21}$ $\quad 49 \cdot 1.5 = 73.5$

$\quad\quad\quad\quad\quad 3.5 \cdot 21 = 73.5$

62. $\dfrac{13}{15} = \dfrac{u}{75}$

$15 \cdot u = 15u$

$13 \cdot 75 = 975$

$15u = 975$

$\dfrac{15u}{15} = \dfrac{975}{15}$

$u = 65$

Verify:

$\dfrac{13}{15} = \dfrac{65}{75}$ $\quad 15 \cdot 65 = 975$

$\quad\quad\quad\quad\quad 13 \cdot 75 = 975$

64. $\dfrac{4}{2} = \dfrac{z}{5\frac{1}{2}}$

$2 \cdot z = 2z$

$4 \cdot 5\dfrac{1}{2} = 4 \cdot \dfrac{11}{2} = 22$

$2z = 22$

$\dfrac{2z}{2} = \dfrac{22}{2}$

$z = 11$

Verify:

$\dfrac{4}{2} = \dfrac{11}{5\frac{1}{2}}$ $\quad 2 \cdot 11 = 22$

$\quad\quad\quad\quad\quad 4 \cdot 5\dfrac{1}{2} = 22$

66. $\dfrac{1.6}{p} = \dfrac{3.2}{0.8}$

$p \cdot 3.2 = 3.2p$

$1.6 \cdot 0.8 = 1.28$

$3.2p = 1.28$

$\dfrac{3.2p}{3.2} = \dfrac{1.28}{3.2}$

$p = 0.4$

Verify:

$\dfrac{1.6}{0.4} = \dfrac{3.2}{0.8}$ $\quad 0.4 \cdot 3.2 = 1.28$

$\quad\quad\quad\quad\quad 1.6 \cdot 0.8 = 1.28$

68. $\dfrac{5}{8} = \dfrac{v}{40}$

$8 \cdot v = 8v$

$5 \cdot 40 = 200$

$8v = 200$

$\dfrac{8v}{8} = \dfrac{200}{8}$

$v = 25$

Verify:

$\dfrac{5}{8} = \dfrac{25}{40}$ $\quad 8 \cdot 25 = 200$

$\quad\quad\quad\quad\quad 5 \cdot 40 = 200$

70. $\dfrac{t}{40} = \dfrac{12}{60}$

$40 \cdot 12 = 480$

$t \cdot 60 = 60t$

$60t = 480$

$\dfrac{60t}{60} = \dfrac{480}{60}$

$t = 8$

Verify:

$\dfrac{8}{40} = \dfrac{12}{60}$ $\quad 40 \cdot 12 = 480$

$\quad\quad\quad\quad\quad 8 \cdot 60 = 480$

72. $\dfrac{0.75}{2} = \dfrac{x}{40}$

$2 \cdot x = 2x$

$0.75 \cdot 40 = 30$

$2x = 30$

$\dfrac{2x}{2} = \dfrac{30}{2}$

$x = 15$

Verify:

$\dfrac{0.75}{2} = \dfrac{15}{40}$ $\quad 2 \cdot 15 = 30$

$\quad\quad\quad\quad\quad 0.75 \cdot 40 = 30$

74. The rate of the sports car is $\dfrac{280}{6}$ miles per hour while the truck's rate is $\dfrac{160}{4}$ miles per hour. To determine if the rates are proportional, compute the cross products: $6 \cdot 160 = 960$ and $280 \cdot 4 = 1120$. The cross products are not equal so the rates are not proportional.

76. The production rate for the first assembly line can be written as $\dfrac{25}{1.5}$ while the competitor's rate can be written as $\dfrac{125}{7.5}$. To see if these rates are proportional, compute the cross products: $1.5 \cdot 125 = 187.5$ and $25 \cdot 7.5 = 187.5$. The cross products are equal so the rates are proportional.

78. Let x denote the amount of medication, in cc, received in 80 hours. Since 438 cc were delivered in 32 hours, we have the proportion $\dfrac{x}{80} = \dfrac{438}{32}$. Cross multiplying gives $32x = 80 \cdot 438 = 35{,}040$ and dividing gives $x = \dfrac{35{,}040}{32} = 1095$. The patient will receive 1095 cc of medication in 80 hours.

80. Let x be the width of the screen in inches. The height is 27 inches and the ratio of height to width is $\dfrac{9}{16}$. Thus x satisfies the proportion $\dfrac{27}{x} = \dfrac{9}{16}$. Solving this proportion gives $9x = 27 \cdot 16 = 432$ and $x = \dfrac{432}{9} = 48$. The television screen is 48 inches wide.

82. Let x denote the length of the line on the blueprint, in inches, that corresponds to the 60 foot wall. Since the ratio of the blueprint lengths to the actual lengths is $\dfrac{1}{4}$ inch to 1 foot, x must satisfy the proportion $\dfrac{x}{60} = \dfrac{\frac{1}{4}}{1}$. Cross multiply to find $1 \cdot x = x = 60 \cdot \dfrac{1}{4} = 15$. The corresponding line on the blueprint will be 15 inches long.

84. Let t be the sales tax on \$1500. Since the tax on \$350 is \$28, t satisfies $\dfrac{t}{1500} = \dfrac{28}{350}$. Solve this proportion to find $350t = 1500 \cdot 28 = 42{,}000$ and so $t = \dfrac{42{,}000}{350} = 120$. The sales tax on \$1500 is \$120.

86. a. Let x be the number of ounces needed to cover 5300 square feet. Since the given rate is 90 ounces per 2400 square feet, x must satisfy $\dfrac{x}{5300} = \dfrac{90}{2400}$. Cross multiply to find $2400x = 90 \cdot 5300 = 477{,}000$. Divide to find $x = \dfrac{477{,}000}{2400} = 198.75$ ounces.

    b. From part a., 198.75 ounces are needed for the job. If the fertilizer comes in 25 ounce bags then $\dfrac{198.75}{25} = 7.95$ bags are needed. Since only whole bags may be purchased, 8 bags are needed.

    c. From part b., 8 of the 25-ounce bags must be purchased. At \$3.25 per bag the total cost will be $8 \cdot \$3.25 = \$26.00$.

88. In 1995, the birth rate was 14.6 per 1000 people. To find the births in a population of 740,000, set up the proportion $\dfrac{b}{740{,}000} = \dfrac{14.6}{1000}$ where b is the number of births. Solving this proportion gives $1000b = 740{,}000 \cdot 14.6 = 10{,}804{,}000$ and $b = \dfrac{10{,}804{,}000}{1000} = 10{,}804$. There were 10,804 births.

90. Let p denote the population of the city in 2001. The city had 1833 births so the rate of births is $\dfrac{1833}{p}$. The National birth rate in 2001 was 14.1 births per 1000 people or $\dfrac{14.1}{1000}$. If the two rates are in proportion then $\dfrac{1833}{p} = \dfrac{14.1}{1000}$ and so $14.1p = 1,833,000$ and $p = \dfrac{1,833,000}{14.1} = 130,000$. The city's population was 130,000.

92. Let b denote the number of births per 1000 people in 2006. Since there were 3,926,000 births per 302,000,000 people, we have the proportion $\dfrac{b}{1000} = \dfrac{3,926,000}{302,000,000}$. Solving this proportion in the usual way gives $302,000,000b = 1000 \cdot 3,926,000$ and $b = \dfrac{3,926,000,000}{302,000,000} = 13$. the birth rate in 2006 was 13.0 births per 1000 people.

94. Let w be the new width, then the ratio of old width to new width and old length to new length are in proportion. The proportion is $\dfrac{12}{w} = \dfrac{18}{24}$. cross multiply to find $18w = 12 \cdot 24 = 288$ and $w = \dfrac{288}{18} = 16$. The new width is will be 16 feet.

96. Let x be the eight of the building in feet. Since the ratio of the height of nearby objects to the lengths of their shadows are in proportion, we have $\dfrac{x}{78} = \dfrac{18}{27}$ since the building is x feet high and casts a shadow of length 78 feet while a pole 18 feet high casts a shadow 27 feet long. Solving this proportion gives $27x = 78 \cdot 18 = 1404$ and $x = \dfrac{1404}{27} = 52$. The building is 52 feet tall.

Cumulative Skills Review

2. $\dfrac{65}{85} = \dfrac{5 \cdot 13}{5 \cdot 17} = \dfrac{13}{17}$

4. a. 12-ounce size:
$$\dfrac{\$4.80}{12 \text{ ounces}} = \dfrac{\$4.80 \div 12}{12 \div 12 \text{ ounces}} = \dfrac{\$0.40}{1 \text{ ounce}}$$
or \$0.40 per ounce.
16-ounce size:
$$\dfrac{\$5.44}{16 \text{ ounces}} = \dfrac{\$5.44 \div 16}{16 \div 16 \text{ ounces}} = \dfrac{\$0.34}{1 \text{ ounce}}$$
or \$0.34 per ounce.

   b. The lowest unit price and so the best buy is the 16-ounce container at 0.34 per ounce.

6. The LCD of $\dfrac{1}{6}$ and $\dfrac{3}{7}$ is the least common multiple of 6 and 7. Start listing multiples of 6 and 7.
   6: 6, 12, 18, 24, 30, 36, 42, 48, …
   7: 7, 14, 21, 28, 35, 42, 49, 56, …
   The smallest multiple common to both lists is 42. The LCD is 42.

8. By the associative property of addition, replace the ? with 3.
$$(3 + 12) + 80 = 3 + (12 + 80)$$

10. $\dfrac{\$13.50}{2 \text{ cakes}} = \dfrac{\$13.50 \div 2}{2 \div 2 \text{ cakes}} = \dfrac{\$6.75}{1 \text{ ounce}}$
The unit price is \$6.75 per cake.

Chapter 4 Numerical Facts Of Life

2. The proportion for determining Mike's calorie burning rate while playing tennis is

$$\frac{540 \text{ calories per hour}}{170 \text{ pounds}} = \frac{y \text{ calories per hour}}{185 \text{ pounds}}$$

which gives

$$170y = 540 \cdot 185$$
$$170y = 99900$$
$$y = \frac{99900}{170} = 587.647...$$

Mike will burn approximately 588 calories per hour while playing tennis.

4. Mike burns 1339 calories per hour running. Assume Mike runs 4 hours per week for 6 weeks. Then each week Mike burns $1339 \cdot 4 = 5356$ calories and so, over 6 weeks, Mike burns a total of $5356 \cdot 6 = 32{,}136$ calories. Let x be the number of pounds Mike lost. Using the fact that 3500 calories make up one pound of fat, we have the following proportion

$$\frac{3500 \text{ calories}}{1 \text{ pound}} = \frac{32{,}136 \text{ calories}}{x \text{ pounds}}.$$

Setting the cross products equal gives $3500x = 32{,}136$ so $x = \frac{32{,}136}{3500} = 9.181...$. To the nearest tenth of a pound, Mike will lose 9.2 pounds.

Chapter 4 Review Exercises

1. The ratio of 3 to 8 may be written

$$3 \text{ to } 8 \quad 3 : 8 \quad \frac{3}{8}$$

2. The ratio of 62 to 7 may be written

$$62 \text{ to } 7 \quad 62 : 7 \quad \frac{62}{7}$$

3. The ratio of 12 to 5.2 may be written

$$12 \text{ to } 5.2 \quad 12 : 5.2 \quad \frac{12}{5.2}$$

4. The ratio of 9 to 14.3 may be written

$$9 \text{ to } 14.3 \quad 9 : 14.3 \quad \frac{9}{14.3}$$

5. The ratio of 3 to $\frac{5}{9}$ may be written

$$3 \text{ to } \frac{5}{9} \quad 3 : \frac{5}{9} \quad \frac{3}{\frac{5}{9}}$$

6. The ratio of $2\frac{1}{2}$ to $\frac{1}{16}$ may be written

$$2\frac{1}{2} \text{ to } \frac{1}{16} \quad 2\frac{1}{2} : \frac{1}{16} \quad \frac{2\frac{1}{2}}{\frac{1}{16}}$$

7. Simplify 10 to 16.

$$\frac{10}{16} = \frac{\overset{5}{\cancel{10}}}{\underset{8}{\cancel{16}}} = \frac{5}{8}$$

8. Simplify 58 to 6.

$$\frac{58}{6} = \frac{\overset{29}{\cancel{58}}}{\underset{3}{\cancel{6}}} = \frac{29}{3}$$

9. Simplify 16 to 52.

$$\frac{16}{52} = \frac{\overset{4}{\cancel{16}}}{\underset{13}{\cancel{52}}} = \frac{4}{13}$$

10. Simplify 24 to 21.

$$\frac{24}{21} = \frac{\overset{8}{\cancel{24}}}{\underset{7}{\cancel{21}}} = \frac{8}{7}$$

11. Simplify 5 to 12.5.

$$\frac{5}{12.5} = \frac{5}{12.5} \cdot \frac{10}{10} = \frac{50}{125} = \frac{\overset{2}{\cancel{50}}}{\underset{5}{\cancel{125}}} = \frac{2}{5}$$

12. Simplify 1.1 to 15.

$$\frac{1.1}{15} = \frac{1.1}{15} \cdot \frac{10}{10} = \frac{11}{150}$$

13. Simplify 2 to $\frac{7}{8}$.

$$\frac{2}{\frac{7}{8}} = \frac{2}{1} \cdot \frac{8}{7} = \frac{16}{7}$$

14. Simplify $\frac{9}{17}$ to 7.

$$\frac{\frac{9}{17}}{7} = \frac{9}{17} \cdot \frac{1}{7} = \frac{9}{119}$$

15. 110 feet to 16 yards
Smaller unit: feet
16 yards = 16·3 feet = 48 feet

$$\frac{110 \text{ feet}}{16 \text{ yards}} = \frac{110}{48} = \frac{55}{24}$$

16. 3 pounds to 20 ounces
Smaller unit: ounces
3 pounds = 3·16 ounces
= 48 ounces

$$\frac{3 \text{ pounds}}{20 \text{ ounces}} = \frac{48}{20} = \frac{12}{5}$$

17. 12 minutes to 220 seconds
Smaller unit: seconds
12 minutes = 12·60 seconds
= 720 seconds

$$\frac{12 \text{ minutes}}{220 \text{ seconds}} = \frac{720}{220} = \frac{36}{11}$$

18. 10,000 feet to 4 miles
Smaller unit: feet
4 miles = 4·5280 feet
= 21,120 feet

$$\frac{10,000 \text{ feet}}{4 \text{ miles}} = \frac{10,000}{21,120} = \frac{125}{264}$$

19. 8500 pounds to 5 tons
Smaller unit: pounds
5 tons = 5·2000 pounds
= 10,000 pounds

$$\frac{8500 \text{ pounds}}{5 \text{ tons}} = \frac{8500}{10,000} = \frac{17}{20}$$

20. 12 quarts to 50 pints
Smaller unit: pints
12 quarts = 12·2 pints
= 24 pints

$$\frac{12 \text{ quarts}}{50 \text{ pints}} = \frac{24}{50} = \frac{12}{25}$$

21. 280 days to 16 weeks
Smaller unit: days
16 weeks = 16·7 days
= 112 days

$$\frac{280 \text{ days}}{16 \text{ weeks}} = \frac{280}{112} = \frac{5}{2}$$

22. 5.5 gallons to 12 quarts
Smaller unit: quarts
5.5 gallons = 5.5·4 quarts
= 22 quarts

$$\frac{5.5 \text{ gallons}}{12 \text{ quarts}} = \frac{22}{12} = \frac{11}{6}$$

23. 75 sprinklers for 6 acres

$$\frac{75 \text{ sprinklers}}{6 \text{ acres}} = \frac{25 \text{ sprinklers}}{2 \text{ acres}}$$

25 sprinklers for every 2 acres

24. 392 avocados for 40 trees

$$\frac{392 \text{ avocados}}{40 \text{ trees}} = \frac{49 \text{ avocados}}{5 \text{ trees}}$$

49 avocados for every 5 trees

25. 38 kittens for 3 pet stores

$$\frac{38 \text{ kittens}}{3 \text{ pet stores}}$$

38 kittens for every 3 pet stores

26. $98 for 4 tires

$$\frac{\$98}{4 \text{ tires}} = \frac{\$49}{2 \text{ tires}}$$

$49 for every 2 tires

27. 30 ponies for 12 trainers

$$\frac{30 \text{ ponies}}{12 \text{ trainers}} = \frac{5 \text{ ponies}}{2 \text{ trainers}}$$

5 ponies for every 2 trainers

28. 120 cheeseburgers for $200

$$\frac{120 \text{ cheeseburgers}}{\$200} = \frac{3 \text{ cheeseburgers}}{\$5}$$

3 cheeseburgers for $5

29. 60 miles in 5 days

$$\frac{60 \text{ miles}}{5 \text{ days}} = \frac{60 \div 5 \text{ miles}}{5 \div 5 \text{ days}} = \frac{12 \text{ miles}}{1 \text{ day}}$$

12 miles per day

30. 1588 pounds in 2 trucks

$$\frac{1588 \text{ pounds}}{2 \text{ trucks}} = \frac{1588 \div 2 \text{ pounds}}{2 \div 2 \text{ trucks}}$$
$$= \frac{794 \text{ pounds}}{1 \text{ truck}}$$

794 pounds per truck

31. 18 yards in 7 minutes

$$\frac{18 \text{ yards}}{7 \text{ minutes}} = \frac{18 \div 7 \text{ yards}}{7 \div 7 \text{ minutes}} = \frac{2.571... \text{ yards}}{1 \text{ minute}}$$

To the nearest tenth, 2.6 yards per minute

32. 9615 jellybeans in 12 bags

$$\frac{9615 \text{ jellybeans}}{12 \text{ bags}} = \frac{9615 \div 12 \text{ jellybeans}}{12 \div 12 \text{ bags}}$$
$$= \frac{801.25 \text{ jellybeans}}{1 \text{ bag}}$$

To the nearest tenth, 801.3 jellybeans per bag

33. 168 cars in 6 lanes

$$\frac{168 \text{ cars}}{6 \text{ lanes}} = \frac{168 \div 6 \text{ cars}}{6 \div 6 \text{ lanes}} = \frac{28 \text{ cars}}{1 \text{ lane}}$$

28 cars per lane

34. 13,005 bees in 9 beehives

$$\frac{13,005 \text{ bees}}{9 \text{ beehives}} = \frac{13,005 \div 9 \text{ bees}}{9 \div 9 \text{ beehives}} = \frac{14458 \text{ bees}}{1 \text{ beehive}}$$

1445 bees per beehive

35. 47 tons of fuels in 3 cruises

$$\frac{47 \text{ tons}}{3 \text{ cruises}} = \frac{47 \div 3 \text{ tons}}{3 \div 3 \text{ cruises}} = \frac{15.666... \text{ tons}}{1 \text{ cruise}}$$

To the nearest tenth, 15.7 tons of fuel per cruise

36. 25 pounds in 8 weeks

$$\frac{25 \text{ pounds}}{8 \text{ weeks}} = \frac{25 \div 8 \text{ pounds}}{8 \div 8 \text{ weeks}} = \frac{3.125 \text{ pounds}}{1 \text{ week}}$$

To the nearest tenth, 3.1 pounds per week

37. 5 tickets for $90

$$\frac{\$90}{5 \text{ tickets}} = \frac{\$90 \div 5}{5 \div 5 \text{ tickets}} = \frac{\$18}{1 \text{ ticket}}$$

The unit price is $18 per ticket.

38. 15 T-shirts for $187.50

$$\frac{\$187.50}{15 \text{ T-shirts}} = \frac{\$187.50 \div 15}{15 \div 15 \text{ T-shirts}} = \frac{\$12.50}{1 \text{ T-shirt}}$$

The unit price is $12.50 per T-shirt.

39. $14 for 2 car washes

$$\frac{\$14}{2 \text{ car washes}} = \frac{\$14 \div 2}{2 \div 2 \text{ car washes}} = \frac{\$7}{1 \text{ car wash}}$$

The unit price is $7 per car wash.

40. $695 for 4 days

$$\frac{\$695}{4 \text{ days}} = \frac{\$695 \div 4}{4 \div 4 \text{ days}} = \frac{\$173.75}{1 \text{ day}}$$

The unit price is $173.75 per day.

41. 6 flight lessons for $510

$$\frac{\$510}{6 \text{ lessons}} = \frac{\$510 \div 6}{6 \div 6 \text{ lessons}} = \frac{\$85.00}{1 \text{ lesson}}$$

The unit price is $85 per flight lesson.

42. 125 sugar cookies for $81.25

$$\frac{\$81.25}{125 \text{ cookies}} = \frac{\$81.25 \div 125}{125 \div 125 \text{ cookies}} = \frac{\$0.65}{1 \text{ cookie}}$$

The unit price is $0.65 per sugar cookie.

43. $4.75 for 3 tennis balls

$$\frac{\$4.75}{3 \text{ balls}} = \frac{\$4.75 \div 3}{3 \div 3 \text{ balls}} = \frac{\$1.5833...}{1 \text{ ball}}$$

The unit price, to the nearest cent, is $1.58 per tennis ball.

44. $12,900 for 3 sales events

$$\frac{\$12,900}{3 \text{ events}} = \frac{\$12,900 \div 3}{3 \div 3 \text{ events}} = \frac{\$4,300}{1 \text{ event}}$$

The unit price is $4,300 per sales event.

45. 9 is to 11 as 36 is to 44.
written as a proportion is
$$\frac{9}{11} = \frac{36}{44}$$

46. 124 graduates is to 3 schools as 248 graduates is to 6 schools.
written as a proportion is
$$\frac{124 \text{ graduates}}{3 \text{ schools}} = \frac{248 \text{ graduates}}{6 \text{ schools}}$$

47. 3 is to 5 as 300 is to 500.
written as a proportion is
$$\frac{3}{5} = \frac{300}{500}$$

48. 2 days is to 95 mail orders as 6 days is to 285 mail orders.
written as a proportion is
$$\frac{2 \text{ days}}{95 \text{ mail orders}} = \frac{6 \text{ days}}{285 \text{ mail orders}}$$

49. 2.1 is to 6.5 as 16.8 is to 52.
written as a proportion is
$$\frac{2.1}{6.5} = \frac{16.8}{52}$$

50. 5 concerts is to 7 days as 15 concerts is to 21 days.
written as a proportion is
$$\frac{5 \text{ concerts}}{7 \text{ days}} = \frac{15 \text{ concerts}}{21 \text{ days}}$$

51. $$\frac{30 \text{ violins}}{5 \text{ orchestras}} = \frac{90 \text{ violins}}{15 \text{ orchestras}}$$
left hand side: 30 violins to 5 orchestras
right hand side: 90 violins to 15 orchestras
Sentence form:
30 violins is to 5 orchestras as 90 violins is to 15 orchestras.

52. $$\frac{9}{13} = \frac{81}{117}$$
left hand side: 9 to 13
right hand side: 81 to 117
Sentence form:
9 is to 13 as 81 is to 117.

53. $$\frac{3 \text{ tours}}{450 \text{ bicycles}} = \frac{6 \text{ tours}}{900 \text{ bicycles}}$$
left hand side: 3 tours to 450 bicycles
right hand side: 6 tours to 900 bicycles
Sentence form:
3 tours is to 450 bicycles as 6 tours is to 900 bicycles.

54. $$\frac{12}{33} = \frac{36}{99}$$
left hand side: 12 to 33
right hand side: 36 to 99
Sentence form:
12 is to 33 as 36 is to 99.

55. $$\frac{8 \text{ swings}}{3 \text{ playgrounds}} = \frac{16 \text{ swings}}{6 \text{ playgrounds}}$$
left hand side: 8 swings to 3 playgrounds
right hand side: 16 swings to 6 playgrounds
Sentence form:
8 swings is to 3 playgrounds as 16 swings is to 6 playgrounds.

56. $$\frac{3.7}{1.2} = \frac{37}{12}$$
left hand side: 3.7 to 1.2
right hand side: 37 to 12
Sentence form:
3.7 is to 1.2 as 37 is to 12.

57. $$\frac{18}{17} \overset{?}{=} \frac{54}{51}$$
$17 \cdot 54 = 918, \quad 18 \cdot 51 = 918$
The cross products are equal. The ratios are proportional.
$$\frac{18}{17} = \frac{54}{51}$$

58. $$\frac{6}{1.9} \overset{?}{=} \frac{18}{5.4}$$
$1.9 \cdot 18 = 34.2, \quad 6 \cdot 5.4 = 32.4$
The cross products are not equal. The ratios are not proportional.

59. $$\frac{39}{28} \overset{?}{=} \frac{13}{9}$$
$28 \cdot 13 = 364, \quad 39 \cdot 9 = 351$
The cross products are not equal. The ratios are not proportional.

60. $\dfrac{35}{21} \stackrel{?}{=} \dfrac{70}{42}$

$21 \cdot 70 = 1470, \quad 35 \cdot 42 = 1470$

The cross products are equal.
The ratios are proportional.

$$\dfrac{35}{21} = \dfrac{70}{42}$$

61. $\dfrac{7.5}{11} \stackrel{?}{=} \dfrac{60}{88}$

$11 \cdot 60 = 660, \quad 7.5 \cdot 88 = 660$

The cross products are equal.
The ratios are proportional.

$$\dfrac{7.5}{11} = \dfrac{60}{88}$$

62. $\dfrac{2.3}{5.5} \stackrel{?}{=} \dfrac{9.2}{22}$

$5.5 \cdot 9.2 = 50.6, \quad 2.3 \cdot 22 = 50.6$

The cross products are equal.
The ratios are proportional.

$$\dfrac{2.3}{5.5} = \dfrac{9.2}{22}$$

63. $\dfrac{2}{5} = \dfrac{14}{g}$

$5 \cdot 14 = 70$

$2 \cdot g = 2g$

$2g = 70$

$\dfrac{2g}{2} = \dfrac{70}{2}$

$g = 35$

Verify:

$\dfrac{2}{5} = \dfrac{14}{35} \qquad 5 \cdot 14 = 70$
$\qquad\qquad\qquad 2 \cdot 35 = 70$

64. $\dfrac{28}{100} = \dfrac{y}{25}$

$100 \cdot y = 100y$

$28 \cdot 25 = 700$

$100y = 700$

$\dfrac{100y}{100} = \dfrac{700}{100}$

$y = 7$

Verify:

$\dfrac{28}{100} = \dfrac{7}{25} \qquad 100 \cdot 7 = 700$
$\qquad\qquad\qquad 28 \cdot 25 = 700$

65. $\dfrac{m}{3} = \dfrac{46}{2}$

$3 \cdot 46 = 138$

$m \cdot 2 = 2m$

$2m = 138$

$\dfrac{2m}{2} = \dfrac{138}{2}$

$m = 69$

Verify:

$\dfrac{69}{3} = \dfrac{46}{2} \qquad 3 \cdot 46 = 138$
$\qquad\qquad\qquad 69 \cdot 2 = 138$

66. $\dfrac{t}{3} = \dfrac{44}{6}$

$3 \cdot 44 = 132$

$t \cdot 6 = 6t$

$6t = 132$

$\dfrac{6t}{6} = \dfrac{132}{6}$

$t = 22$

Verify:

$\dfrac{22}{3} = \dfrac{44}{6} \qquad 3 \cdot 44 = 132$
$\qquad\qquad\qquad 22 \cdot 6 = 132$

67. $\dfrac{18}{0.5} = \dfrac{a}{3}$

$0.5 \cdot a = 0.5a$

$18 \cdot 3 = 54$

$0.5a = 54$

$\dfrac{0.5a}{0.5} = \dfrac{54}{0.5}$

$a = 108$

Verify:

$\dfrac{18}{0.5} = \dfrac{108}{3} \qquad 0.5 \cdot 108 = 54$
$\qquad\qquad\qquad 18 \cdot 3 = 54$

68. $\dfrac{1.6}{f} = \dfrac{4}{40}$

$f \cdot 4 = 4f$

$1.6 \cdot 40 = 64$

$4f = 64$

$\dfrac{4f}{4} = \dfrac{64}{4}$

$f = 16$

Verify:

$\dfrac{1.6}{16} = \dfrac{4}{40} \qquad 16 \cdot 4 = 64$
$\qquad\qquad\qquad 1.6 \cdot 40 = 64$

69. $\dfrac{4}{u} = \dfrac{24}{18}$

$u \cdot 24 = 24u$

$4 \cdot 18 = 72$

$24u = 72$

$\dfrac{24v}{24} = \dfrac{72}{24}$

$u = 3$

Verify:

$\dfrac{4}{3} = \dfrac{24}{18} \qquad 3 \cdot 24 = 72$
$\qquad\qquad\qquad 4 \cdot 18 = 72$

70. $\dfrac{b}{2} = \dfrac{30}{12}$

$2 \cdot 30 = 60$

$b \cdot 12 = 12b$

$12b = 60$

$\dfrac{12b}{12} = \dfrac{60}{12}$

$b = 5$

Verify:

$\dfrac{5}{2} = \dfrac{30}{12} \qquad 2 \cdot 30 = 60$
$\qquad\qquad\qquad 5 \cdot 12 = 60$

71. $\dfrac{q}{7} = \dfrac{20}{3.5}$

$7 \cdot 20 = 140$

$q \cdot 3.5 = 3.5q$

$3.5q = 140$

$\dfrac{3.5q}{3.5} = \dfrac{140}{3.5}$

$q = 40$

Verify:

$\dfrac{40}{7} = \dfrac{20}{3.5} \qquad 7 \cdot 20 = 140$
$\qquad\qquad\qquad 40 \cdot 3.5 = 140$

72. $\dfrac{2.5}{10} = \dfrac{r}{12}$

$10 \cdot r = 10r$

$2.5 \cdot 12 = 30$

$10r = 30$

$\dfrac{10r}{10} = \dfrac{30}{10}$

$r = 3$

Verify:

$\dfrac{2.5}{10} = \dfrac{3}{12}$ $10 \cdot 3 = 30$

$2.5 \cdot 12 = 30$

73. $\dfrac{2\frac{1}{4}}{h} = \dfrac{9}{12}$

$h \cdot 9 = 9h$

$2\dfrac{1}{4} \cdot 12 = \dfrac{9}{4} \cdot 12 = 27$

$9h = 27$

$\dfrac{9h}{9} = \dfrac{27}{9}$

$h = 3$

Verify:

$\dfrac{2\frac{1}{4}}{3} = \dfrac{9}{12}$ $3 \cdot 9 = 27$

$2\dfrac{1}{4} \cdot 12 = 27$

74. $\dfrac{3\frac{1}{4}}{6\frac{1}{2}} = \dfrac{4}{x}$

$6\dfrac{1}{2} \cdot 4 = \dfrac{13}{2} \cdot 4 == 26$

$3\dfrac{1}{4} \cdot x = \dfrac{13}{4}x$

$\dfrac{13}{4}x = 26$

$\dfrac{\frac{13}{4}x}{\frac{13}{4}} = \dfrac{26}{\frac{13}{4}}$

$x = 26 \cdot \dfrac{4}{13} = 8$

Verify:

$\dfrac{3\frac{1}{4}}{6\frac{1}{2}} = \dfrac{4}{8}$ $6\dfrac{1}{2} \cdot 4 = 26$

$3\dfrac{1}{4} \cdot 8 = 26$

75. a. Given 14 girls and 27 boys, the ratio of girls to boys can be written in the following ways:

14 to 27, 14:27, $\dfrac{14}{27}$.

b. The total number of students is $14 + 27 = 41$. There are 27 boys. The ratio of boys to the total may be written as: 27 to 41, 27:41, $\dfrac{27}{41}$.

76. a. There are 125 condominium units and 33 townhouses. The ratio of condominium units to townhouses may be written as: 125 to 33, 125:33, $\dfrac{125}{33}$.

b. The total number of homes is $125 + 33 = 158$. There are 125 condominiums. The ratio of condominiums to the total may be written as: 158 to 125, 158:125, $\dfrac{158}{125}$.

77. a. The ratio of Randy's Monday mileage to his Wednesday mileage is $\dfrac{65}{25} = \dfrac{5 \cdot 13}{5 \cdot 5} = \dfrac{13}{5}$.

    b. The ratio of Randy's Tuesday mileage to his Thursday mileage is $\dfrac{40}{50} = \dfrac{4 \cdot 10}{5 \cdot 10} = \dfrac{4}{5}$.

    c. Randy traveled a total of $65 + 40 + 25 + 50 = 180$ miles with 65 of those miles on Monday. The simplified ratio of Monday mileage to the total is $\dfrac{65}{180} = \dfrac{5 \cdot 13}{5 \cdot 36} = \dfrac{13}{36}$.

78. a. The number of associate in science degrees is 225 and the number of bachelor degrees awarded was 60. The simplified ratio of associate in science degrees to bachelor degrees is $\dfrac{225}{60} = \dfrac{15 \cdot 15}{15 \cdot 4} = \dfrac{15}{4}$.

    b. The number of associates in art degrees and science degrees were 150 and 225 respectively. The ratio of associate arts degrees to science degrees is $\dfrac{150}{225} = \dfrac{75 \cdot 2}{75 \cdot 3} = \dfrac{2}{3}$.

    c. The total number of degrees awarded was $150 + 225 + 60 = 435$ of which 60 were bachelor degrees. The simplified ratio of bachelor degrees to total degrees is $\dfrac{60}{435} = \dfrac{15 \cdot 4}{15 \cdot 29} = \dfrac{4}{29}$.

79. a. The coffeemaker can brew 4 cups of coffee in 3 minutes. As a rate, this may be written as $\dfrac{4 \text{ cups of coffee}}{3 \text{ minutes}}$.

    b. The unit rate for part a. is $\dfrac{4 \text{ cups of coffee}}{3 \text{ minutes}} = \dfrac{4 \div 3 \text{ cups of coffee}}{3 \div 3 \text{ minute}} = \dfrac{1\frac{1}{3} \text{ cups of coffee}}{1 \text{ minute}}$ or $1\frac{1}{3}$ cups of coffee per minute.

    c. The unit price is $\dfrac{\$1.80}{4 \text{ cups}} = \dfrac{\$1.80 \div 4}{4 \div 4 \text{ cups}} = \dfrac{\$0.45}{1 \text{ cup}}$ or \$0.45 per cup.

80. a. The machine requires 27 oranges for 5 pints of orange juice. As a rate, this is written as $\dfrac{27 \text{ oranges}}{5 \text{ pints}}$.

    b. The unit rate for part a. is $\dfrac{27 \text{ oranges}}{5 \text{ pints}} = \dfrac{27 \div 5 \text{ oranges}}{5 \div 5 \text{ pints}} = \dfrac{5\frac{2}{5} \text{ oranges}}{1 \text{ pint}}$ or $5\frac{2}{5}$ oranges per pint.

    c. We are given the cost of 27 oranges is \$11.50. Note, we are looking for the unit price per pint not per orange. From part a., 27 oranges produce 5 pints of juice. The unit price is $\dfrac{\$11.50}{5 \text{ pints}} = \dfrac{\$11.50 \div 5}{5 \div 5 \text{ pints}} = \dfrac{\$2.30}{1 \text{ pint}}$ or \$2.30 per pint.

81. The 10-ounce bag has a unit price of $\dfrac{\$1.20}{10 \text{ ounces}} = \dfrac{\$0.12}{1 \text{ ounce}}$ or \$0.12 per ounce. The 13-ounce bag has a unit price of $\dfrac{\$1.69}{13 \text{ ounces}} = \dfrac{\$0.13}{1 \text{ ounce}}$. The best buy (lowest unit price) is 10-ounces at \$0.12 per ounce.

82. The table below shows the unit prices for each number of rides.

No. of rides	Price	Unit price
3	$9.75	$9.75 \div 3 = 3.25 per ride
6	$18.00	$18.00 \div 6 = 3.00 per ride
12	$34.80	$34.80 \div 12 = 2.90 per ride

The best buy is 12 rides at $2.90 per ride.

83. Two dozen bagels have a unit price of $5.95 \div 2 = 2.975 per dozen while three dozen bagels have a unit price of $8.75 \div 3 = $2.9166...$ per dozen. The latter unit price is the smaller of the two so the best buy, rounding to the nearest cent, is three dozen bagels at $2.92 per dozen.

84. The table below shows the unit prices for each number of classes.

No. of classes	Price	Unit price
9	$50.00	$50.00 \div 9 = $5.555...$ per class
12	$64.20	$64.20 \div 12 = 5.35 per class
15	$84.75	$84.75 \div 15 = 5.65 per class

The best buy is 12 classes at $5.35 per class.

85. We must determine the validity of the proportion $\dfrac{152,000}{1600} \overset{?}{=} \dfrac{185,250}{1950}$. Compute the cross products: $1600 \cdot 185,250 = 296,400,000$ and $152,000 \cdot 1950 = 296,400,000$. Since the cross products are equal, the ratios are in proportion and we may write the cost per square feet proportion as $\dfrac{\$152,000}{1600 \text{ sq. ft.}} = \dfrac{\$185,250}{1950 \text{ sq. ft.}}$.

86. The prints-to-time ratio for the first printer is $\dfrac{5}{7}$ while this ratio for the second printer is $\dfrac{7}{9}$. To determine if these rates are proportional, compute the cross products: $7 \cdot 7 = 49$ and $5 \cdot 9 = 45$. The cross products are not equal so the rates are not proportional.

87. The question is whether the rates 15 acres for every 3 hours and 19 acres for every 4 hours are proportional rates, or equivalently is $\dfrac{15}{3} \overset{?}{=} \dfrac{19}{4}$ a valid proportion. Compute the cross products: $3 \cdot 19 = 57$ and $15 \cdot 4 = 60$. The cross products are not equal so the rates are not proportional.

88. Harold's fuel consumption rate, in dollars per days, is $\dfrac{52}{8}$ while Jenna's is $\dfrac{32.50}{5}$. The cross products for these two rates are $8 \cdot 32.50 = 260$ and $52 \cdot 5 = 260$. The cross products are equal so the rates are proportional which can be written $\dfrac{\$52.00}{8 \text{ days}} = \dfrac{\$32.50}{5 \text{ days}}$.

89. The ratio of puppies to instructors is 5 to 3. If p is the number of puppies that can attend a class with 9 instructors then $\dfrac{p}{9} = \dfrac{5}{3}$. Cross multiply to find $3p = 9 \cdot 5 = 45$ and then divide to find $p = \dfrac{45}{3} = 15$. In a class with 9 instructors, 15 puppies can attend.

90. Let x denote the total square feet in the new corral which will hold 12 horses. If the corrals are proportional then the ratios of each corral's area to the number of horses will be proportional. Thus, $\dfrac{x}{12} = \dfrac{1500}{5}$ and so $5x = 12 \cdot 1500 = 18{,}000$ and $x = \dfrac{18{,}000}{5} = 3600$. The new corral should contain 3600 square feet.

91. The ratio of notebooks to students is $\dfrac{45}{20}$. Let n be the number of notebooks needed for 60 students, then $\dfrac{n}{60} = \dfrac{45}{20}$. Solving this proportion gives $20n = 60 \cdot 45 = 2700$ and so $n = \dfrac{2700}{20} = 135$. A class of 60 students needs 135 notebooks.

92. Let p the price of the 26-ounce soda. For the prices to be proportional, p must satisfy $\dfrac{p}{26} = \dfrac{2.50}{20}$. Now, cross multiply to find the equation $20p = 26 \cdot 2.50 = 65$. To find p, divide by 20 to get $p = \dfrac{65}{20} = 3.25$. The 26-ounce size should sell for \$3.25.

93. Shaun's work minutes-to-break minutes ratio is $\dfrac{50}{5}$. Let w be the amount of time Shaun needs to work to earn 30 minutes break time. Then w satisfies the proportion $\dfrac{50}{5} = \dfrac{w}{30}$. Solving this proportion gives $5w = 50 \cdot 30 = 1500$ and $w = \dfrac{1500}{5} = 300$ minutes. Shaun must work 300 minutes or 5 hours.

94. Let c be the number of classes in 12 semesters. Alicia's class-to-semester ratio is $\dfrac{10}{3}$, so c satisfies the proportion $\dfrac{c}{12} = \dfrac{10}{3}$. Cross multiplying gives $3c = 12 \cdot 10 = 120$ and so $c = \dfrac{120}{3} = 40$. Alicia will take 40 classes in 12 semesters.

95. Let n be the number of nails used in 20 minutes. If the nail gun uses nails at a rate of 65 nails for every $1\frac{1}{2}$ minutes, then n satisfies the proportion $\dfrac{n}{20} = \dfrac{65}{1\frac{1}{2}}$. Solve this proportion in the usual way:

$$1\tfrac{1}{2} \cdot n = 20 \cdot 65 = 1300 \text{ and } n = \dfrac{1300}{1\frac{1}{2}} = \dfrac{1300}{\frac{3}{2}} = 1300 \cdot \dfrac{2}{3} = \dfrac{2600}{3} = 866.666\ldots \text{. To the nearest whole nail, 867}$$

nails will be used in 20 minutes.

96. Let p be the amount of peaches, in pounds, needed for a recipe having 2 cups of sugar. Since 3 pounds of peaches correspond to $\dfrac{3}{4}$ cup of sugar, p satisfies the proportion $\dfrac{p}{2} = \dfrac{3}{\frac{3}{4}}$. By cross multiplying, $\dfrac{3}{4}p = 2 \cdot 3 = 6$. Dividing by $\dfrac{3}{4}$, or multiplying by $\dfrac{4}{3}$, gives the value $p = \dfrac{4}{3} \cdot 6 = \dfrac{24}{3} = 8$. Eight pounds of peaches are needed.

97. Let b be the number of pairs of work boots Brad will buy in 2 years. Brad buys 3 pairs every 6 months. When setting up a proportion, the units must agree, so first express 2 years as 24 months and then write the proportion $\dfrac{b}{24} = \dfrac{3}{6}$. Solving this proportion gives $6b = 24 \cdot 3 = 72$ and $b = \dfrac{72}{6} = 12$. Brad will buy 12 pairs of boots in 2 years.

98. Claudia's car gets 28 miles for every 1 gallon. Let g be the gallons of gasoline needed for a 1498 mile trip. Then g satisfies the proportion $\dfrac{1498}{g} = \dfrac{28}{1}$. Cross multiplying yields the equation $28g = 1498$ and dividing by 28 gives $g = \dfrac{1498}{28} = 53.5$. Claudia needs 53.5 gallons of gasoline for the trip.

99. Let v be the number of viewers expected over 7 nights where v is in millions. Since 3 million viewers are expected over 4 nights, v satisfies the proportion $\dfrac{v}{7} = \dfrac{3}{4}$. Solve this proportion in the usual way:

$4v = 7 \cdot 3 = 21$ and $v = \dfrac{21}{4} = 5.25$. Thus, 5.25 million or 5,250,000 million viewers are expected.

100. Suppose w is the amount of water, in gallons, used in 1 hour by the sprinkler. The sprinkler uses 20 gallons of water in 5 minutes so x satisfies the proportion $\dfrac{x}{60} = \dfrac{20}{5}$. Note the rate on the right hand side is expressed as gallons over minutes so the denominator on the left must also be in minutes so 1 hour was converted to its equivalent of 60 minutes. Now solve by cross multiplying: $5x = 60 \cdot 20 = 1200$ and $x = \dfrac{1200}{5} = 240$. The sprinkler will use 240 gallons in one hour.

101. Since the pots are similar geometric figures, the ratio of distances across the top is proportional to the ratio of heights of the smaller to larger pot. Let x be the height of the smaller pot, then $\dfrac{6}{9} = \dfrac{x}{12}$. Cross multiplying yields the equation $9x = 6 \cdot 12 = 72$. Dividing by 9 gives $x = \dfrac{72}{9} = 8$. The smaller pot is 8 inches high.

102. Since the new pool is built proportional to the old pool, the ratio of a side in the smaller pool to the corresponding side in the larger pool is in proportion to any other such ratio. Let z be the unknown side of the larger pool. The side of length 12 feet in the smaller pool corresponds to the side of length 30 feet in the new pool. Similarly, the side of length 20 feet in the smaller pool corresponds to the side of length z in the new pool. Thus, $\dfrac{12}{30} = \dfrac{20}{z}$ and, by comparing cross products, $12z = 30 \cdot 20 = 600$. Lastly, divide by 12 to find $z = \dfrac{600}{12} = 50$. The side of the new pool is 50 feet long.

103. Let x be the height of the mast in feet. A nearby piling has a height-to-shadow length ratio of $\dfrac{10}{14}$. Since the mast casts a shadow of length 56 feet, x must satisfy the proportion $\dfrac{x}{56} = \dfrac{10}{14}$. By comparing cross products, $14x = 56 \cdot 10 = 560$ and so $x = \dfrac{560}{14} = 40$. The mast is 40 feet tall.

104. Let x represent the height of the building in feet. We know the building casts a shadow 60 feet long. The ratio of the crane's height to shadow length is 80 to 25. Since the two are next to each other their height-to-

shadow ration are in proportion and so $\dfrac{x}{60} = \dfrac{80}{25}$. Solving in the usual manner gives $25x = 60 \cdot 80 = 4800$ and $x = \dfrac{4800}{25} = 192$. The building is 192 feet tall.

105. The wingspan of the Boeing 787 is given as 186 feet. The wingspan of the Airbus A330 is shown as 198 feet. Simplifying the ratio of the Boeing's wingspan to that of the Airbus gives $\dfrac{186}{198} = \dfrac{6 \cdot 31}{6 \cdot 33} = \dfrac{31}{33}$. The three ways to write this simplified ratio are 31 to 33, 31:33, and $\dfrac{31}{33}$.

106. Using the measurements in the diagrams, the ratio of the 787's length to that of the 767 is $\dfrac{182}{180} = \dfrac{2 \cdot 91}{2 \cdot 90} = \dfrac{91}{90}$. This ratio can be written as 91 to 90, 91:90, and $\dfrac{91}{90}$.

107. The cruising speed of the Airbus A330 is given as 635 mph while that for the Boeing 767 is 530 mph. First, write their ratio as a fraction and simplify $\dfrac{635}{530} = \dfrac{5 \cdot 127}{5 \cdot 106} = \dfrac{127}{106}$. Next write the simplified ratio in word form: 127 miles per hour of the Airbus A330 for every 106 miles per hour of the Boeing 767.

108. The passenger capacity of the Boeing 787 is specified as 200 people while that for the model 767 is 218 people. First write the 787-to-767 passenger ratio as a fraction and simplify: $\dfrac{200}{218} = \dfrac{2 \cdot 100}{2 \cdot 109} = \dfrac{100}{109}$. The word form for the simplified ratio is: 100 passengers on the boeing 787 for every 109 passengers on the Boeing 767.

109. a. From the drawing, the wingspan of the base model Boeing 787 is 186 feet and the length is 182 feet. The wingspan-to-length ratio is $\dfrac{186}{182} = \dfrac{2 \cdot 93}{2 \cdot 91} = \dfrac{93}{91}$.

   b. The length of the new "stretch" model will be 198 feet. Let w denote the wingspan of the short model in feet. Since the wingspan-to-length ratio will be the same as determined in part a., we have the proportion $\dfrac{w}{198} = \dfrac{93}{91}$. Cross multiply to find $91w = 198 \cdot 93 = 18{,}414$. Then $w = \dfrac{18{,}414}{91} = 202.35\ldots$. To the nearest foot, the wingspan of the new model should be 202 feet.

110. a. From the diagram, the wingspan of the base model A330 is 198 feet and the length is 194 feet. The wingspan-to-length ratio is $\dfrac{198}{194} = \dfrac{2 \cdot 99}{2 \cdot 97} = \dfrac{99}{97}$.

   b. The wingspan of the new "short" model will be 180 feet. Let x denote the length of the short model in feet. Since the wingspan-to-length ratio will be the same as determined in part a., we have the proportion $\dfrac{180}{x} = \dfrac{99}{97}$. Cross multiply to find $99x = 180 \cdot 97 = 17{,}460$. Then $x = \dfrac{17{,}460}{99} = 176.36\ldots$. To the nearest foot, the length of the new model should be 176 feet.

Chapter 4 Assessment Test

1. The ratio of 28 to 65 may be written

    28 to 65   28 : 65 $\dfrac{28}{65}$

2. The ratio of 5.8 to 2.1 may be written

    5.8 to 2.1   5.8 : 2.1 $\dfrac{5.8}{2.1}$

3. Simplify 16 to 24.

    $$\dfrac{16}{24} = \dfrac{\overset{2}{\cancel{16}}}{\underset{3}{\cancel{24}}} = \dfrac{2}{3}$$

4. Simplify 15 to 6.

    $$\dfrac{15}{6} = \dfrac{\overset{5}{\cancel{15}}}{\underset{2}{\cancel{6}}} = \dfrac{5}{2}$$

5. Simplify 68 to 36.

    $$\dfrac{68}{36} = \dfrac{\overset{17}{\cancel{68}}}{\underset{9}{\cancel{36}}} = \dfrac{17}{9}$$

6. Simplify 2.5 to 75.

    $$\dfrac{2.5}{75} = \dfrac{25}{750} = \dfrac{\overset{1}{\cancel{25}}}{\underset{30}{\cancel{750}}} = \dfrac{1}{30}$$

7. 2 days to 15 hours
    Smaller unit: hours
    2 days = 2 · 24 hours = 48 hours

    $$\dfrac{2 \text{ days}}{15 \text{ hours}} = \dfrac{48}{15} = \dfrac{16}{5}$$

8. 5 quarts to 3 pints
    Smaller unit: pints
    5 quarts = 5 · 2 pints = 10 pints

    $$\dfrac{5 \text{ quarts}}{3 \text{ pints}} = \dfrac{10}{3}$$

9. 56 apples for 10 baskets
    in fraction form is

    $$\dfrac{56 \text{ apples}}{10 \text{ baskets}} = \dfrac{28 \text{ apples}}{5 \text{ baskets}}.$$

    In sentence form, the simplified
    fraction form is "28 apples for
    every 5 baskets."

10. 12 cabinets for 88 files
    in fraction form is

    $$\dfrac{12 \text{ cabinets}}{88 \text{ files}} = \dfrac{3 \text{ cabinets}}{22 \text{ files}}.$$

    In sentence form, the simplified
    fraction form is "3 cabinets for
    every 22 files."

11. 385 miles for 12 gallons in fraction

    is $\dfrac{385 \text{ gallons}}{12 \text{ miles}}$. Divide to get a

    denominator of 1,

    $$\dfrac{385 \text{ gallons}}{12 \text{ miles}} = \dfrac{32.0833... \text{ gallons}}{1 \text{ mile}}$$

    To the nearest tenth, the unit rate is
    32.1 gallons per mile.

12. 12 birds in 4 cages in fraction form

    is $\dfrac{12 \text{ birds}}{4 \text{ cages}}$. Divide to get a

    denominator of 1,

    $$\dfrac{12 \text{ birds}}{4 \text{ cages}} = \dfrac{3 \text{ birds}}{1 \text{ cage}}$$

    The unit rate is 3 birds per cage.

13. $675 for 4 dining room chairs
    Write in fraction form, then divide
    by the denominator:

    $$\dfrac{\$675}{4 \text{ chairs}} = \dfrac{\$675 \div 4}{4 \div 4 \text{ chair}} = \dfrac{\$168.75}{1 \text{ chair}}$$

    The unit price is $168.75 per chair.

14. $5.76 for 12 tropical fish
    Write in fraction form, then divide
    by the denominator:

    $$\dfrac{\$5.76}{12 \text{ fish}} = \dfrac{\$5.76 \div 12}{12 \div 12 \text{ fish}} = \dfrac{\$0.48}{1 \text{ fish}}$$

    The unit price is $0.48 per fish.

15. 3 is to 45 as 18 is to 270
    written as a proportion is

    $$\dfrac{3}{45} = \dfrac{18}{270}$$

16. 9 labels is to 4 folders as 45 labels is to 20 folders
    written as a proportion is

    $$\dfrac{9 \text{ labels}}{4 \text{ folders}} = \dfrac{45 \text{ labels}}{20 \text{ folders}}$$

17. Given the proportion $\dfrac{2}{17}=\dfrac{6}{51}$

left hand side: 2 to 17
right hand side: 6 to 51
Sentence form:
2 is to 17 as 6 is to 51.

18. Given the proportion $\dfrac{12 \text{ photos}}{5 \text{ hours}}=\dfrac{24 \text{ photos}}{10 \text{ hours}}$

left hand side: 12 photos to 5 hours
right hand side: 24 photos to 10 hours
Sentence form:
12 photos is to 5 hours as 24 photos is to 10 hours.

19. $\dfrac{7}{16}\overset{?}{=}\dfrac{35}{80}$

Compute cross products:
$16\cdot35=560,\ \ 7\cdot80=560$

The cross products are equal so the
ratios are proportional.

20. $\dfrac{22}{18}\overset{?}{=}\dfrac{14}{12}$

Compute cross products:
$18\cdot14=252,\ \ 22\cdot12=264$

The cross products are not equal so the
ratios are not proportional.

21. $\dfrac{5}{p}=\dfrac{125}{150}$

Cross multiply: $125p=5\cdot150=750$

Solve: $p=\dfrac{125p}{125}=\dfrac{750}{125}=6$

Verify:

$\dfrac{5}{6}=\dfrac{125}{150}\qquad \begin{array}{l}6\cdot125=750\\5\cdot150=750\end{array}$

22. $\dfrac{8}{13}=\dfrac{c}{52}$

Cross multiply: $13c=8\cdot52=416$

Solve: $c=\dfrac{13c}{13}=\dfrac{416}{13}=32$

Verify:

$\dfrac{8}{13}=\dfrac{32}{52}\qquad \begin{array}{l}13\cdot32=416\\8\cdot52=416\end{array}$

23. $\dfrac{22}{19}=\dfrac{55}{m}$

Cross multiply: $22m=19\cdot55=1045$

Solve: $m=\dfrac{22m}{22}=\dfrac{1045}{22}=47.5$

Verify:

$\dfrac{22}{19}=\dfrac{55}{47.5}\qquad \begin{array}{l}19\cdot55=1045\\22\cdot47.5=1045\end{array}$

24. $\dfrac{t}{3.5}=\dfrac{27}{10.5}$

Cross multiply: $10.5t=3.5\cdot27=94.5$

Solve: $t=\dfrac{10.5c}{10.5}=\dfrac{94.5}{10.5}=9$

Verify:

$\dfrac{9}{3.5}=\dfrac{27}{10.5}\qquad \begin{array}{l}3.5\cdot27=94.5\\9\cdot10.5=94.5\end{array}$

25. a. The player ran 160 yards in 12 carries. As a fraction, his performance can be expressed as the ratio
$\dfrac{160}{12}=\dfrac{40}{3}$. Two other ways to express this ratio are $40:3$ and   40 to 3.

b. From part a., the fraction representing his performance is $\dfrac{40}{3}=13.333.....$. This fraction to the nearest
tenth is 13.3. and represents the ratio of yards to carry. The unit rate is then 13.3 yards per carry.

26. Five pounds of bananas for \$7.25 is a unit rate of $\dfrac{7.25}{5}=1.45$ dollars per pound. Three pounds of bananas
for \$4.20 is a unit rate of $\dfrac{4.20}{3}=1.40$ dollars per pound which is the smaller unit rate. Three pounds are the
better buy.

27. The unit rates are

18 ounces of sugar for \$3.60, the unit rate is $\dfrac{3.60}{18}=0.20$ dollars per ounce,

24 ounces of sugar for \$4.08, the unit rate is $\dfrac{4.08}{24} = 0.17$ dollars per ounce,

32 ounces of sugar for \$5.76, the unit rate is $\dfrac{5.76}{32} = 0.18$ dollars per ounce.

The smallest unit rate is \$0.17 per ounce so the 24 ounce deal is the best.

28. The ratio representing the first assembly lines production is $\dfrac{45}{4}$, while for the second line it is $\dfrac{78}{7}$. The question is whether $\dfrac{45}{4} \overset{?}{=} \dfrac{78}{8}$ is a valid proportion. Compute cross products to find $4 \cdot 78 = 312$ and $45 \cdot 8 = 360$. Since 312 is not equal to 360, the cross products are not equal and the rates of operation are not proportional.

29. Let x denote the actual distance between the cities. Then solve the proportion $\dfrac{4}{35} = \dfrac{2.6}{x}$. First, cross multiply to find $4x = 2.6 \cdot 35 = 91$. Then divide to find x, $x = \dfrac{4x}{4} = \dfrac{91}{4} = 22.75$. The distance is 22.75 miles.

30. Let x denote the height of the building in feet. Then solve the proportion $\dfrac{x}{130} = \dfrac{12}{20}$. First, cross multiply to find $20x = 130 \cdot 12 = 1560$. Then divide to find x, $x = \dfrac{20x}{20} = \dfrac{1560}{20} = 78$. The building is 78 feet high.

Chapter 5 Percents

Section 5.1 Introduction to Percents

Concept Check

2. The % symbol is called the __percent__ __sign__ .

4. To convert a percent to a decimal, multiply the number preceding the percent sign by __0.01__ . Alternatively, drop the percent sign and move the decimal point two places to the __left__ .

6. To convert a fraction to a percent, first convert the fraction to a __decimal__ .

8. a. What percent is represented by the shaded area? __67%__
   Note the figure is divided into $10 \times 10 = 100$ squares, 67 of which are shaded, hence 67% is shaded.

   b. What percent is represented by the unshaded area? __33%__
   Note the figure is divided into $10 \times 10 = 100$ squares, 33 of which are unshaded, hence 33% is unshaded.

Guide Problems

10. Consider 19.5%

   a. Convert 19.5% to a fraction.

   $$19.5\% = \frac{19.5}{100} \cdot \frac{10}{10} = \frac{195}{1000}$$

   To convert a percent to a fraction, write the value before the percent sign over a denominator of 100. Remove any decimal points by multiplying numerator and denominator by the same power of 10.

   b. Simplify the fraction in part a.

   $$\frac{195}{1000} = \frac{39}{200}$$

   Divide out a factor of 5.

12. Convert 29.3% to a decimal.

   To convert a percent to a decimal, drop the percent sign and multiply by 0.01.

   $$29.3\% = 29.3 \cdot 0.01 = \underline{0.293}$$

In Problems 14 through 40, percents are converted to fractions as follows. The value to the left of the percent sign becomes the numerator of a fraction with 100 as the denominator. If decimal values are involved, the fraction is multiplied by 1 in the form n/n where n is a power of 10 chosen to clear all decimal points. If a mixed numbers is involved, the mixed number is rewritten as a fraction . Lastly, the fraction is simplified.

14. $40\% = \dfrac{40}{100} = \dfrac{2}{5}$

16. $80\% = \dfrac{80}{100} = \dfrac{4}{5}$

18. $22\% = \dfrac{22}{100} = \dfrac{11}{50}$

20. $56\% = \dfrac{56}{100} = \dfrac{14}{25}$

22. $18\dfrac{1}{2}\% = \dfrac{18\frac{1}{2}}{100} = \dfrac{\frac{37}{2}}{100}$

$= \dfrac{37}{2} \cdot \dfrac{1}{100} = \dfrac{37}{200}$

24. $11\dfrac{1}{4}\% = \dfrac{11\frac{1}{4}}{100} = \dfrac{\frac{45}{4}}{100}$

$= \dfrac{45}{400} = \dfrac{9}{80}$

26. $18\dfrac{3}{4}\% = \dfrac{18\frac{3}{4}}{100} = \dfrac{\frac{75}{4}}{100}$

$= \dfrac{75}{400} = \dfrac{3}{16}$

28. $4.5\% = \dfrac{4.5}{100} = \dfrac{4.5}{100} \cdot \dfrac{10}{10}$

$= \dfrac{45}{1000} = \dfrac{9}{200}$

30. $11.5\% = \dfrac{11.5}{100} = \dfrac{11.5}{100} \cdot \dfrac{10}{10}$

$= \dfrac{115}{1000} = \dfrac{23}{200}$

32. $13.25\% = \dfrac{13.25}{100} = \dfrac{13.25}{100} \cdot \dfrac{100}{100}$

$= \dfrac{1325}{10,000} = \dfrac{52}{400}$

34. $17.6\% = \dfrac{17.6}{100} = \dfrac{17.6}{100} \cdot \dfrac{10}{10}$

$= \dfrac{176}{1000} = \dfrac{22}{125}$

36. $140\% = \dfrac{140}{100} = \dfrac{7}{5} = 1\dfrac{2}{5}$

38. $125\% = \dfrac{125}{100} = \dfrac{5}{4} = 1\dfrac{1}{4}$

40. $118\% = \dfrac{118}{100} = \dfrac{59}{50} = 1\dfrac{9}{50}$

In Exercises 42 through 68 a percent is converted to a decimal as follows. If the numerical value to the right of the percent sign contains a fraction, the value is first written in decimal form. The percent is converted to a decimal by dropping the percent sign and multiplying by 0.01. Alternatively, drop the percent sign and move the decimal point two places to left.

42. $69\% = 69 \cdot 0.01 = 0.69$

44. $86\% = 86 \cdot 0.01 = 0.86$

46. $186\% = 186 \cdot 0.01 = 1.86$

48. $371\% = 371 \cdot 0.01 = 3.71$

50. $71\dfrac{1}{2}\% = 71\dfrac{5}{10}\% = 71.5\%$

$= 71.5 \cdot 0.01 = 0.715$

52. $6\dfrac{3}{5}\% = 6\dfrac{6}{10}\% = 6.6\%$

$= 6.6 \cdot 0.01 = 0.066$

54. $32\dfrac{1}{2}\% = 32\dfrac{5}{10}\% = 32.5\%$

$= 32.5 \cdot 0.01 = 0.325$

56. $43\dfrac{1}{5}\% = 43\dfrac{2}{10}\% = 43.2\%$

$= 43.2 \cdot 0.01 = 0.432$

58. $47.1\% = 47.1 \cdot 0.01 = 0.471$

60. $66.24\% = 66.24 \cdot 0.01 = 0.6624$

62. $93.6\% = 93.6 \cdot 0.01 = 0.936$

64. $0.53\% = 0.53 \cdot 0.01 = 0.0053$

66. $0.75\% = 0.75 \cdot 0.01 = 0.0075$

68. $0.572\% = 0.572 \cdot 0.01 = 0.00572$

Guide Problems

70. Convert 0.247 to a percent.

Multiply by 100%.

$0.247 \cdot 100\% = 24.7\%$

Alternatively, move the decimal
two places to the right and append
a percent sign.

72. Consider $3\frac{1}{5}$.

a. Convert the mixed number to a decimal.

$$3\frac{1}{5} = \underline{\ 3.2\ }$$

b. Convert the decimal in part a to a percent.
Multiply by 100%.

$\underline{\ 3.2\ } \cdot 100\% = 320\%$

In each of Exercises 74 through 100 a decimal value is converted to a percent. In all cases, the conversion is done by multiplying by 100%. Alternatively, the conversion can be done by moving the decimal point in the given value two places to the right and adding % symbol.

74. $0.35 = 0.35 \cdot 100\% = 35\%$ 76. $0.6 = 0.6 \cdot 100\% = 60\%$ 78. $0.09 = 0.09 \cdot 100\% = 9\%$

80. $0.832 = 0.832 \cdot 100\% = 83.2\%$

82. $0.981 = 0.981 \cdot 100\% = 98.1\%$

84. $0.0312 = 0.0312 \cdot 100\% = 3.12\%$

86. $0.0074 = 0.0074 \cdot 100\% = 0.74\%$

88. $5 = 5 \cdot 100\% = 500\%$

90. $23 = 23 \cdot 100\% = 2300\%$

92. $2.278 = 2.278 \cdot 100\% = 227.8\%$

94. $5.34 = 5.34 \cdot 100\% = 534\%$

96. $8.3 = 8.3 \cdot 100\% = 830\%$

98. $14.3 = 14.3 \cdot 100\% = 1430\%$

100. $17.2 = 17.2 \cdot 100\% = 1720\%$

In each of Exercises 102 through 128, a fraction or mixed fraction is converted to a percent. In each case, the fraction is first converted to an equivalent decimal value using the methods of chapter 3. The resulting decimal is then converted to a percent using the techniques of Exercises 72 through 100 above.

102. $\dfrac{7}{10} = 0.7 = 0.7 \cdot 100\% = 70\%$

104. $\dfrac{1}{4} = 0.25 = 0.25 \cdot 100\% = 25\%$

106. $\dfrac{19}{100} = 0.19 = 0.19 \cdot 100\% = 19\%$

108. $\dfrac{43}{100} = 0.43 = 0.43 \cdot 100\% = 43\%$

110. $\dfrac{17}{50} = 0.34 = 0.34 \cdot 100\% = 34\%$

112. $\dfrac{3}{50} = 0.06 = 0.06 \cdot 100\% = 6\%$

114. $\dfrac{11}{8} = 1.375 = 1.375 \cdot 100\% = 137.5\%$

116. $\dfrac{19}{16} = 1.1875 = 1.1875 \cdot 100\% = 118.75\%$

118. $\dfrac{23}{8} = 2.875 = 2.875 \cdot 100\% = 287.5\%$

120. $1\dfrac{3}{10} = 1.3 = 1.3 \cdot 100\% = 130\%$

122. $1\dfrac{33}{50} = 1.66 = 1.66 \cdot 100\% = 166\%$

124. $1\dfrac{13}{25} = 1.52 = 1.52 \cdot 100\% = 152\%$

126. $2\dfrac{1}{4} = 2.25 = 2.25 \cdot 100\% = 225\%$

128. $1\dfrac{18}{25} = 1.72 = 1.72 \cdot 100\% = 172\%$

130. 18% as a decimal is 0.18 (drop the % symbol and move the decimal two places to the left).

132. The decimal 0.788 represents 78.8% since $0.788 = 0.788 \cdot 100\% = 78.8\%$.

134. The decimal form of 3.2% is $3.2\% = 3.2 \cdot 0.01 = 0.032$.

136. The decimal represented by 57% is $57\% = 57 \cdot 0.01 = 0.57$.

138. In decimal form 22% is $22\% = 22 \cdot 0.01 = 0.22$.

140. The decimal 0.427 represents 42.7% since $0.427 = 0.427 \cdot 100\% = 42.7\%$.

Cumulative Skills Review

2. In word form 8.625 is "eight and six hundred twenty-five thousandths."

4. $\dfrac{9}{16} \div \dfrac{1}{4} = \dfrac{9}{16} \cdot \dfrac{4}{1} = \dfrac{9}{\overset{}{\underset{4}{\cancel{16}}}} \cdot \dfrac{\overset{1}{\cancel{4}}}{1} = \dfrac{9}{4} = 2\dfrac{1}{4}$

6. $\dfrac{\$18.00}{20 \text{ ribbons}} = \dfrac{\$0.90}{1 \text{ ribbon}}$ or $0.90 per ribbon

8. Multiply vertically: $\begin{array}{r} \overset{3}{68} \\ \times\ 4 \\ \hline 272 \end{array}$

10. $\dfrac{15}{36} = \dfrac{\overset{5}{\cancel{15}}}{\underset{12}{\cancel{36}}} = \dfrac{5}{12}$

Section 5.2   Solve Percent Problems Using Equations

Concept Check

2. An equation is a mathematical statement containing an _equal_ sign.

4. When writing an equation, the words *what*, *what number*, and *what percent* represent the_unknown_ quantity.

6. In a percent problem, the _percent_ is the number that defines what part the amount is of the whole.

8. The percent equation is written as _Amount = Percent · Base_ .

10. When solving for the percent, we can use the formula _$\text{Percent} = \dfrac{\text{Amount}}{\text{Base}}$_ as a variation of the percent equation.

12. When solving the percent equation for the percent, the answer is converted from a _decimal_ to a _percent_.

Guide Problems

14. Fill in the following to complete the percent equation.

$$45\% \quad \text{of} \quad \underline{\text{what number}} \quad \text{is} \quad 29?$$

$$\downarrow \quad \downarrow \qquad \downarrow \qquad \qquad \downarrow \quad \downarrow$$

$$45\% \quad \cdot \qquad b \qquad \qquad = \quad 29$$

Recall that in a percent problem, the word *is* indicates an equal sign and the word *of* indicates multiplication. Phrases such as *what, what number*, and *what percent* indicate an unknown quantity represented by a variable. Here we use *b* since the unknown quantity is the whole or base.

In Problems 16 through 26 a percent problem is written as an equation. The word " is" typically translates into an equal sign while the word "of" becomes multiplication. The phrases what, what number, and what percent indicate an unknown to be represented by a variable. If the unknown quantity is a percent, the variable p is used, otherwise a and b are used. Note how the resulting equation compares to the percent equation, Amount = Percent · Base *.*

16. $57 \quad \text{is} \quad 80\% \quad \text{of} \quad \underline{\text{what number?}}$

$$\downarrow \quad \downarrow \quad \downarrow \quad \downarrow \qquad \downarrow$$

$$57 \quad = \quad 80\% \quad \cdot \qquad b$$

18. $336 \quad \text{is} \quad 15\% \quad \text{of} \quad \underline{\text{what number?}}$

$$\downarrow \quad \downarrow \quad \downarrow \quad \downarrow \qquad \downarrow$$

$$336 \quad = \quad 15\% \quad \cdot \qquad b$$

20. $10\% \quad \text{of} \quad \underline{\text{what number}} \quad \text{is} \quad 64?$

$$\downarrow \quad \downarrow \qquad \downarrow \qquad \downarrow \quad \downarrow$$

$$10\% \quad \cdot \qquad b \qquad = \quad 64$$

22. $\underline{\text{What number}} \quad \text{is} \quad 25\% \quad \text{of} \quad 924?$

$$\downarrow \qquad \downarrow \quad \downarrow \quad \downarrow \quad \downarrow$$

$$a \qquad = \quad 25\% \quad \cdot \quad 924$$

24. $\underline{\text{What number}} \quad \text{is} \quad 62.5\% \quad \text{of} \quad 720?$

$$\downarrow \qquad \downarrow \quad \downarrow \quad \downarrow \quad \downarrow$$

$$a \qquad = \quad 62.5\% \quad \cdot \quad 720$$

26. $\underline{\text{What percent}} \quad \text{of} \quad 5000 \quad \text{is} \quad 250?$

$$\downarrow \qquad \downarrow \quad \downarrow \quad \downarrow \quad \downarrow$$

$$p \qquad \cdot \quad 5000 \quad = \quad 250$$

Guide Problems

28. 40% of what number is 48?

a. Identify the parts of the percent problem.

amount: __48__
rate: __40%__
base: __unknown, *b*__

The phrase "what number" after "40% of" tells you the base is unknown and the amount must be 48.

b. Write the problem as a percent equation.

Use   Amount = Percent · Base .
$$40\% \cdot b = 48$$

c. Convert the percent to a decimal.

$$0.4b = 48$$

d. Solve the equation.

$$\text{Divide: } \frac{0.4b}{0.4} = \frac{48}{0.4}$$
$$b = 120$$

30. What percent of 1400 is 1050?

amount: 1050
percent: unknown, p
base: 1400

$$\text{Percent} \cdot \text{Base} = \text{Amount}$$
$$p \cdot 1400 = 1050$$
$$\frac{p \cdot 1400}{1400} = \frac{1050}{1400}$$
$$p = 0.75$$
$$p = 0.75 \cdot 100\%$$
$$p = 75\%$$

32. 52 is 80% of what number?

amount: 52
percent: 80%
base: unknown, b

$$\text{Percent} \cdot \text{Base} = \text{Amount}$$
$$80\% \cdot b = 52$$
$$0.8b = 52$$
$$\frac{0.8b}{0.8} = \frac{52}{0.8}$$
$$b = 65$$

34. What number is 1% of 8700?

amount: unknown, a
percent: 1%
base: 8700

$$\text{Amount} = \text{Percent} \cdot \text{Base}$$
$$a = 1\% \cdot 8700$$
$$a = 0.01 \cdot 8700$$
$$a = 87$$

36. 1180 is 20% of what number?

amount: 1180
percent: 20%
base: unknown, b

$$\text{Percent} \cdot \text{Base} = \text{Amount}$$
$$20\% \cdot b = 1180$$
$$0.2b = 1180$$
$$\frac{0.2b}{0.2} = \frac{1180}{0.2}$$
$$b = 5900$$

38. 6380 is what percent of 11,000?

amount: 6380
percent: unknown, p
base: 11,000

$$\text{Percent} \cdot \text{Base} = \text{Amount}$$
$$p \cdot 11,000 = 6380$$
$$\frac{p \cdot 11,000}{11,000} = \frac{6380}{11,000}$$
$$p = 0.58$$
$$p = 0.58 \cdot 100\%$$
$$p = 58\%$$

40. What is 15% of 540?

amount: unknown, a
percent: 32%
base: 11,000

$$\text{Amount} = \text{Percent} \cdot \text{Base}$$
$$a = 15\% \cdot 540$$
$$a = 0.15 \cdot 540$$
$$a = 81$$

42. What percent is 117 of 900?

$$p \cdot 900 = 117$$
$$\frac{p \cdot 900}{900} = \frac{117}{900}$$
$$p = 0.13$$
$$p = 13\%$$

44. What percent is 170 of 1700?

$$p \cdot 1700 = 170$$
$$\frac{p \cdot 1700}{1700} = \frac{170}{1700}$$
$$p = 0.1$$
$$p = 10\%$$

46. 1328 is what percent of 1600?

$$p \cdot 1600 = 1328$$
$$\frac{p \cdot 1600}{1600} = \frac{1328}{1600}$$
$$p = 0.83$$
$$p = 83\%$$

48. 5680 is 40% of what number?

$$40\% \cdot b = 5680$$
$$0.4b = 5680$$
$$\frac{0.4b}{0.4} = \frac{5680}{0.4}$$
$$b = 14,200$$

50. 270 is 36% of what number?

$$36\% \cdot b = 270$$
$$0.36b = 270$$
$$\frac{0.36b}{0.36} = \frac{270}{0.36}$$
$$b = 750$$

52. What is 81% of 599?

$$a = 81\% \cdot 599$$
$$a = 0.81 \cdot 599$$
$$a = 485.19$$

54. 338.4 is 72% of what number?

$$72\% \cdot b = 338.4$$
$$0.72b = 338.4$$
$$\frac{0.72b}{0.72} = \frac{338.4}{0.72}$$
$$b = 470$$

56. What number is 12% of 623?

$$a = 12\% \cdot 623$$
$$a = 0.12 \cdot 623$$
$$a = 74.76$$

58. What percent of 394 is 39.4?

$$p \cdot 394 = 39.4$$
$$\frac{p \cdot 394}{394} = \frac{39.4}{394}$$
$$p = 0.1$$
$$p = 10\%$$

60. a. The total cost of the car represents the base, $1200 is the amount and 4%, the percent so the percent equation says $0.04b = 1200$. Solving gives $b = \frac{1200}{0.04} = 30,000$. The total car cost is $30,000.

    b.   The dealer charge is 1% of the total cost or $1\% \cdot \$30,000 = 0.01 \cdot \$30,000 = \$300$.

62. The problem asks what percent of $400 is $160? From the percent equation $p \cdot 400 = 160$ or

    $p = \frac{160}{400} = 0.4 = 40\%$.

64. Only 2% of the 450 Fords tested were allowed to have major damage or $2\% \cdot 450 = 0.02 \cdot 450 = 9$ Fords.

66. a. The question is "what percent of 352 is 88?" Solving $p \cdot 352 = 88$ gives $p = \frac{88}{352} = 0.25 = 25\%$.

    b. Since all of the seats constitute 100% and 25% were occupied, $100\% - 25\% = 75\%$ were not occupied.

68. The underlying percent problem is: what percent is 4 of 7? The corresponding percent equation is
$p \cdot 7 = 4$ so $p = \dfrac{4}{7} = 0.571 = 0.571 \cdot 100\% = 57.1\%$.

70. The workers installed 1400 square feet of tile which represents 20% of the total so the question is "20% of what number is 1400?" ?" Using the percent equation, we have $20\% \cdot b = 1400$ so $0.2b = 1400$ and $b = \dfrac{1400}{0.2} = 7000$. A total of 7000 square feet of tile was installed.

72. The question asked here is what percent 8 acres is 5 acres. From the percent equation, the unknown percent satisfies $p \cdot 8 = 5$ so the percent is $p = \dfrac{5}{8} = 0.625 = 0.625 \cdot 100\% = 62.5\%$.

74. There were 58 of 160 workers absent. The percent of workers absent was $p = \dfrac{58}{160} = 0.3625 = 36.25\%$.

76. a. The problem is the same as the percent problem: what percent is 71 of 300? The percent equation is
$p \cdot 300 = 71$ and the solution is $p = \dfrac{71}{300} = 0.23666... = 23.7\%$ to the nearest tenth of a percent.

    b. The store sold 18% of 250 English textbooks. The number English textbooks sold was
$a = 18\% \cdot 250 = 0.18 \cdot 250 = 45$. The number left over is then $250 - 45 = 205$.

78. The store has used 22 of 160 ounces of raw silver so $160 - 22 = 138$ ounces remaining. The percent remaining is $p = \dfrac{138}{160} = 0.8625 = 86.25\%$.

80. The tax on the condominium is $2820.80 which represents 1.6% of the condo's value. Thus the unknown value of the condo is the base in the percent equation $1.6\% \cdot b = 2820.80$. Solving the equation $0.016 \cdot b = 2820.80$ gives $b = \dfrac{2820.80}{0.016} = 176,300$. The condo is valued at $176,300.

82. Since 20 grams represents 7% of the recommended daily value or DV, the DV is the base in the percent equation $7\% \cdot b = 20$. Solving this equation gives $b = \dfrac{20}{0.07} = 285.7$ or about 286 grams for the DV.

84. Using the total population of 280 million from the previous exercise and the fact that 69.1 million people bowl, the percent that bowl is $p = \dfrac{69.1}{280} = .247 = 24.7\%$.

86. If 30% of the total population of 280 million play no sports at all then $30\% \cdot 280 = 0.30 \cdot 280 = 84$ million people do not play a sport.

88. From the graph, 40.8 million people golf. If 0.02% of these have scored a hole-in-one in the last year, then $0.02\% \cdot 40.8 = 0.0002 \cdot 40.8 = 0.00816$ million have scored a hole-in-one. Equivalently 0.00816 million $= 0.00816 \cdot 1,000,000 = 8160$ golfers have scored a hole-in-one in the last 12 months.

Cumulative Skills Review

2. $0.6 = 0.6 \cdot 100\% = 60\%$

4. Convert the smaller unit, seconds, to minutes:

$$120 \text{ seconds} = \frac{120 \text{ seconds}}{1} \cdot \frac{1 \text{ minute}}{60 \text{ seconds}} = \frac{\overset{2}{\cancel{120} \text{ seconds}}}{1} \cdot \frac{1 \text{ minute}}{\underset{1}{\cancel{60} \text{ seconds}}} = 2 \text{ minutes}$$

Then $\dfrac{1.5 \text{ minutes}}{120 \text{ seconds}} = \dfrac{1.5 \text{ minutes}}{2 \text{ minutes}} = \dfrac{1.5 \cancel{\text{ minutes}}}{2 \cancel{\text{ minutes}}} = \dfrac{1.5}{2} = \dfrac{1.5}{2} \cdot \dfrac{10}{10} = \dfrac{15}{20} = \dfrac{3}{4}$.

6. To convert to a decimal, drop the percent sign and multiply by 0.01 so $78\% = 78 \cdot 0.01 = 0.78$.

8.
$$\begin{array}{r} 9.25 \\ \times \;\; 0.33 \\ \hline 2775 \\ 2775 \;\;\; \\ \hline 3.0525 \end{array}$$

10. $\dfrac{12}{30} = \dfrac{2 \cdot 2 \cdot 3}{2 \cdot 3 \cdot 5} = \dfrac{\cancel{2} \cdot 2 \cdot \cancel{3}}{\cancel{2} \cdot \cancel{3} \cdot 5} = \dfrac{2}{5}$

Section 5.3   Solve Percent Problems Using Proportions

Concept Check

2. Lists the steps to write and solve a percent proportion.

Step 1. Identify the amount, base, and part.
Step 2. Assign a letter to the unknown number. Substitute the known numbers and letter in the percent proportion.
Step 3. Simplify the fractions in the percent proportion, if possible.
Step 4. Cross-multiply to find the cross-products. Set the cross-products equal.
Step 5. Divide both sides of the equation by the number on the side with the unknown.

Guide Problems

4. What percent of 200 is 60?

    a. Identify the parts of the percen problem.

    amount: __60__
    part: __unknown, p__
    base: __200__

    Recall the base typically follows
    of in the problem statement.
    The word *what* indicates the
    unknown and the part precedes
    the % symbol.

    b. Write the percent proportion.

    $$\frac{\text{Amount}}{\text{Base}} = \frac{\text{Part}}{100}$$

    c. Substitute the values of proportion, base, and part into the proportion.

    $$\frac{60}{200} = \frac{p}{100}$$

6.   What percent of 370 is 74?   8.   1700 is 34% of what number?   10.   432.25 is 45.5% of what number?

amount: _74_
part: _unknown, p_
base: _370_

$$\frac{\text{Amount}}{\text{Base}} = \frac{\text{Part}}{100}$$

$$\frac{74}{370} = \frac{p}{100}$$

amount: _1700_
part: _34_
base: _unknown, b_

$$\frac{\text{Amount}}{\text{Base}} = \frac{\text{Part}}{100}$$

$$\frac{1700}{b} = \frac{34}{100}$$

amount: _432.25_
part: _45.5_
base: _unknown, b_

$$\frac{\text{Amount}}{\text{Base}} = \frac{\text{Part}}{100}$$

$$\frac{432.25}{b} = \frac{45.5}{100}$$

Guide Problems

12.   What number is 40% of 180?

   a. Identify the parts of the percent problem.

     amount: _unknown, a_
     part: _40_
     base: _180_

     Recall the base follows *of*.

   b. Substitute the values of amount, base, and part into the proportion.

$$\frac{\text{Amount}}{\text{Base}} = \frac{\text{Part}}{100}$$
$$\frac{a}{180} = \frac{40}{100}$$

   c. Simplify the fractions in the percent proportion, if possible.

$$\frac{a}{180} = \frac{2}{5}$$

   d. Cross-multiply and set the cross-products equal.

$$180 \cdot 2 = a \cdot 5$$
$$360 = 5a$$

   e. Divide both sides of the equation by the number on the side with the unknown.

$$\frac{5a}{5} = \frac{360}{5}$$
$$a = 72$$

     _72_ is 40% of 180.

14.   8% of what number is 50?

   a. Identify the parts of the percent problem.

     amount: _50_
     part: _8_
     base: _unknown, b_

     Recall the base follows *of*.

   b. Substitute the values of amount, base, and part into the proportion.

$$\frac{\text{Amount}}{\text{Base}} = \frac{\text{Part}}{100}$$
$$\frac{50}{b} = \frac{8}{100}$$

   c. Simplify the fractions in the percent proportion, if possible.

$$\frac{50}{b} = \frac{2}{25}$$

   d. Cross-multiply and set the cross-products equal.

$$b \cdot 2 = 50 \cdot 25$$
$$2b = 1250$$

   e. Divide both sides of the equation by the number on the side with the unknown.

$$\frac{2b}{2} = \frac{1250}{2}$$
$$b = 625$$

     8% of _625_ is 50.

In Problems 16 through 40, the same steps are followed to solve the percent problem as a proportion. First, the parts of the percent problem are identified with one part an unknown. The parts are substituted into the percent proportion $\dfrac{\text{Amount}}{\text{Base}} = \dfrac{\text{Part}}{100}$. *Fractions are simplified, if possible, then the cross-products are computed and set equal to each other. Lastly, each side is divided by the number on the side with the unknown.*

16. What is 20% of 2740?

amount: __unknown, a__
part: __20__
base: __2740__

$$\frac{\text{Amount}}{\text{Base}} = \frac{\text{Part}}{100}$$

$$\frac{a}{2740} = \frac{20}{100}$$

$$\frac{a}{2740} = \frac{1}{5}$$

$$2740 \cdot 1 = a \cdot 5$$

$$5a = 2740$$

$$\frac{5a}{5} = \frac{2740}{5}$$

$$a = 548$$

548 is 20% of 2740

18. 546 is what percent of 1400?

amount: __546__
part: __unknown, p__
base: __1400__

$$\frac{\text{Amount}}{\text{Base}} = \frac{\text{Part}}{100}$$

$$\frac{546}{1400} = \frac{p}{100}$$

$$\frac{39}{100} = \frac{p}{100}$$

$$100 \cdot p = 39 \cdot 100$$

$$100p = 3900$$

$$\frac{100p}{100} = \frac{3900}{100}$$

$$p = 39$$

546 is 39% of 1400

20. What percent of 370 is 148?

amount: __148__
part: __unknown, p__
base: __370__

$$\frac{\text{Amount}}{\text{Base}} = \frac{\text{Part}}{100}$$

$$\frac{148}{370} = \frac{p}{100}$$

$$\frac{2}{5} = \frac{p}{100}$$

$$5 \cdot p = 2 \cdot 100$$

$$5p = 200$$

$$\frac{5p}{5} = \frac{200}{5}$$

$$p = 40$$

40% of 370 is 148

22. 650 is 40% of what number?

$$\frac{650}{b} = \frac{40}{100}$$

$$\frac{650}{b} = \frac{2}{5}$$

$$b \cdot 2 = 650 \cdot 5$$

$$2b = 3250$$

$$b = \frac{3250}{2} = 1625$$

650 is 40% of 1625.

24. 13,014 is 54% of what number?

$$\frac{13,014}{b} = \frac{54}{100}$$

$$\frac{13,014}{b} = \frac{27}{50}$$

$$b \cdot 27 = 13,014 \cdot 50$$

$$27b = 650,700$$

$$b = \frac{650,700}{27} = 24,100$$

13,014 is 54% of 24,100.

26. 6501 is 33% of what number?

$$\frac{6501}{b} = \frac{33}{100}$$

$$\frac{6501}{b} = \frac{33}{100}$$

$$b \cdot 33 = 6501 \cdot 100$$

$$33b = 650,100$$

$$b = \frac{650,100}{33} = 19,700$$

6501 is 33% of 19,700.

28. 1% of 4200 is what number?

$$\frac{a}{4200} = \frac{1}{100}$$
$$4200 \cdot 1 = a \cdot 100$$
$$100a = 4200$$
$$a = \frac{4200}{100} = 42$$

1% of 4200 is 42.

30. What percent of 1100 is 121?

$$\frac{121}{1100} = \frac{p}{100}$$
$$\frac{11}{100} = \frac{p}{100}$$
$$100 \cdot p = 11 \cdot 100$$
$$100p = 1100$$
$$p = \frac{1100}{100} = 11$$

11% of 1100 is 121.

32. What percent of 570 is 285?

$$\frac{285}{570} = \frac{p}{100}$$
$$\frac{1}{2} = \frac{p}{100}$$
$$2 \cdot p = 1 \cdot 100$$
$$2p = 100$$
$$p = \frac{100}{2} = 50$$

50% of 570 is 285.

34. 80% of what number is 7200?

$$\frac{7200}{b} = \frac{80}{100}$$
$$\frac{7200}{b} = \frac{4}{5}$$
$$b \cdot 4 = 7200 \cdot 5$$
$$4b = 36,000$$
$$b = \frac{36,000}{2} = 9000$$

80% of 9000 is 7200.

36. What number is 28.5% of 460?

$$\frac{a}{460} = \frac{28.5}{100}$$
$$\frac{a}{460} = \frac{285}{1000} = \frac{57}{200}$$
$$460 \cdot 57 = a \cdot 200$$
$$200a = 26,220$$
$$a = \frac{26,220}{200} = 131.1$$

131.1 is 28.5% if 460.

38. 1.5% of 600 is what number?

$$\frac{a}{600} = \frac{1.5}{100}$$
$$\frac{a}{600} = \frac{1.5}{100} = \frac{15}{1000} = \frac{3}{200}$$
$$600 \cdot 3 = a \cdot 200$$
$$200a = 1800$$
$$a = \frac{1800}{200} = 9$$

1.5% of 600 is 9.

40. What number is 28% of 799?

$$\frac{a}{799} = \frac{28}{100}$$
$$\frac{a}{799} = \frac{7}{25}$$
$$799 \cdot 7 = a \cdot 25$$
$$25a = 5593$$
$$a = \frac{5593}{25} = 223.72$$

223.72 is 28% of 799.

42. a. First, identify the parts of a percent proportion problem. The total number of batteries is the unknown base, b. The amount is 330 and the part out of 100 is 37. The corresponding proportion is $\frac{330}{b} = \frac{37}{100}$. Cross-multiplying gives $b \cdot 37 = 330 \cdot 100$ and solving for b gives $b = \frac{33,000}{37} = 891.892$. Rounding to a whole number, there were 892 batteries at the beginning of the month.

b. The battery sales totaled 330 which is now the base. The percentage 20% says the part out of 100 is 20. The unknown amount, a, is found by solving $\frac{a}{330} = \frac{20}{100}$ or $\frac{a}{330} = \frac{1}{5}$. Cross-multiplying gives $5a = 330$ and so $a = \frac{330}{5} = 66$ sales included a set of new cables.

44. The total number of minutes, 750, is the base of which Ian has used 40%. The number of minutes used is the unknown amount, a. Using the percent proportion gives $\dfrac{a}{750} = \dfrac{40}{100} = \dfrac{2}{5}$. Cross-multiplying yields the equation $5a = 750 \cdot 2 = 1500$. Dividing by 5 gives the $a = 300$ so Ian has used 300 minutes of his plan.

46. a. Rephrased the problem is "45 is 25% of what number?" The base is b, the amount, 45 and the part, 25. Solving the percent proportion: $\dfrac{45}{b} = \dfrac{25}{100} = \dfrac{1}{4}$ gives $b = 4 \cdot 45 = 180$ invitations were sent out.

    b. The problem is asking "what percent of 60 is 18?" The part, p, is unknown, the amount is 18 and the base is 60. The percent proportion is $\dfrac{18}{60} = \dfrac{p}{100}$ and so $\dfrac{p}{100} = \dfrac{18}{60} = \dfrac{9}{30}$ and $30p = 900$. Lastly, $p = \dfrac{900}{30} = 30$. The realtor had sold 30% of the condos.

48. Renee will receive 75% of $1242 so the part is 75, the base is $1242 and the amount, a, is unknown. The percent proportion is $\dfrac{a}{1242} = \dfrac{75}{100} = \dfrac{3}{4}$. Cross-multiplying gives $4a = 3 \cdot 1242 = 3726$ and so $a = \dfrac{3726}{4} = 931.5$. Renee will receive $931.50.

50. The amount, a, is the unknown. The base is $78,000 and the part is 35. The percent proportion is solved as follows: $\dfrac{a}{78,000} = \dfrac{35}{100} = \dfrac{7}{20}$, SO $20a = 7 \cdot 78,000 = 546,000$ and so $a = \dfrac{546,000}{20} = 27,300$. Paul will pay $27,300 in taxes.

52. The amount, a, of the discount can be found from the percent proportion $\dfrac{a}{450} = \dfrac{20}{100}$. Solving the proportion gives $\dfrac{a}{450} = \dfrac{20}{100} = \dfrac{1}{5}$ so $5a = 450$ and $a = \dfrac{450}{5} = 90$. The discount is $90 so the cost of a membership after the discount is $450 - $90 = 360.

54. a. Identify the components of the percent proportion. Amount: $2,400,00 part: 4 base: b. The proportion is $\dfrac{2,400,000}{b} = \dfrac{4}{100} = \dfrac{1}{25}$. Cross-multiplying gives $b = 2,400,000 \cdot 25 = 60,000,000$. Total sales were $60,000,000.

    b. What percent of 50 is 42? Solve $\dfrac{42}{50} = \dfrac{p}{100}$ or $\dfrac{21}{25} = \dfrac{p}{100}$ giving $25p = 2100$ or $p = \dfrac{2100}{25} = 84$. The company has offices in 84% of the 50 states.

56. Since 120 dinners were pasta dinners, the remaining $200 - 120 = 80$ dinners were non-pasta dinners so the problem is asking what percent of 200 is 80? The percent proportion $\dfrac{80}{200} = \dfrac{p}{100}$ reduces to $\dfrac{2}{5} = \dfrac{p}{100}$. Cross-multiplying gives the equation $5p = 200$ and division gives $p = \dfrac{200}{5} = 40$. Thus, 40% of the dinners were non-pasta dinners.

58. The total Northeast sales is the unknown base, b. The amount is \$513,600 and the part is 64.2. The percent proportion is $\dfrac{513,600}{b} = \dfrac{64.2}{100}$. Cross-multiplying gives the equation $64.2b = 51,360,000$ and so $b = \dfrac{51,360,000}{64.2} = 800,000$. Northeast sales totaled \$800,000 last year.

60. The problem can be rephrased as "what is 40% of 12 liters?". The corresponding percent proportion is $\dfrac{a}{12} = \dfrac{40}{100}$. Solving the proportion in the usual fashion gives $\dfrac{a}{12} = \dfrac{2}{5}$ and $5a = 24$ so $a = \dfrac{24}{5} = 4.8$. The container of solution has 4.8 liters of hydrochloric acid.

62. a. 8% of what number is 12,344,000? Solve $\dfrac{12,344,000}{b} = \dfrac{8}{100} = \dfrac{2}{25}$, $2b = 25 \cdot 12,344,000 = 308,600,00$. Dividing by 2 gives the total market as 154,300,000 subscribers.

    b. Using the result of part a., the problem here is "what is 8.51% of 154,300,000?" The proportion is $\dfrac{a}{154,300,000} = \dfrac{8.51}{100}$ or $100a = 1,313,093,000$. Dividing by 100 gives $a = 13,130,930$ subscribers.

    c. As in b. above, we have $\dfrac{a}{154,300,000} = \dfrac{29.8}{100}$ or $100a = 4,598,140,000$. So $a = 45,981,400$. subscribers.

In Problems 64-66, the problem is rephrased into one the standard forms, the parts of the percent problem are identified and substituted into the percent proportion which is then solved.

64. What percent of 117.5 million is 67.5 million? Base: 117.5, amount: 67.5, part: p.
$$\dfrac{67.5}{117.5} = \dfrac{p}{100}, \qquad 117.5p = 100 \cdot 67.5 = 6750, \qquad p = \dfrac{6750}{117.5} = 57.447$$
Elton John's album sales are about 57% of that of Elvis Presley.

66. What percent of 78.5 million is 15 million? Base: 78.5, amount: 15, part: p.
$$\dfrac{15}{78.5} = \dfrac{p}{100}, \qquad 78.5p = 15 \cdot 100 = 1500, \qquad p = \dfrac{1500}{78.5} = 19.108$$
Billy Joel's overseas sales account for 19.1% of his total album sales.

Cumulative Skills Review

2. In 896,155 the digit to the right of the hundreds digit is 5 so round up when rounding to the hundreds place to get $896,200$.

4. $\dfrac{1}{4} = 0.25 = 0.25 \cdot 100\% = 25\%$

6. $\dfrac{855 \text{ miles}}{15 \text{ gallons}} = \dfrac{15 \cdot 57 \text{ miles}}{15 \text{ gallons}} = \dfrac{57 \text{ miles}}{1 \text{ gallon}}$

   or 57 miles per gallon

8. Subtract vertically:
$$\begin{array}{r} 5\overset{4}{\cancel{6}}\,\overset{12}{\cancel{2}} \\ 1\,2\,9 \\ \hline 4\,2\,3 \end{array}$$

10. Since $\dfrac{\$9.90}{6 \text{ songs}} = \dfrac{\$1.65}{1 \text{ song}}$ the unit cost is \$1.65 per song.

Section 5.4   Solve Percent Application Problems

Concept Check

2.   When numbers go up, the percent change is referred to as a percent   <u>increase</u> .

4.   Write the formula for percent change. $\text{Percent change} = \dfrac{\text{Change amount}}{\text{Original amount}}$

6.   Write the sales tax equation. $\text{Sales tax} = \text{Sales tax rate} \cdot \text{Item cost}$

8.   A form of compensation based on a percent of sales is called   <u>commission</u> .

10. Write the discount equation. $\text{Discount} = \text{Discount rate} \cdot \text{Original cost}$

Guide Problems

12. If a number changes from 565 to 300,
     what is the percent change?

     a. What is the change amount?

     The new amount is smaller than the
     original amount, so the amount has
     decreased and the change amount is
     found by subtracting the new amount
     from the original amount.

     $565 - 300 = 265$

     b. Set up the percent change formula.

     $\text{Percent change} = \dfrac{\text{Change amount}}{\text{Original amount}}$

     $= \dfrac{265}{565}$

     c. Solve and state the percent change as an increase or decrease.

     $\dfrac{265}{565} = 0.469 = 46.9\%$

     The percent change is a 46.9% decrease.

In completing the table for exercises 14 – 22, the following strategy is used. To determine the Amount Of Change, compute New Amount − Original Amount *, if the new amount is greater than the original amount. If the new amount is less than the original amount, compute* Original Amount − New Amount *. The Percent Change is found by computing* $\dfrac{\text{Change amount}}{\text{Original amount}}$ *and writing the result as a percent. Lastly, the percent change is an increase if the new amount is greater than the original amount and a decrease if the new amount is less than the original amount. Percents are rounded to the nearest whole percent.*

	Original Amount	New Amount	Amount Of Change	Percent Change
14.	15	12.75	Orig. − New = 15 − 12.75 = 2.25	$\dfrac{2.25}{15} = 0.15 = 15\%$ decrease
16.	$65	$50	Orig. − New = $65 − $50 = $15	$\dfrac{15}{65} = 0.23 = 23\%$ decrease

18.	875	900	New − Orig. = 900 − 875 = 25	$\dfrac{25}{875} = 0.03 = 3\%$ increase
20.	$10	$50	New − Orig. = $50 − $10 = $40	$\dfrac{40}{10} = 4.0 = 400\%$ increase
22.	48.2	60	New − Orig. = 60 − 48.2 = 11.8	$\dfrac{11.8}{48.2} = 0.24 = 24\%$ increase

Guide Problems

24. Mary Lou's dinner tab was $23.25. She wants to leave a 20% tip.

    a. Write the tip formula.
       Tip = Tip rate · Bill amount

    b. Substitute the values in the formula.

       $t = 20\% \cdot \$23.25$

    c. Calculate the tip.

       $t = 20\% \cdot \$23.25 = 0.2 \cdot \$23.25$
       $= \$4.65$

    d. Determine the total.

       Bill amount + Tip = Total
       $\$23.25 + \$4.65 = \$27.90$

26. At Harrison's Department Store, leather handbags are on sale. If the original price is $150 and the discount is 50%, what is the amount of the discount and the sale price?

    a. Write the discount formula.
       Discount = Discount rate · Original cost

    b. Substitute the values in the formula.

       $d = 50\% \cdot \$150$

    c. Calculate the discount.

       $d = 50\% \cdot \$150 = 0.5 \cdot \$150 = \$75$

    d. Determine the sale price.
       Original price − Discount = Sale price
       $\$150 - \$75 = \$75$

28. Item cost: $12.95   Sales tax rate: 5.4%
    Sales tax = Sales tax rate · Item cost
    $= 5.4\% \cdot \$12.95 = 0.054 \cdot \$12.95$
    $= \$0.6993$ or $\$0.70$

30. a. Item cost: $250,000   Sales tax rate: 7%
    Sales tax = Sales tax rate · Item cost
    $= 7\% \cdot \$250,000 = 0.07 \cdot \$250,000$
    $= \$17,500$

    b. Total purchase price
       = Item Cost + Sales Tax
       $= \$250,000 + \$17,500 = \$267,500$

32. Bill amount: $55.20   Tip rate: 22%
    Tip = Tip rate · Bill amount
    $= 22\% \cdot \$55.20 = 0.22 \cdot \$55.20$
    $= \$12.144$ or $\$12.14$
    Total = Bill amount + Tip
    $= \$55.20 + \$12.14 = \$67.34$

34. The bill amount is $780 while the total is $1000. The tip is then $\$1000 - \$780 = \$220$.

    Let r represent the tip rate. Then from the tip equation
       Tip = Tip rate · Bill amount
       $\$220 = r \cdot \$780$
       $\$780r = \$220$

    Solving for r give a tip rate of
       $r = \dfrac{220}{780} = \dfrac{11}{39} = 0.282... = 28\%$.

36. Commission rate: 6%
    Total sales: $3575
    Commission
    $$= \text{Commission rate} \cdot \text{Sales amount}$$
    $$= 6\% \cdot \$3575 = 0.06 \cdot \$3575$$
    $$= \$214.50$$
    Mardell earned $214.50 on the sale.

38. Commission: $50,000
    Total sales: $800,000
    Let r denote the unknown commission rate.
    Then from the commission equation
    $$\$50,000 = r \cdot \$800,000$$
    Solving for r gives a commission rate of
    $$r = \frac{50,000}{800,000} = \frac{1}{16} = 0.0625 = 6.25\%$$

40. a. Discount = Discount rate $\cdot$ Original cost
    $$= 60\% \cdot \$50 = 0.6 \cdot \$50 = \$30$$

    b. Sale price = Original price − Discount
    $$= \$50 - \$30 = \$20$$
    The sale price of the toy car is $20.

42. The original price was $1250 and the sale price
    was $790. The amount of the discount was then
    $1250 − $790 = 460. Let r denote the unknown
    discount rate. From the discount equation.

    Discount = Discount rate $\cdot$ Original cost
    $$\$460 = r \cdot \$1250$$
    Solve for r, $r = \dfrac{460}{1250} = \dfrac{46}{125} = 0.368 = 36.8\%$.
    The computer was discounted 36.8%.

44. The original price is $90 and the discount rate is 20%. The discount equation gives

    Discount = Discount rate $\cdot$ Original cost
    Discount $= 20\% \cdot \$90 = 0.2 \cdot \$90 = \$18$

    The sale price of the software is

    Sale price = Original price − Discount
    $$= \$90 - \$18 = \$72$$

Guide Problems

46. The number of employees at Armstrong Corporation declined 15% to 306. How many employees did the
    company have before the decrease?

    a. Because the number of employees decreased, subtract the percent change from 100%.
       $$100\% - \underline{\ \ 15\% \ \ } = \underline{\ \ 85\% \ \ }$$

    b. Substitute the new number of employees and the percent from part a. into the percent equation. The
       percent equation is
          Amount = Percent $\cdot$ Base
       and the base amount, b, is the unknown original number of employees.

       $$306 \text{ employees} = 85\% \cdot b$$

    c. Determine the original number of employees.

$$306 \text{ employees} = 85\% \cdot b = 0.85b$$

$$\frac{306 \text{ employees}}{0.85} = b$$

$$b = 360 \text{ employees}$$

In exercises 48-60, the table is completed as follows. In each exercise, the percent equation is solved to find either the unknown original amount or the unknown new amount. The original amount corresponds to the base, b, in the percent equation, while the new amount is the amount, a. The percent is $100\% + \text{Percent Change}$ *if an increase is indicated or* $100\% - \text{Percent Change}$ *if a decrease is indicated.*

	Original Amount	Percent Change	Increase or Decrease	New Amount
48.	Amount = Percent · Base $\$80 = (100\% + 78\%) \cdot b$ $\$80 = 178\% \cdot b = 1.78b$ $b = \dfrac{\$80}{1.78} = \$44.94$ or $45 rounded	78%	increase	$80
50.	1850	84%	increase	Amount = Percent · Base $a = (100\% + 84\%) \cdot 1850 = 184\% \cdot 1850$ $a = 1.84 \cdot 1850 = 3404$
52.	500	262%	increase	$a = (100\% + 262\%) \cdot 500 = 362\% \cdot 500$ $a = 3.62 \cdot 500 = 1810$
54.	$30 = (100\% - 47\%) \cdot b$ $30 = 53\% \cdot b = 0.53b$ $b = \dfrac{30}{0.53} = 56.6$ or 57 rounded	47%	decrease	30
56.	$\$450 = (100\% + 50\%) \cdot b$ $\$450 = 150\% \cdot b = 1.50b$ $b = \dfrac{\$450}{1.50} = \$300$	50%	increase	$450
58.	$26 = (100\% - 15\%) \cdot b$ $26 = 85\% \cdot b = 0.85b$ $b = \dfrac{26}{0.85} = 30.588$ or 31 rounded	15%	decrease	26
60.	$105 = (100\% + 133\%) \cdot b$ $105 = 233\% \cdot b = 2.33b$ $b = \dfrac{105}{2.33} = 45.064$ or 45 rounded	133%	increase	105

62. If 6 feet were cut from 15 feet then $15 - 6 = 9$ feet remain. The percent this represents is found by solving $9 = p \cdot 15$ to find $p = \dfrac{9}{15} = \dfrac{3}{5} = 0.6 = 60\%$. Alternatively, note that the percent cut from the roll is the percent of 15 that is 6 or $p = \dfrac{6}{15} = \dfrac{2}{5} = 0.4 = 40\%$ so the percent remaining is $100\% - 40\% = 60\%$.

64. a. The percent change in service locations is an increase of $\dfrac{\text{Change amount}}{\text{Original amount}} = \dfrac{10}{200} = 0.05 = 5\%$.

    b. If the weekly revenue increase by 22% the percent change is $100\% + 22\% = 122\%$. The new revenue is $a = 122\% \cdot \$4000 = 1.22 \cdot \$4000 = \$4880$ per store.

66. Since the propane level has decreased by 26%. the new level is $100\% - 26\% = 74\%$ of the original level. Since $74\% \cdot 170 = 125.8$ the new level is about 126 gallons.

68. Since there is an increase of 40%, the new page count is $100\% + 40\% = 140\%$ of the original page count of 750. From the percent equation, the new page count is $a = 140\% \cdot 750 = 1.4 \cdot 750 = 1050$ pages.

70. The change amount of Greg's bill is $\$23 - \$16 = \$7$ which represents a percent decrease of $\dfrac{7}{23} = 0.30$ or 30%

72. a. The change amount of volunteers is $500 - 180 = 320$. This represents a percent increase of $\dfrac{320}{180} = \dfrac{16}{9} = 1.78 = 178\%$.

    b. The expected change amount in houses built is $7 - 5 = 2$. This represents a percent increase of $\dfrac{2}{5} = 0.4 = 40\%$.

74. The predicted increase in Department of Education spending is $\$64 - \$31 = \$33$ billion dollars. This represents a percent increase from 1993 of $\dfrac{33}{31} = 1.064 = 106.4\%$ or 106% rounded to the nearest whole percent.

76. Since the 2005 cost represents a 91.7% increase, the 2005 cost is $100\% + 91.7\% = 191.7\%$ of the 1995 cost. The 2005 cost was $2.3 million. If b is the 1995 cost in millions, the percent equation states $191.7\% \cdot b = 1.917b = 2.3$. Solving gives $b = \dfrac{2.3}{1.917} = 1.2$ million dollars for a Supper Bowl ad in 1995.

78. The change in laptop orders is $22 - 12 = 10$ laptops. The percent change from the 12 laptops last year is $\dfrac{10}{12} = \dfrac{5}{6} = 0.8333 = 83.33\%$. After rounding, there was an 83% increase in laptop orders.

80. The change in the number of dogs is an increase of $73.9 - 52.9 = 21$ million. This represents a percent increase from the 1996 number of 52.9 million of $\dfrac{21}{52.9} = 0.397 = 39.7\%$.

82. From 1996 to 2006 the amount spent on pet care increased by $\$26.6 - \$11.1 = \$15.5$ billion. This represents a percent increase from the 1996 $11.1 billion figure of $\dfrac{15.5}{11.1} = 1.396 = 139.6\%$.

84. The change in mobile users from 2004 to 2006 was $163.7 - 154.2 = 9.5$ million users which represents a percent increase of $\dfrac{9.5}{154.2} = 0.06161 = 6.161\%$ or 6.2% to the nearest tenth of a percent.

86. A 2% increase means the 2008 usage, a, is $100\% + 2\% = 102\%$ of the 167.5 million recorded in 2007. From the percent equation, $a = 102\% \cdot 167.5 = 1.02 \cdot 167.5 = 170.85$ million users or 170,850,000 users in 2008.

Cumulative Skills Review

2. In fraction notation, the first value in the ratio "8 is to 13" becomes the numerator and the second, the denominator. In fraction notation, "8 is to 13" is $\dfrac{8}{13}$.

4. $5.2\% = 5.2 \cdot 0.01 = 0.052$ or, equivalently, drop the % symbol and move the decimal to the left two places.

6. In "what percent of 65 is 3", the base is 65, the amount is 3 and the percent, p, is unknown. The percent equation is $\text{Amount} = \text{Percent} \cdot \text{Base}$. Substituting gives $p \cdot 65 = 3$ or $65p = 3$.

8. The ratio "4 is to 7" can be written as a fraction, with a colon, or with the word "to" as below:

$$\frac{4}{7} \qquad 4:7 \qquad 4 \text{ to } 7.$$

10. Use the percent equation, $\text{Amount} = \text{Percent} \cdot \text{Base}$ so $a = 65\% \cdot 1000 = 0.65 \cdot 1000 = 650$.

Chapter 5 Numerical Facts Of Life

First summarize Toby Kaluzny's income and his current obligations.

Monthly income: $4650.00   Non-housing monthly obligations: $615.00

If Toby qualifies for the mortgage, his monthly housing expense will be $1230.00.

a. Toby's housing expense ratio is

$$\text{Housing expense ratio} = \frac{\text{Monthly housing expense}}{\text{Monthly gross income}} = \frac{1230.00}{4650.00} = 0.2645 = 26.5\%$$

to a tenth of a percent.

b. With the mortgage, Toby's total monthly financial obligations will be $615 + $1230 = 1845. Toby's obligations ratio is

$$\text{Total obligations ratio} = \frac{\text{Total monthly financial obligations}}{\text{Monthly gross income}} = \frac{1845.00}{4650.00} = 0.3967 = 39.7\%$$

to a tenth of a percent.

c. Toby's housing expense ratio of 26.5% is below the 29% maximum required for an FHA mortgage and below the 28% percent maximum for a conventional mortgage. However, his 39.7% total obligations ratio exceeds the allowable maximum of 36% for a conventional mortgage and so Toby would be denied a conventional mortgage. Fortunately, 39.7% does not exceed the maximum total obligations ratio of 41% for an FHA mortgage and so Toby qualifies for an FHA mortgage.

Chapter 5 Review Exercises

1. $4.5\% = \dfrac{4.5}{100} = \dfrac{4.5}{100} \cdot \dfrac{10}{10}$
   $= \dfrac{45}{1000} = \dfrac{9}{200}$

2. $284\% = \dfrac{284}{100} = 2\dfrac{84}{100}$
   $= 2\dfrac{21}{25}$

3. $8\% = \dfrac{8}{100} = \dfrac{2}{25}$

4. $75\% = \dfrac{75}{100} = \dfrac{3}{4}$

5. $32.5\% = \dfrac{32.5}{100} = \dfrac{32.5}{100} \cdot \dfrac{10}{10}$
   $= \dfrac{325}{1000} = \dfrac{13}{40}$

6. $0.25\% = \dfrac{0.25}{100} = \dfrac{0.25}{100} \cdot \dfrac{100}{100}$
   $= \dfrac{25}{10,000} = \dfrac{1}{400}$

7. $37.5\% = 37.5 \cdot 0.01 = 0.375$

8. $56\dfrac{4}{5}\% = 56.8\%$
   $= 56.8 \cdot 0.01$
   $= 0.568$

9. $95\% = 95 \cdot 0.01 = 0.95$

10. $40.01\% = 40.01 \cdot 0.01$
    $= 0.4001$

11. $88\% = 88 \cdot 0.01 = 0.88$

12. $77\dfrac{1}{2}\% = 77.5\% = 77.5 \cdot 0.01$
    $= 0.775$

13. $1.65 = 1.65 \cdot 100\% = 165\%$

14. $0.2 = 0.2 \cdot 100\% = 20\%$

15. $9.0 = 9.0 \cdot 100\% = 900\%$

16. $0.45 = 0.45 \cdot 100\% = 45\%$

17. $0.0028 = 0.0028 \cdot 100\%$
    $= 0.28\%$

18. $0.31 = 0.31 \cdot 100\% = 31\%$

19. $2\dfrac{1}{5} = 2.2 = 2.2 \cdot 100\%$
    $= 220\%$

20. $1\dfrac{1}{2} = 1.5 = 1.5 \cdot 100\%$
    $= 150\%$

21. $\dfrac{21}{25} = 0.84 = 0.84 \cdot 100\%$
    $= 84\%$

22. $\dfrac{17}{50} = 0.34 = 0.34 \cdot 100\%$
    $= 34\%$

23. $\dfrac{7}{8} = 0.875 = 0.875 \cdot 100\%$
    $= 87.5\%$

24. $3\dfrac{2}{5} = 3.4 = 3.4 \cdot 100\%$
    $= 340\%$

	FRACTION	DECIMAL	PERCENT
25.	$60\% = \dfrac{60}{100} = \dfrac{3}{5}$	$60\% = 60 \cdot 0.01 = 0.60$	60% (given)
26.	$1\dfrac{5}{8}$ (given)	$1\dfrac{5}{8} = 1.625$	$1\dfrac{5}{8} = 1.625 = 1.625 \cdot 100\% = 162.5\%$
27.	$0.81 = \dfrac{81}{100}$	0.81 (given)	$0.81 = 0.81 \cdot 100\% = 81\%$
28.	$\dfrac{2}{5}$ (given)	$\dfrac{2}{5} = 0.4$	$\dfrac{2}{5} = 0.4 = 0.4 \cdot 100\% = 40\%$

	FRACTION	DECIMAL	PERCENT
29.	$68\% = \dfrac{68}{100} = \dfrac{17}{25}$	$68\% = 68 \cdot 0.01 = 0.68$	68% (given)
30.	$0.14 = \dfrac{14}{100} = \dfrac{7}{50}$	0.14 (given)	$0.14 = 0.14 \cdot 100\% = 14\%$
31.	$\dfrac{17}{400}$ (given)	$\dfrac{17}{400} = 0.0425$	$\dfrac{17}{400} = 0.0425 = 0.0425 \cdot 100\% = 4.25\%$
32.	$79\% = \dfrac{79}{100}$	$79\% = \dfrac{79}{100} = 0.79$	79% (given)

33. What number is 22% of 1980?

$$\text{Amount} = \text{Percent} \cdot \text{Base}$$
$$a = 0.22 \cdot 1980$$
$$a = 435.6$$

34. 120 is 80% of what number?

$$\text{Base} = \frac{\text{Amount}}{\text{Percent}}$$
$$b = \frac{120}{0.8}$$
$$b = 150$$

35. What percent of 50 is 7.5?

$$\text{Percent} = \frac{\text{Amount}}{\text{Base}}$$
$$p = \frac{7.5}{50}$$
$$= \frac{15}{100} = 15\%$$

36. 245 is 49% of what number?

$$\text{Base} = \frac{\text{Amount}}{\text{Percent}}$$
$$b = \frac{245}{0.49}$$
$$b = 500$$

37. 2200 is what percent of 4400?

$$\text{Percent} = \frac{\text{Amount}}{\text{Base}}$$
$$p = \frac{2200}{4400}$$
$$= 0.5 = 50\%$$

38. 70% of 690 is what number?

$$\text{Amount} = \text{Percent} \cdot \text{Base}$$
$$a = 0.7 \cdot 690$$
$$a = 483$$

39. 392 is 28% of what number?

$$\text{Base} = \frac{\text{Amount}}{\text{Percent}}$$
$$b = \frac{392}{0.28}$$
$$b = 1400$$

40. What is 60% of 300?

$$\text{Amount} = \text{Percent} \cdot \text{Base}$$
$$a = 0.60 \cdot 300$$
$$a = 180$$

41. What percent is 64 of 400?

$$\text{Percent} = \frac{\text{Amount}}{\text{Base}}$$
$$p = \frac{64}{400}$$
$$= \frac{16}{100} = 16\%$$

42. What is 30% of 802?

$$\text{Amount} = \text{Percent} \cdot \text{Base}$$
$$a = 0.3 \cdot 802$$
$$a = 240.6$$

43. 13 is what percent of 65?

$$\text{Percent} = \frac{\text{Amount}}{\text{Base}}$$
$$p = \frac{13}{65}$$
$$= \frac{1}{5} = 20\%$$

44. 64.08 is 72% of what number?

$$\text{Base} = \frac{\text{Amount}}{\text{Percent}}$$
$$b = \frac{64.08}{0.72}$$
$$b = 89$$

45. What number is 7% of 2000?

$$\frac{\text{Amount}}{\text{Base}} = \frac{\text{Part}}{100}$$
$$\frac{a}{2000} = \frac{7}{100}$$
$$100a = 14{,}000$$
$$a = 140$$

46. 261 is what percent of 450?

$$\frac{\text{Amount}}{\text{Base}} = \frac{\text{Part}}{100}$$
$$\frac{261}{450} = \frac{p}{100}$$
$$\frac{29}{50} = \frac{p}{100}$$
$$50p = 2900$$
$$p = 58$$
261 is 58% of 450.

47. 30 is 20% of what number?

$$\frac{\text{Amount}}{\text{Base}} = \frac{\text{Part}}{100}$$
$$\frac{30}{b} = \frac{20}{100}$$
$$\frac{30}{b} = \frac{1}{5}$$
$$b = 150$$

48. 50 is what percent of 50?

$$\frac{\text{Amount}}{\text{Base}} = \frac{\text{Part}}{100}$$
$$\frac{50}{50} = \frac{p}{100}$$
$$\frac{1}{1} = \frac{p}{100}$$
$$p = 100$$
50 is 100% of 50.

49. What is 15% of 8000?

$$\frac{\text{Amount}}{\text{Base}} = \frac{\text{Part}}{100}$$

$$\frac{a}{8000} = \frac{15}{100}$$

$$\frac{a}{8000} = \frac{3}{20}$$

$$20a = 24{,}000$$

$$a = 1200$$

50. 136 is 34% of what number?

$$\frac{\text{Amount}}{\text{Base}} = \frac{\text{Part}}{100}$$

$$\frac{136}{b} = \frac{34}{100}$$

$$\frac{136}{b} = \frac{17}{50}$$

$$17b = 6800$$

$$b = 400$$

51. What is 9% of 540?

$$\frac{\text{Amount}}{\text{Base}} = \frac{\text{Part}}{100}$$

$$\frac{a}{540} = \frac{9}{100}$$

$$100a = 4860$$

$$a = 48.6$$

52. 136 is 40% of what number?

$$\frac{\text{Amount}}{\text{Base}} = \frac{\text{Part}}{100}$$

$$\frac{136}{b} = \frac{40}{100}$$

$$\frac{136}{b} = \frac{2}{5}$$

$$2b = 680$$

$$b = 340$$

53. 516 is what percent of 645?

$$\frac{\text{Amount}}{\text{Base}} = \frac{\text{Part}}{100}$$

$$\frac{516}{645} = \frac{p}{100}$$

$$\frac{4}{5} = \frac{p}{100}$$

$$5p = 400$$

$$p = 80$$

516 is 80% of 645.

54. 210 is 56% of what number?

$$\frac{\text{Amount}}{\text{Base}} = \frac{\text{Part}}{100}$$

$$\frac{210}{b} = \frac{56}{100}$$

$$\frac{210}{b} = \frac{14}{25}$$

$$14b = 5250$$

$$b = 375$$

55. 245 is what percent of 100?

$$\frac{\text{Amount}}{\text{Base}} = \frac{\text{Part}}{100}$$

$$\frac{245}{100} = \frac{p}{100}$$

$$\frac{49}{20} = \frac{p}{100}$$

$$20p = 4900$$

$$p = 245$$

245 is 245% of 100.

56. What number is 70% of 833?

$$\frac{\text{Amount}}{\text{Base}} = \frac{\text{Part}}{100}$$

$$\frac{a}{833} = \frac{70}{100}$$

$$\frac{a}{833} = \frac{7}{10}$$

$$10a = 5831$$

$$a = 583.1$$

57. The change amount is an increase of $\$3{,}000{,}000 - \$2{,}500{,}000 = \$500{,}000$. The percent change is given by

$$\text{Percent change} = \frac{\text{Change amount}}{\text{Original amount}} = \frac{500,000}{2,500,000} = \frac{1}{5} = 20\%$$

so a 20% increase in sales is expected.

58. The change amount is a decrease of $\$11,000 - \$8400 = \$2600$. The percent change is given by

$$\text{Percent change} = \frac{\text{Change amount}}{\text{Original amount}} = \frac{2600}{11,000} = 0.236 = 23.6\%$$

so a 23.6% decrease in monthly long distance charges resulted from changing providers.

59. The amount of change in staffing is a decrease of $600 - 550 = 50$. The percent change is given by

$$\text{Percent change} = \frac{\text{Change amount}}{\text{Original amount}} = \frac{50}{600} = 0.0833... = 8\%$$

so there was a 8% decrease in employees.

60. The change in sales is an increase of $120 - 40 = 80$ surfboards. The percent change is given by

$$\text{Percent change} = \frac{\text{Change amount}}{\text{Original amount}} = \frac{80}{40} = 2 = 200\%$$

so there is a 200% increase in sales from the regular season to the summer months.

61. a. The tip is found from the tip equation, $\text{Tip} = \text{Tip rate} \cdot \text{Bill amount} = 0.20 \cdot \$79.50 = \$15.90$.

    b. The total bill is $\$79.50 + \$15.90 = \$95.40$.

62. a. The sales tax on *one* car is found from the sales tax equation
    $$\text{Sales tax} = \text{Sales tax rate} \cdot \text{Item cost} = 0.058 \cdot \$12,500 = \$725.$$
    The total sales tax for three cars is $3 \cdot \$725 = \$2175$.

    b. The total purchase price is the total item cost, $3 \cdot \$12,500 = \$37,500$, plus the total sales tax or
    $$\$37,500 + \$2175 = \$39,675.$$

63. Clay's commission is given by the commission equation
    $$\text{Commission} = \text{Commission rate} \cdot \text{Sales amount} = 0.075 \cdot \$1,500,000 = \$112,500.$$

64. a. The discount amount is $\text{Discount rate} \cdot \text{Original cost} = 0.10 \cdot \$16 = \$1.60$.

    b. The sale price is $\$16 - \$1.60 = \$14.40$.

65. The number of jobs increased by 15% so the new amount is 115% of last month's figure. Last month's figure forms the base of the percent equation and is found to be
    $$\text{Base} = \frac{\text{Amount}}{\text{Percent}} = \frac{144,900}{1.15} = 126,000 \text{ employees.}$$

66. Since car rental rates have decreased 16%, the current rate is $100\% - 16\% = 84\%$ of the original or base rate. The original rate can be found using the percent equation

    $$\text{Base} = \frac{\text{Amount}}{\text{Percent}} = \frac{42}{0.84} = 50 \text{ or } \$50 \text{ per day.}$$

67. The new mortgage payment is 22% less than the rental amount of $900. Equivalently, the mortgage payment is $100\% - 22\% = 78\%$ *of* the rental amount. The mortgage payment is $\$900 \cdot 0.78 = \$702$.

68. Tracy's weekly gasoline cost has decreased by $36 - 26 = 10$ dollars. The percent change is $\dfrac{10}{36} = 0.28 = 28\%$. Her weekly cost has decreased 28%.

69. From 2001 to 2002, snack food sales grew by $\$22.5 - \$21.8 = \$0.7$ billion. This represents a percent increase of
$$\frac{0.7}{21.8} = 0.032 = 3.2\%.$$

70. If sales in 2007 represent a 10% increase from 2002, then 2007 sales are 110% of 2002 sales or $1.1 \cdot 22.5 = 24.75$ billion. To the nearest tenth of a billion, 2007 sales were $24.8 billion.

71. Nut sales make up 8.4% of the snack food market so the question is what number is 8.4% of $20.7 billion, the total revenue in 2000. Since $0.084 \cdot 20.7 = 1.7388$ billion, the revenue from nut sales is $1,738,800,000.

72. Tortilla chip sales make up 19.9% of the snack food market so the question is what number is 19.9% of $21.8 billion, the total revenue in 2001. Since $0.199 \cdot 21.8 = 4.3382$ billion, the revenue from tortilla chips in 2001 was $4,338,200,000.

Chapter 5 Assessment Test

1. $76\% = \dfrac{76}{100} = \dfrac{19}{25}$

2. $3\% = \dfrac{3}{100}$

3. $13.5\% = 13.5 \cdot 0.01 = 0.135$

4. $68.8\% = 68.8 \cdot 0.01 = 0.688$

5. $0.57 = 0.57 \cdot 100\% = 57\%$

6. $6.45 = 6.45 \cdot 100\% = 645\%$

7. $\dfrac{11}{8} = 1\dfrac{3}{8} = 1.375 = 1.375 \cdot 100\% = 137.5\%$

8. $10\dfrac{1}{2} = 10.5 = 10.5 \cdot 100\% = 1050\%$

9. What percent of 610 is 106.75?

$$\text{Percent} = \frac{\text{Amount}}{\text{Base}}$$
$$p = \frac{106.75}{610} = \frac{10,675}{61,000}$$
$$= \frac{7}{40} = 0.175 = 17.5\%$$

10. 186 is 62% of what number?

$$\text{Base} = \frac{\text{Amount}}{\text{Percent}}$$
$$b = \frac{186}{0.62}$$
$$b = 300$$

11. What is 47% of 450?

$$\text{Amount} = \text{Percent} \cdot \text{Base}$$
$$a = 0.47 \cdot 450$$
$$a = 211.5$$

12. 367 is 20% of what number?

$$\text{Base} = \frac{\text{Amount}}{\text{Percent}}$$
$$b = \frac{367}{0.2}$$
$$b = 1835$$

13. What number is 80% of 4560?

$$\text{Amount} = \text{Percent} \cdot \text{Base}$$
$$a = 0.80 \cdot 4560$$
$$a = 3648$$

14. 77 is what percent of 280?

$$\text{Percent} = \frac{\text{Amount}}{\text{Base}}$$
$$p = \frac{77}{280} = \frac{11}{40}$$
$$= 0.275 = 27.5\%$$

15. 560 is 14% of what number?

$$\frac{\text{Amount}}{\text{Base}} = \frac{\text{Part}}{100}$$
$$\frac{560}{b} = \frac{14}{100}$$
$$\frac{560}{b} = \frac{7}{50}$$
$$7b = 28,000$$
$$b = 4000$$

16. 95 is what percent of 380?

$$\frac{\text{Amount}}{\text{Base}} = \frac{\text{Part}}{100}$$
$$\frac{95}{380} = \frac{p}{100}$$
$$\frac{1}{4} = \frac{p}{100}$$
$$4p = 100$$
$$p = 25$$
95 is 25% of 380.

17. What is 83% of 180?

$$\frac{\text{Amount}}{\text{Base}} = \frac{\text{Part}}{100}$$
$$\frac{a}{180} = \frac{83}{100}$$
$$100a = 14,940$$
$$a = 149.4$$

18. What percent of 490 is 196?

$$\frac{\text{Amount}}{\text{Base}} = \frac{\text{Part}}{100}$$
$$\frac{196}{490} = \frac{p}{100}$$
$$\frac{2}{5} = \frac{p}{100}$$
$$5p = 200$$
$$p = 40$$
196 is 40% of 490.

19. What number is 29% of 158?

$$\frac{\text{Amount}}{\text{Base}} = \frac{\text{Part}}{100}$$

$$\frac{a}{158} = \frac{29}{100}$$

$$100a = 4582$$

$$a = 45.82$$

20. 245 is 35% of what number?

$$\frac{\text{Amount}}{\text{Base}} = \frac{\text{Part}}{100}$$

$$\frac{245}{b} = \frac{35}{100}$$

$$\frac{245}{b} = \frac{7}{20}$$

$$7b = 4900$$

$$b = 700$$

21. The change in the number of small pizzas is $5600 - 3500 = 2100$ and represents a decrease. The percent change is $\frac{2100}{5600} = \frac{3}{8} = 0.375 = 37.5\%$. Sales of small pizzas have decreased 37.5%.

22. Gilbert has increased his rates by $\$575 - \$500 = \$75$. The percent change is $\frac{75}{500} = \frac{3}{20} = 0.15 = 15\%$. Gilbert's rate has increased by 15%.

23. The tax payment has decreased by $\$16,800 - \$13,600 = \$3200$. The percent change is $\frac{3200}{16,800} = \frac{4}{21} = 0.19 = 19\%$. Their taxes decreased by 19%.

24. The change in rent is $\$1500 - \$800 = \$700$. The percent change is $\frac{700}{800} = \frac{7}{8} = 0.875$. Andrew's rent has increased approximately 88%.

25. From the sales tax formula, the tax on $20 is $\text{Sales tax rate} \cdot \text{Item cost} = 0.07 \cdot \$20 = \$1.40$. Adding the tax to the cost of the item gives a total purchase price of $\$20 + \$1.40 = \$21.40$.

26. Since the lunch cost $52.50 and the sales tax is $3.10, the sales tax equation, with p representing the unknown tax rate, gives $52.50p = 3.10$. Thus $p = \frac{3.10}{52.50} = 0.059 = 5.9\%$. The sales tax rate in that area is 5.9%.

27. Since Sylvan lost 8% of his original weight, his new weight represents 92% of his original weight of 190 pounds. His new weight is given by the formula $\text{Amount} = \text{Percent} \cdot \text{Base} = 0.92 \cdot 190 = 175$ pounds.

28. A 30% increase means the number of packages today is 130% of the number yesterday. The number of packages delivered today is $54 \cdot 130\% = 54 \cdot 1.3 = 70.2$ or 70 packages.

29. If the pump lost 40% of its pressure, the new pressure, 168 pounds per square inch, is 60% of the original pressure. The original pressure is given by the formula $\text{Base} = \frac{\text{Amount}}{\text{Percent}} = \frac{168}{0.6} = 280$ pounds per square inch.

30. A 22% increase means the current temperature, 90°F, is 122% of what it was. The original temperature is given by the formula $\text{Base} = \frac{\text{Amount}}{\text{Percent}} = \frac{90}{1.22} = 73.77$ degrees or, to the nearest degree, 74°F.

Chapter 6   Measurement

Section 6.1   The U.S. Customary System

Concept Check

2. Two different systems of measurement are used in the United States, the __U.S. Customary__ System and the __metric__ system.

4. A __unit__ __ratio__ is a ratio that is equivalent to 1.

6. To convert between measurement units, __multiply__ the original measure by the appropriate unit ratio, dividing out the common original units and leaving only the new units in the answer.

8. __Capacity__ is a measure of a liquid's content or volume.

Guide Problems

10. Convert 65 feet to inches.

a. Write an appropriate unit ratio.
We know 1 ft = 12 in. . The unit ratio must have the new unit (inches) in the numerator and the original unit (feet) in the denominator. Thus

$$\text{Unit ratio} = \frac{\text{New units}}{\text{Original units}}$$

$$= \frac{12 \text{ in.}}{1 \text{ ft}}$$

b. Multiply the original measure by the unit fraction.

$$65 \text{ ft} \cdot \frac{12 \text{ in.}}{1 \text{ ft}}$$

$$= 65 \cancel{\text{ ft}} \cdot \frac{12 \text{ in.}}{1 \cancel{\text{ ft}}}$$

$$= 65 \cdot 12 \text{ in.} = \underline{780 \text{ in.}}$$

In Problems 12 through 22, the same procedure is followed to perform the indicated conversion. First find the appropriate unit ratio. The unit ratio will have the desired new unit in the numerator and the original or given unit in the denominator. Convert the given measure by multiplying it by the unit ratio. The units in the denominator will always cancel with those in the original measure.

12. 13.5 feet to inches
Unit ratio:
$$\frac{\text{New unit}}{\text{Old unit}} = \frac{12 \text{ inches}}{1 \text{ foot}}$$
Convert:
$$13.5 \text{ feet} \cdot \frac{12 \text{ inches}}{1 \text{ foot}}$$
$$= 13.5 \cancel{\text{ feet}} \cdot \frac{12 \text{ inches}}{1 \cancel{\text{ foot}}}$$
$$= 13.5 \cdot 12 \text{ inches}$$
$$= 162 \text{ inches}$$

14. 14 miles to yards
Unit ratio:
$$\frac{\text{New unit}}{\text{Old unit}} = \frac{1760 \text{ yards}}{1 \text{ miles}}$$
Convert:
$$14 \text{ miles} \cdot \frac{1760 \text{ yards}}{1 \text{ miles}}$$
$$= 14 \cancel{\text{ miles}} \cdot \frac{1760 \text{ yards}}{1 \cancel{\text{ miles}}}$$
$$= 14 \cdot 1760 \text{ yards}$$
$$= 24,640 \text{ yards}$$

16. 9000 inches to feet
$$\text{Unit ratio: } \frac{1 \text{ foot}}{12 \text{ inches}}$$
Convert:
$$9000 \text{ inches} \cdot \frac{1 \text{ foot}}{12 \text{ inches}}$$
$$= \frac{9000}{12} \text{ feet}$$
$$= 750 \text{ feet}$$

18. 11,440 yards to miles

Unit ratio: $\dfrac{1 \text{ mile}}{1760 \text{ yards}}$

Convert:

$11{,}440 \text{ miles} \cdot \dfrac{1 \text{ mile}}{1760 \text{ yards}}$

$= \dfrac{11{,}440}{1760} \text{ miles} = 6.5 \text{ miles}$

20. $\dfrac{1}{4}$ mile to feet

Unit ratio: $\dfrac{5280 \text{ feet}}{1 \text{ mile}}$

Convert:

$\dfrac{1}{4} \text{ mile} \cdot \dfrac{5280 \text{ feet}}{1 \text{ mile}}$

$= \dfrac{5280}{4} \text{ feet}$

$= 1320 \text{ feet}$

22. $\dfrac{1}{8}$ foot to inches

Unit ratio: $\dfrac{12 \text{ inches}}{1 \text{ foot}}$

Convert:

$\dfrac{1}{8} \text{ foot} \cdot \dfrac{12 \text{ inches}}{1 \text{ foot}}$

$= \dfrac{12}{8} \text{ inches}$

$= 1\dfrac{1}{2} \text{ inches}$

Guide Problems

24. Convert 16,000 pounds to tons.

a. Write an appropriate unit ratio. We know $1 \text{ ton} = 2{,}000 \text{ lb}$. The unit ratio must have the new unit (t) in the numerator and the original unit (lb) in the denominator. Thus

Unit ratio $= \dfrac{\text{New units}}{\text{Original units}}$

$= \dfrac{1 \text{ t}}{2000 \text{ lb}}$

b. Multiply the original measure by the unit fraction.

$16{,}000 \text{ lb} \cdot \dfrac{1 \text{ t}}{2000 \text{ lb}}$

$= 16{,}000 \cancel{\text{ lb}} \cdot \dfrac{1 \text{ t}}{2000 \cancel{\text{ lb}}}$

$= \dfrac{16{,}000}{2000} \text{ t} = \underline{8 \text{ t}}$

26. 2 pounds to ounces

Unit ratio: $\dfrac{\text{New unit}}{\text{Old unit}} = \dfrac{16 \text{ oz}}{1 \text{ lb}}$

Convert:

$2 \text{ lb} \cdot \dfrac{16 \text{ oz}}{1 \text{ lb}}$

$= 2 \cancel{\text{ lb}} \cdot \dfrac{16 \text{ oz}}{1 \cancel{\text{ lb}}}$

$= 2 \cdot 16 \text{ oz} = 32 \text{ ounces}$

28. 160 ounces to pounds

Unit ratio: $\dfrac{\text{New unit}}{\text{Old unit}} = \dfrac{1 \text{ lb}}{16 \text{ oz}}$

Convert:

$160 \text{ oz} \cdot \dfrac{1 \text{ lb}}{16 \text{ oz}}$

$= 160 \cancel{\text{ oz}} \cdot \dfrac{1 \text{ lb}}{16 \cancel{\text{ oz}}}$

$= \dfrac{160}{16} \text{ lb} = 10 \text{ pounds}$

30. 12 tons to pounds

Unit ratio: $\dfrac{2000 \text{ lb}}{1 \text{ t}}$

Convert:

$12 \text{ t} \cdot \dfrac{2000 \text{ lb}}{1 \text{ t}}$

$= 12 \cdot 2000 \text{ lb}$

$= 24{,}000 \text{ pounds}$

32. 14,500 pounds to tons

Unit ratio: $\dfrac{1 \text{ t}}{2000 \text{ lb}}$

Convert:

$14{,}500 \text{ lb} \cdot \dfrac{1 \text{ t}}{2000 \text{ lb}}$

$= \dfrac{14{,}500}{2000} \text{ t} = 7.25 \text{ tons}$

34. 496,000 ounces to tons
First convert ounces to pounds

using $\dfrac{1 \text{ lb}}{16 \text{ oz}}$.

$496{,}000 \text{ oz} \cdot \dfrac{1 \text{ lb}}{16 \text{ oz}}$

$= \dfrac{496{,}000}{16} \text{ lb} = 31{,}000 \text{ lb}$

Next convert pounds to tons

using $\dfrac{1 \text{ t}}{2000 \text{ lb}}$.

$31{,}000 \text{ lb} \cdot \dfrac{1 \text{ t}}{2000 \text{ lb}}$

$= \dfrac{31{,}000}{2000} \text{ t} = 15.5 \text{ tons}$

36. 1 ton to ounces
First convert tons to pounds

using $\dfrac{2000 \text{ lb}}{1 \text{ t}}$.

$1 \text{ t} \cdot \dfrac{2000 \text{ lb}}{1 \text{ t}} = 2000 \text{ lb}$

Next convert pounds to ounces

using $\dfrac{16 \text{ oz}}{1 \text{ lb}}$.

$2000 \text{ lb} \cdot \dfrac{16 \text{ oz}}{1 \text{ lb}}$

$= 2000 \cdot 16 \text{ oz}$

$= 32{,}000 \text{ ounces}$

Guide Problems

38. Convert 4 quarts to pints.

a. Write an appropriate unit ratio.
We know 1 qt = 2 pt. The
unit ratio must have the new unit
(pt) in the numerator and the
original unit (qt) in the
denominator. Thus

$\text{Unit ratio} = \dfrac{\text{New units}}{\text{Original units}}$

$= \dfrac{2 \text{ pt}}{1 \text{ qt}}$

b. Multiply the original measure by
the unit fraction.

$4 \text{ qt} \cdot \dfrac{2 \text{ pt}}{1 \text{ qt}}$

$= 4 \ \cancel{\text{qt}} \cdot \dfrac{2 \text{ pt}}{1 \ \cancel{\text{qt}}}$

$= 4 \cdot 2 \text{ pt} = \underline{8} \text{ pt}$

40. 10 quarts to pints

Unit ratio: $\dfrac{\text{New unit}}{\text{Old unit}} = \dfrac{2 \text{ pt}}{1 \text{ qt}}$

Convert:

$10 \text{ qt} \cdot \dfrac{2 \text{ pt}}{1 \text{ qt}}$

$= 10 \ \cancel{\text{qt}} \cdot \dfrac{2 \text{ pt}}{1 \ \cancel{\text{qt}}}$

$= 10 \cdot 2 \text{ pt} = 20 \text{ pints}$

42. $\dfrac{1}{2}$ gallon to quarts

Unit ratio: $\dfrac{\text{New unit}}{\text{Old unit}} = \dfrac{4 \text{ qt}}{1 \text{ gal}}$

Convert:

$\dfrac{1}{2} \text{ gal} \cdot \dfrac{4 \text{ qt}}{1 \text{ gal}}$

$= \dfrac{1}{2} \ \cancel{\text{gal}} \cdot \dfrac{4 \text{ qt}}{1 \ \cancel{\text{gal}}}$

$= \dfrac{1}{2} \cdot 4 \text{ qt} = 2 \text{ quarts}$

44. $\dfrac{5}{2}$ pints to quarts

Unit ratio: $\dfrac{1 \text{ qt}}{2 \text{ pt}}$

Convert:

$\dfrac{5}{2} \text{ pt} \cdot \dfrac{1 \text{ qt}}{2 \text{ pt}}$

$= \dfrac{5}{2} \cdot \dfrac{1}{2} \text{ qt}$

$= \dfrac{5}{4} \text{ quart}$

46. 45 pints to fluid ounces
Multiply unit ratios to find
the desired unit ratio:

$$\frac{8 \text{ fl oz}}{1 \text{ c}} \cdot \frac{2 \text{ c}}{1 \text{ pt}}$$

$$= \frac{8 \text{ fl oz}}{1 \cancel{\text{c}}} \cdot \frac{2 \cancel{\text{c}}}{1 \text{ pt}}$$

$$= \frac{16 \text{ fl oz}}{1 \text{ pt}}$$

Convert:

$$45 \text{ pt} \cdot \frac{16 \text{ fl oz}}{1 \text{ pt}}$$

$$= 45 \cdot 16 \text{ fl oz}$$

$$= 720 \text{ fluid ounces}$$

48. 18 tablespoons to teaspoons

Unit ratio: $\dfrac{3 \text{ tsp}}{1 \text{ tbs}}$

Convert:

$$18 \text{ tbs} \cdot \frac{3 \text{ tsp}}{1 \text{ tbs}}$$

$$= 18 \cdot 3 \text{ tsp}$$

$$= 54 \text{ teaspoons}$$

50. 1 gallon to cups
We need to multiply by
several unit fractions to
convert.

$$1 \text{ gal} \cdot \frac{2 \text{ c}}{1 \text{ pt}} \cdot \frac{2 \text{ pt}}{1 \text{ qt}} \cdot \frac{4 \text{ qt}}{1 \text{ gal}}$$

$$= 1 \text{ gal} \cdot \frac{2 \text{ c}}{1 \cancel{\text{pt}}} \cdot \frac{2 \cancel{\text{pt}}}{1 \cancel{\text{qt}}} \cdot \frac{4 \cancel{\text{qt}}}{1 \text{ gal}}$$

$$= 1 \text{ gal} \cdot \frac{16 \text{ c}}{1 \text{ gal}}$$

$$= 16 \text{ cups}$$

52. Multiplying by the appropriate unit ratio, Essex Dancer is $6.5 \text{ ft} \cdot \dfrac{12 \text{ in}}{1 \text{ ft}} = 6.5 \cdot 12 \text{ in} = 78$ inches tall.

54. To convert yards to inches, multiply by the unit ratio $\dfrac{36 \text{ in.}}{1 \text{ yd}}$. Thirty yards is equivalent to

$$30 \text{ yd} \cdot \frac{36 \text{ in.}}{1 \text{ yd}} = 30 \cancel{\text{yd}} \cdot \frac{36 \text{ in.}}{1 \cancel{\text{yd}}} = 30 \cdot 36 \text{ in.} = 1080 \text{ inches.}$$

56. a. In pounds, the 50 ton shipment weights $50 \text{ t} \cdot \dfrac{2000 \text{ lb}}{1 \text{ t}} = 50 \cdot 2000 \text{ lb} = 100,000$ pounds.

   b. At 4000 pounds per car, there are $\dfrac{100,000}{4000} = 25$ cars.

58. To convert ounces to pounds, use the unit ratio $\dfrac{1 \text{ lb}}{16 \text{ oz}}$. In pounds, the tomato weighs in at

$$552 \text{ oz} \cdot \frac{1 \text{ lb}}{16 \text{ oz}} = \frac{552}{16} \text{ lb} = 34.5 \text{ pounds.}$$

60. In pounds, the 16 ton truck weighs $16 \text{ t} \cdot \dfrac{2000 \text{ lb}}{1 \text{ t}} = 16 \cdot 2000 \text{ lb} = 32,000$ pounds which is less than the 40,000 pound limit. The truck is safe crossing the bridge.

62. To convert cups to quarts, multiply by the unit ratios $\dfrac{1 \text{ pt}}{2 \text{ c}}$ and $\dfrac{1 \text{ qt}}{2 \text{ pt}}$. So 8 cups is equivalent to

$$8 \text{ c} \cdot \frac{1 \text{ pt}}{2 \text{ c}} \cdot \frac{1 \text{ qt}}{2 \text{ pt}} = 8 \cancel{\text{c}} \cdot \frac{1 \cancel{\text{pt}}}{2 \cancel{\text{c}}} \cdot \frac{1 \text{ qt}}{2 \cancel{\text{pt}}} = \frac{8}{2 \cdot 2} \text{ qt} = 2 \text{ qt.}$$ A dieter will drink 2 quarts of water each day.

64. a. Since Germaine packs 4800 ounces each *half* hour, then in an hour, Germaine packs $2 \cdot 4800 = 9600$

   ounces. In pounds, this is $9600 \text{ oz} \cdot \dfrac{1 \text{ lb}}{16 \text{ oz}} = \dfrac{9600}{16} \text{ lb} = 600$ pounds.

   b. In tons, the 50,000 pounds shipped are equivalent to $50,000 \text{ lb} \cdot \dfrac{1 \text{ t}}{2000 \text{ lb}} = \dfrac{50,000}{2000} \text{ t} = 25 \text{ t.}$ Since 25 tons is less than 30 tons, the distributor stayed within the limits.

Cumulative Skills Review

2. $43\% = \dfrac{43}{100} = 0.43$

4.   The three different ways to write the ratio of 12 to 17 are

$$12 \text{ to } 17 \quad 12{:}17 \quad \dfrac{12}{7}$$

6. $\dfrac{3}{4} = 0.75 = 0.75 \cdot 100\% = 75\%$

8.   Set the cross products of $\dfrac{3}{15} = \dfrac{x}{60}$ equal to get
$$15 \cdot x = 3 \cdot 60 \ \text{ or } \ 15x = 180.$$
Divide to find
$$x = \dfrac{180}{15} = 12.$$

10.   Move from left to right in 2.8989 and 2.8993, comparing digits as you go. The first place where the numbers differ is in the thousandths place where we find the digits 8 and 9 respectively. Since 8 is less than 9, we have 2.8989 < 2.8993.

Section 6.2   Denominate Numbers

Concept Check

2.   A number without an associated unit of measure is called an abstract number.

4.   When adding and subtracting denominate numbers, arrange the denominate numbers so that like units are vertically aligned.

Guide Problems

6.   Express 67 pints in terms of quarts and pints.

a. How many pints are in a quart? 2
   There are two pints in a quart.

b. Divide 67 by the answer to part a.

$$\begin{array}{r} 33 \ \ R \ \ 1 \\ 2\overline{)67} \\ \underline{66} \\ 1 \end{array}$$

c. 67 pints = 33 quarts 1 pint

The quotient, 33, is the number of quarts. The remainder 1 is the number of pints left over.

8.   There are 12 inches in a foot. Since 74 divided by 12 is 6 with a remainder of 2, we have
$$74 \text{ inches} = 6 \text{ feet } 2 \text{ inches}.$$

10.   There are 8 fluid ounces in a cup. Since 15 divided by 8 is 1 R 7,
$$\begin{aligned} 15 \text{ fluid ounces} \\ = 1 \text{ cup } 7 \text{ fluid ounces}. \end{aligned}$$

12. There are 5280 feet in a mile.
Dividing 10,897 by 5280

$$
\begin{array}{r}
2 \\
5280{\overline{\smash{\big)}\,10897}} \\
\underline{10560} \\
337
\end{array}
$$

gives a quotient of 2 and remainder of 337. Thus, 10,897 feet = 2 miles 337 feet.

Guide Problems

14. Simplify 5 gallons 7 quarts.

   a. How many quarts are in a gallon? 4

   b. Since 7 quarts is greater than 4 quarts, express 7 quarts as gallons and quarts.

   7 quarts = 4 quarts + 3 quarts

   = _1_ gallon + _3_ quarts

   Then,

   5 gallons 7 quarts

   = 5 gallons + _1_ gallon + _3_ quarts

   = _6_ gallons + _3_ quarts

16. 5280 ft = 1 mi

   3 miles 6000 feet

   = 3 miles + 6000 feet

   = 3 miles + 5280 feet + 720 feet

   = 3 miles + 1 mile + 720 feet

   = 4 miles + 720 feet

   = 4 miles 720 feet

18. 2000 lb = 1 t

   1 ton 8532 pounds

   = 1 ton + 8532 pounds

   = 1 ton + 8000 pounds + 532 pounds

   = 1 ton + 4 tons + 532 pounds

   = 5 tons + 532 pounds

   = 5 tons 532 pounds

20. 3 tsp = 1 tbs

   10 tablespoons 12 teaspoons

   = 10 tablespoons + 12 teaspoons

   = 10 tablespoons + 4 tablespoons

   = 14 tablespoons

Guide Problems

22. Subtract.
Subtract along each column. If a number is smaller than the one below it, borrow 1 from the larger unit to the left and rewrite as an equivalent denominate number. For example, since 4 is less than 7, borrow 1 c = 8 fl oz from the cup column.

$$
\begin{array}{r}
5\text{ c}\quad 4\text{ fl oz} \\
-\ 3\text{ c}\quad 7\text{ fl oz} \\
\end{array}
$$

$$
\begin{array}{r}
4\text{ c}\quad 12\text{ fl oz} \\
\cancel{5}\text{c}\quad \cancel{4\text{ fl oz}} \\
-\ 3\text{ c}\quad 7\text{ fl oz} \\
\hline
1\text{ c}\quad 5\text{ fl oz}
\end{array}
$$

24.
$$
\begin{array}{r}
6\text{ yd}\ 2\text{ ft} \\
+\ 8\text{ yd}\ 2\text{ ft} \\
\hline
14\text{ yd}\ 4\text{ ft}
\end{array}
$$

26.
$$
\begin{array}{r}
5\text{ lb}\ 14\text{ oz} \\
+\ 7\text{ lb}\ 12\text{ oz} \\
\hline
12\text{ lb}\ 26\text{ oz}
\end{array}
$$

28.
$$
\begin{array}{r}
3\text{ lb}\ 3\text{ oz} \\
8\text{ lb}\ 9\text{ oz} \\
+\ 1\text{ lb}\ 15\text{ oz} \\
\hline
12\text{ lb}\ 27\text{ oz}
\end{array}
$$

$$= 14 \text{ yd} + 3 \text{ ft} + 1 \text{ ft} \qquad\qquad = 12 \text{ lb} + 16 \text{ oz} + 10 \text{ oz} \qquad\qquad = 12 \text{ lb} + 16 \text{ oz} + 11 \text{ oz}$$
$$= 14 \text{ yd} + 1 \text{ yd} + 1 \text{ ft} \qquad\qquad = 12 \text{ lb} + 1 \text{ lb} + 10 \text{ oz} \qquad\qquad = 12 \text{ lb} + 1 \text{ lb} + 11 \text{ oz}$$
$$= 15 \text{ yd} \;\; 1 \text{ ft} \qquad\qquad\qquad = 13 \text{ lb} \;\; 10 \text{ oz} \qquad\qquad\qquad = 13 \text{ lb} \;\; 11 \text{ oz}$$

30.　 42 ft 7 in.　　　　32.　 10 tbs　　　　　34.　 3 t   800 lb
　 − 15 ft 2 in.　　　　　 − 9 tbs 1 tsp　　　　　 − 1 t 1200 lb
　　 27 ft 5 in.

$$\begin{array}{ll} & \overset{9\text{ tbs}}{\cancel{10\text{ tbs}}} \quad 3\text{ tsp} \\ - & 9\text{ tbs} \quad 1\text{ tsp} \\ \hline & \qquad\qquad 2\text{ tsp} \end{array}$$

$$\begin{array}{ll} & \overset{2\text{ t}}{\cancel{3\text{ t}}} \quad \overset{2800\text{ lb}}{\cancel{800\text{ lb}}} \\ - & 1\text{ t} \quad 1200\text{ lb} \\ \hline & 1\text{ t} \quad 1600\text{ lb} \end{array}$$

Guide Problems

36. Divide 16 ft 9 in. by 3.

a. Divide 3 into 16 ft.
   When dividing a denominate number by an abstract number, begin by dividing the abstract number into the number of the larger unit.

$$\begin{array}{r} 5\text{ ft} \\ 3\overline{)16\text{ ft} \;\; 9\text{ in.}} \\ \underline{15\text{ ft}} \\ 1\text{ ft} \;\; 9\text{ in.} \end{array}$$

   Subtract as usual.

b. Add 1 ft to 9.
   After subtracting, convert the difference to be in terms of the smaller unit.

   $1\text{ ft} + 9\text{ in.} = \underline{12}\text{ in.} + 9\text{ in.} = \underline{21}\text{ in.}$

c. Complete the division.
   Compete the division by dividing the abstract number into the rewritten difference.

$$\begin{array}{r} 5\text{ ft} \;\; \underline{7}\text{ in.} \\ 3\overline{)16\text{ ft} \;\; 9\text{ in.}} \\ \underline{15\text{ ft}} \\ \underline{21}\text{ in.} \end{array}$$

   Since 21 in. divided by 3 is 7 in.

38.　 12 ft　3 in.
　 ×　　　　7
　　 84 ft 21 in.
　　 $= 84 \text{ ft} + 12 \text{ in.} + 9 \text{ in.}$
　　 $= 84 \text{ ft} + 1 \text{ ft} + 9 \text{ in.}$
　　 $= 85 \text{ ft} \;\; 9 \text{ in.}$

40.　　 3 qt　1 pt
　 ×　　　　 5
　　 15 qt 5 pt
　　 $= 15 \text{ qt} + 4 \text{ pt} + 1 \text{ pt}$
　　 $= 15 \text{ qt} + 2 \text{ qt} + 1 \text{ pt}$
　　 $= 17 \text{ qt} \;\; 1 \text{ pt}$

42.　　 2 tbs　1 tsp
　 ×　　　　 11
　　 22 tbs 11 tsp
　　 $= 22 \text{ tbs} + 9 \text{ tsp} + 2 \text{ tsp}$
　　 $= 22 \text{ tbs} + 3 \text{ tbs} + 2 \text{ tsp}$
　　 $= 25 \text{ tbs} \;\; 2 \text{ tsp}$

44.
$$\begin{array}{r} 8\text{ tbs} \;\; 1\text{ tsp} \\ 2\overline{)16\text{ tbs} \;\; 2\text{ tsp}} \\ \underline{16\text{ tbs}} \\ 2\text{ tsp} \end{array}$$

46.
$$\begin{array}{r} 2\text{ t} \;\; 1100\text{ lb} \\ 2\overline{)5\text{ t} \;\; 200\text{ lb}} \\ \underline{4\text{ t}} \\ 1\text{ t} \;\; 200\text{ lb} \quad (= 2200\text{ lb}) \end{array}$$

48.
$$\begin{array}{r} 1\text{ ft} \;\; 8\text{ in.} \\ 5\overline{)8\text{ ft} \;\; 4\text{ in.}} \\ \underline{5\text{ ft}} \\ 3\text{ ft} \;\; 4\text{ in.} \quad (= 40\text{ in.}) \end{array}$$

50. Convert 18 quarts to gallons: $18 \text{ qt} \cdot \dfrac{1 \text{ gal}}{4 \text{ qt}} = \dfrac{18}{4} \text{ qt} = 4.5$ gallons. The smallest bucket that will hold 4.5 gallons is the 6-gallon bucket.

52.   120 ft 6 in.
   + 250 ft 3 in.
   ─────────────
      370 ft 9 in.

The combined height is 370 feet 9 inches.

54.   6 lb   9 oz
       12 lb   14 oz
   +   8 lb   8 oz
   ─────────────
      26 lb   31 oz

$= 26 \text{ lb} + 16 \text{ oz} + 15 \text{ oz}$

$= 26 \text{ lb} + 1 \text{ lb} + 15 \text{ oz}$

$= 27 \text{ lb} \quad 15 \text{ oz}$

The deli sold 27 pounds 15 ounces of turkey breast.

56. a. Subtract the old weight from the new weight:

         180 lb   24 oz
      ~~181 lb~~   ~~8 oz~~
   −   176 lb   14 oz
   ─────────────
        4 lb   10 oz

Rusty gained 4 pounds 10 ounces.

b. Subtract the amount lost from his current weight:

      181 lb   8 oz
   −   7 lb   2 oz
   ─────────────
      174 lb   6 oz

Rusty now weighs 174 pounds 6 ounces.

58. Multiply by 3 and simplify:

      50 lb 12 oz
   ×   3
   ─────────────
     150 lb 36 oz

$= 150 \text{ lb} + 32 \text{ oz} + 4 \text{ oz}$

$= 150 \text{ lb} + 2 \text{ lb} + 4 \text{ oz}$

$= 152 \text{ lb} \quad 4 \text{ oz}$

Jarrod can bench press 152 pounds 4 ounces.

60. Multiply by 4 and simplify:

      21 gal   3 qt
   ×   4
   ─────────────
      84 gal 12 qt

$= 84 \text{ gal} + 12 \text{ qt}$

$= 84 \text{ gal} + 3 \text{ gal} = 87 \text{ gal}$

The new tank holds 87 gallons.

62. The average distance is computed as

$$3\overline{)\begin{array}{c} 1 \text{ mi} \quad 600 \text{ yd} \\ 4 \text{ mi} \quad 40 \text{ yd} \end{array}}$$

      3 mi
   ─────────────
      1 mi   40 yd $(= 1800 \text{ yd})$

for an average of 1 mile 600 yards each day.

Cumulative Skills Review

2. $\dfrac{3}{16} \cdot \dfrac{6}{14} = \dfrac{3}{16} \cdot \dfrac{\overset{3}{\cancel{6}}}{\underset{7}{\cancel{14}}} = \dfrac{3 \cdot 3}{16 \cdot 7} = \dfrac{9}{112}$

4. $\dfrac{10}{12} = \dfrac{5 \cdot 2}{6 \cdot 2} = \dfrac{5}{6}$ or "5 to 6"

6. $224 \text{ oz} \cdot \dfrac{1 \text{ lb}}{16 \text{ oz}} = \dfrac{224}{16} \text{ lb} = 14 \text{ lb}$

224 ounces = 14 pounds

8. Using the percent proportion
    $$\frac{\text{Amount}}{\text{Base}} = \frac{\text{Part}}{100}$$
    we have $\dfrac{22.75}{65} = \dfrac{p}{100}$. Equate

    cross products and solve to find
    $$65p = 22.75 \cdot 100$$
    $$65p = 2275$$
    $$p = \frac{2275}{65} = 35$$
    22.75 is 35% of 65.

10. Convert to unit rates:
     $$\frac{\$80}{2 \text{ tickets}} = \frac{\overset{\$40}{\cancel{\$80}}}{\underset{1}{\cancel{2}} \text{ tickets}} = \frac{\$40}{1 \text{ ticket}}$$

     $$\frac{\$120}{4 \text{ tickets}} = \frac{\overset{\$30}{\cancel{\$120}}}{\underset{1}{\cancel{4}} \text{ tickets}} = \frac{\$30}{1 \text{ ticket}}$$

     The smaller unit rate, belonging to
     $120 for four tickets, is the best buy.

Section 6.3   The Metric System

Concept Check

2. The basic unit of weight or mass in the metric system is the __gram__ .

4. Deci-, centi-, and milli- represent multiples __smaller__ than the basic unit.

6. __Mass__ is the measure of the amount of material in an object, whereas __weight__ is a measure of an object's heaviness.

8. A __liter__ is the capacity or volume of a cube whose sides measure 10 centimeters.

Guide Problems

10. Convert 30 hectometers to centimeters.
     Move the decimal point __4__ places to the __right__ . Note cm is four units to the right of hm
     in the list below.
           km __hm__ dam m dm __cm__ mm
     Thus, 30 hectometers = __300,000__ centimeters.

Each of Problems 12 through 18 can be done in two ways. First by multiplying by the appropriate unit ration or by moving the decimal point the number of places indicated by examining the list of metric units with prefixes
           kilo- hector- deka- base deci- centi- milli-
where base represents the base unit of measurement.

12. 59 meters to millimeters

     Unit ratio: $\dfrac{1000 \text{ mm}}{1 \text{ m}}$

     Convert: $59 \text{ m} \cdot \dfrac{1000 \text{ mm}}{1 \text{ m}} = 59 \cdot 1000 \text{ mm}$

                                  $= 59,000 \text{ mm}$
     59 meters = 59,000 millimeters

14. 42 hectometers to centimeters
     In the list
           km __hm__ dam m dm __cm__ mm
     cm is four places to the *right* of hm so move the
     decimal four places to the right.
           42 hectometers = 420,000 centimeters

16. 35,600 millimeters to hectometers
    In the list
        km <u>hm</u> dam m dm cm <u>mm</u>
    hm is five places to the *left* of mm so move the
    decimal five places to the left.
        35,600 millimeters = 0.356 hectometers

18. 5 kilometers to decimeters
    In the list
        <u>km</u> hm dam m <u>dm</u> cm mm
    dm is four places to the *right* of hm so move the
    decimal four places to the right.
        5 kilometers = 50,000 decimeters

Guide Problems

20. Convert 10 kilograms to grams.

    a. Write an appropriate unit ratio.
       Since there are 1000 grams in a kilogram
       and grams are the new unit, the unit ratio
       is

       $$\text{Unit ratio} = \frac{\text{New units}}{\text{Original units}}$$
       $$= \frac{1000 \text{ g}}{1 \text{ kg}}$$

    b. Multiply the original measure by
       the unit fraction.

       $$10 \text{ kg} \cdot \frac{1000 \text{ g}}{1 \text{ kg}}$$
       $$= 10 \ \cancel{\text{kg}} \cdot \frac{1000 \text{ g}}{1 \ \cancel{\text{kg}}}$$
       $$= 10 \cdot 1000 \text{ g} = 10,000 \text{ g}$$

       Alternatively, move the decimal point __3__ places
       to the __right__. Note g is three units to the right of
       kg in the list below.
           <u>kg</u> hg dag <u>g</u> dg cg mg
       Thus 10 kilograms = __10,000__ grams.

22. 12 kilograms to grams
    Unit ratio: $\dfrac{1000 \text{ g}}{1 \text{ kg}}$

    Convert: $12 \text{ kg} \cdot \dfrac{1000 \text{ g}}{1 \text{ kg}} = 12 \cdot 1000 \text{ g}$
    $$= 12,000 \text{ g}$$
    12 kilograms = 12,000 grams

24. 440 grams to hectograms
    Unit ratio: $\dfrac{1 \text{ hg}}{100 \text{ g}}$

    Convert: $440 \text{ g} \cdot \dfrac{1 \text{ hg}}{100 \text{ g}} = \dfrac{440}{100} \text{ hg}$
    $$= 4.4 \text{ hg}$$
    440 grams = 4.4 hectograms

26. 130 hectograms to decigrams
    In the list
        kg <u>hg</u> dag g <u>dg</u> cg mg
    dg is three places to the *right* of hg so move the
    decimal three places to the right.
        130 hectograms = 130,000 grams

28. 50 milligrams to decigrams
    In the list
        kg hg dag g <u>dg</u> cg <u>mg</u>
    dg is two places to the *left* of mg so move the
    decimal two places to the left.
        50 milligrams = 0.5 decigrams

30. 0.9 decigrams to centigrams
    In the list
        kg hg dag g <u>dg</u> <u>cg</u> mg
    cg is one place to the *right* of dg so move the
    decimal one place to the right.
        0.9 decigrams = 9 centigrams

Guide Problems

32. Convert 25 centiliters to dekaliters.
    Move the decimal point __3__ places to the __left__ . Note daL is three units to the left of cL
    in the list below.

kL hL <u>daL</u> L dL <u>cL</u> mL
Thus, 25 centiliters = <u>0.025</u> dekaliters.

34. 800 liters to hectoliters

Unit ratio: $\dfrac{1 \text{ hL}}{100 \text{ L}}$

Convert: $800 \text{ L} \cdot \dfrac{1 \text{ hL}}{100 \text{ L}} = \dfrac{800}{100} \text{ hL}$
$= 8 \text{ hL}$

800 liters = 8 hectoliters

36. 6589 liters to kiloliters

Unit ratio: $\dfrac{1 \text{ kL}}{1000 \text{ L}}$

Convert: $6589 \text{ L} \cdot \dfrac{1 \text{ kL}}{1000 \text{ L}} = \dfrac{6589}{1000} \text{ kL}$
$= 6.589 \text{ kL}$

6589 liters = 6.589 kiloliters

38. 5025 deciliters to milliliters
In the list
      kL hL daL L <u>dL</u> cL <u>mL</u>
mL is two places to the *right* of dL so move the
decimal two places to the right.
5025 deciliters = 502,500 milliliters

40. 901 centiliters to hectoliters
In the list
      kL <u>hL</u> daL L dL <u>cL</u> mL
hL is four places to the *left* of cL so move the
decimal four places to the left.
901 centiliters = 0.0901 hectoliters

42. a. Multiplying by a unit ratio, a height of 8.5 kilometers is the same as

$8.5 \text{ km} \cdot \dfrac{1000 \text{ m}}{1 \text{ km}} = 8.5 \cdot 1000 \text{ m} = 8500 \text{ meters}.$

b. First convert 3200 meters to kilometers: $3200 \text{ m} \cdot \dfrac{1 \text{ km}}{1000 \text{ m}} = \dfrac{3200}{1000} \text{ km} = 3.2$ kilometers. Given a height
of 8.5 kilometers, you have $8.5 - 3.2 = 5.3$ kilometers left to reach the top.

44. a. In the list: kL hL daL L <u>dL</u> cL <u>mL</u>, the unit mL is two places to the right of dL so to convert dL to
mL, move the decimal two places to the right. Henry has 65 deciliters or 6500 milliliters of chemicals.

b. A 5-liter jar holds $5 \text{ L} \cdot \dfrac{1000 \text{ mL}}{1 \text{ L}} = 5 \cdot 1000 \text{ mL} = 5000$ milliliters. Since Henry has $6500 > 5000$
milliliters, he needs a larger jar.

46. Matthew took $500 \text{ mg} \cdot \dfrac{1 \text{ g}}{1000 \text{ mg}} = \dfrac{500}{1000} \text{ g} = 0.5$ grams of headache medication.

48. a. Since the dosage is 1 milligram per kilogram of body weight, a 109-kilogram person would receive 109
milligrams.

b. Using the result of part a., convert 109 milligrams to grams: $109 \text{ mg} \cdot \dfrac{1 \text{ g}}{1000 \text{ mg}} = \dfrac{109}{1000} \text{ g} = 0.109$ grams.

50. At a dosage of 1 mg for every kilogram of weight, a person weighing 100 kg would receive 100 mg of
Lovenox. This dosage expressed in grams would be $100 \text{ mg} \cdot \dfrac{1 \text{ g}}{1000 \text{ mg}} = \dfrac{100}{1000} \text{ g} = 0.1$ grams.

Cumulative Skills Review

2. Move from left to right in 3.462 and 3.4619, comparing digits as you go. The first place where the numbers differ is in the thousandths place where we find the digits 2 and 1 respectively. Since 2 is greater than 1, we have
    $3.462 > 3.4619$

4. $\dfrac{45}{250} = \dfrac{5 \cdot 9}{5 \cdot 50} = \dfrac{9}{50} = 0.18$
    $= 0.18 \cdot 100\% = 18\%$

6. $18,000 \text{ in} \cdot \dfrac{1 \text{ ft}}{12 \text{ in}} = \dfrac{18,000}{12} \text{ ft} = 1500 \text{ ft}$
    $18,000 \text{ inches} = 1500 \text{ feet}$

8. The part, or amount, is unknown so use the variable a to represent it. From the percent equation
    $$\text{Amount} = \text{Percent} \cdot \text{Base}$$
    we have
    $$a = 12\% \cdot 5000$$
    or $\quad a = 0.12 \cdot 5000$

10. There are 4 quarts in a gallon so divide 23 by 4. The result is 5 R 3, so
    23 quarts = 5 gallons 3 quarts.

Section 6.4   Converting between the U.S. System and the Metric System

Concept Check

2. To convert between the U.S. Customary System and the metric system, we use __unit__ ratios.

Guide Problems

4. Convert 120 kilograms to pounds.

    a. Write an appropriate unit ratio. Since there are roughly 2.2 pounds in a kilogram and pounds are the new unit, the unit ratio is
    $$\text{Unit ratio} = \dfrac{\text{New units}}{\text{Original units}}$$
    $$\approx \dfrac{2.2 \text{ lb}}{1 \text{ kg}}$$

    b. Multiply the original measure by the unit fraction.
    $$120 \text{ kg} \cdot \dfrac{2.2 \text{ lb}}{1 \text{ kg}}$$
    $$= 120 \ \cancel{\text{kg}} \cdot \dfrac{2.2 \text{ lb}}{1 \ \cancel{\text{kg}}}$$
    $$= \dfrac{120 \cdot 2.2 \text{ lb}}{1} = 264 \text{ lb}$$
    Thus $120 \text{ kg} \approx$ __264__ pounds.

In Exercises 6 through 22 a conversion is made from a denominate number in the U.S. system to an equivalent number in the metric system or vice versa. In each case, the given number is multiplied by an appropriate unit ratio based on the conversion table in the text. Since most U.S.-to-metric conversion factors are approximations, the symbol $\approx$ is used to indicate when a conversion is approximate.

6. 800 yards to meters
    Unit ratio:
    $$\frac{\text{New units}}{\text{Original units}} \approx \frac{0.91 \text{ m}}{1 \text{ yd}}$$
    Convert:
    $$800 \text{ yd} \cdot \frac{0.91 \text{ m}}{1 \text{ yd}} = 800 \cdot 0.91 \text{ m}$$
    $$= 728 \text{ m}$$

    800 yards ≈ 728 meters

8. 1989 centimeters to inches
    Unit ratio:
    $$\frac{\text{New units}}{\text{Original units}} \approx \frac{0.39 \text{ in}}{1 \text{ cm}}$$
    Convert:
    $$1989 \text{ cm} \cdot \frac{0.39 \text{ in}}{1 \text{ cm}} = 1989 \cdot 0.39 \text{ in}$$
    $$= 775.71 \text{ in}$$

    1989 centimeters = 775.71 inches

10. 90 miles to kilometers
    Unit ratio: $\dfrac{1.61 \text{ km}}{1 \text{ mi}}$
    Convert:
    $$90 \text{ mi} \cdot \frac{1.61 \text{ km}}{1 \text{ mi}} = 90 \cdot 1.61 \text{ km}$$
    $$= 144.9 \text{ km}$$

    90 miles ≈ 144.9 kilometers

12. 2500 pounds to kilograms
    Unit ratio: $\dfrac{0.45 \text{ kg}}{1 \text{ lb}}$
    Convert:
    $$2500 \text{ lb} \cdot \frac{0.45 \text{ kg}}{1 \text{ lb}} = 2500 \cdot 0.45 \text{ kg}$$
    $$= 1125 \text{ kg}$$

    2500 pounds ≈ 1125 kilograms

14. 1700 kilograms to pounds
    Unit ratio: $\dfrac{2.2 \text{ lb}}{1 \text{ kg}}$
    Convert:
    $$1700 \text{ kg} \cdot \frac{2.2 \text{ lb}}{1 \text{ kg}} = 1700 \cdot 2.2 \text{ lb}$$
    $$= 3740 \text{ lb}$$

    1700 kilograms ≈ 3740 pounds

16. 105 grams to ounces
    Unit ratio: $\dfrac{0.035 \text{ oz}}{1 \text{ g}}$
    Convert:
    $$105 \text{ g} \cdot \frac{0.035 \text{ oz}}{1 \text{ g}} = 105 \cdot 0.035 \text{ oz}$$
    $$3.675 \text{ oz}$$
    $$\approx 3.68 \text{ oz}$$

    105 grams ≈ 3.68 ounces

18. 70 quarts to liters
    Unit ratio: $\dfrac{0.95 \text{ liters}}{1 \text{ qt}}$
    Convert:
    $$70 \text{ qt} \cdot \frac{0.95 \text{ liters}}{1 \text{ qt}} = 70 \cdot 0.95 \text{ liter}$$
    $$= 66.5 \text{ liter}$$

    70 quarts ≈ 66.5 liters

20. 12,560 fluid ounces to liters
    Unit ratio: $\dfrac{0.03 \text{ liters}}{1 \text{ fl oz}}$
    Convert:
    $$12,560 \text{ fl oz} \cdot \frac{0.03 \text{ liters}}{1 \text{ fl oz}}$$
    $$= 12,560 \cdot 0.03 \text{ liters}$$
    $$= 376.8 \text{ liters}$$

    12,560 fluid ounces ≈ 376.8 liters

22. 200 liters to gallons
    Unit ratio: $\dfrac{0.26 \text{ gal}}{1 \text{ liter}}$
    Convert:
    $$200 \text{ liters} \cdot \frac{0.26 \text{ gal}}{1 \text{ liter}} = 200 \cdot 0.26 \text{ gal}$$
    $$= 52 \text{ gal}$$

    200 liters ≈ 52 gallons

24. Convert 15 gallons to liters: $15 \text{ gal} \cdot \dfrac{3.78 \text{ liters}}{1 \text{ gal}} = 15 \cdot 3.78 \text{ liters} = 56.7 \text{ liters}$. It takes 56.7 liters to fill the tank.

26. The dairy farm produced $2130 \text{ liters} \cdot \dfrac{0.26 \text{ gal}}{1 \text{ liter}} = 2130 \cdot 0.26 \text{ gal} = 553.8$ gallons of milk.

28. First, convert 165 pounds to kilograms: $165 \text{ lb} \cdot \dfrac{0.45 \text{ kg}}{1 \text{ lb}} = 165 \cdot 0.45 \text{ kg} = 74.25$ kilograms. Since the standard dosage is 1 milligram for each kilogram of body weight, the dosage should be 74.25 milligrams.

30. a. The unit ratio for converting milliliters to drops is $\dfrac{15 \text{ drops}}{1 \text{ mL}}$ so 120 milliliters is equivalent to

    $$120 \text{ mL} \cdot \frac{15 \text{ drops}}{1 \text{ mL}} = 1800 \text{ drops}.$$

b. The unit ratio for converting drops to teaspoons is $\dfrac{1 \text{ tsp}}{60 \text{ drops}}$. Using the result of part a. 1800 drops is

equivalent to $1800 \text{ drops} \cdot \dfrac{1 \text{ tsp}}{60 \text{ drops}} = \dfrac{1800}{60} \text{ tsp} = 30 \text{ tsp}$. There are 30 1-teaspoon doses available.

32. Since 1 milligram is equivalent to 1000 micrograms, A dosage of 0.075 mg is equivalent to

$0.075 \text{ mg} \cdot \dfrac{1000 \text{ micrograms}}{1 \text{ mg}} = 0.075 \cdot 1000 \text{ micrograms} = 75 \text{ micrograms}.$

34. A single dose of 0.09 milligrams is equivalent to

$0.09 \text{ mg} \cdot \dfrac{1000 \text{ micrograms}}{1 \text{ mg}} = 0.09 \cdot 1000 \text{ micrograms} = 90 \text{ micrograms}.$

This amount is taken 4 times a day for a total of $4 \cdot 90 = 360$ micrograms.

Cumulative Skills Review

2. Four of the ten sections are shaded or
$\dfrac{4}{10} = 0.4 = 0.4 \cdot 100\% = 40\%.$

4. Noting that m is three places to the right of km in the list
<u>km</u> hm dam <u>m</u> dm cm mm
so move the decimal place in 45 three places to the right to convert from kilometers to meters: 45 kilometers = 45,000 meters.

6. $\dfrac{\$450}{5 \text{ shirts}} = \dfrac{\overset{\$90}{\cancel{\$450}}}{\underset{1}{\cancel{5}} \text{ shirts}} = \dfrac{\$90}{1 \text{ shirt}}$
The unit price is $90 per shirt.

8.
$$\begin{array}{r} 21 \text{ lb} \quad 6 \text{ oz} \\ 2\overline{)42 \text{ lb} \quad 12 \text{ oz}} \\ \underline{42 \text{ lb}} \\ 12 \text{ oz} \\ \underline{12 \text{ oz}} \\ 0 \end{array}$$

10. Move from left to right in 0.9922 and 0.9921, comparing digits as you go. The first place where the numbers differ is in the ten-thousandths place where we find the digits 2 and 1 respectively. Since 2 is greater than 1, we have $0.9922 > 0.9921$.

Section 6.5 Time and Temperature

Concept Check

2. One hour is equivalent to <u>60</u> minutes.

4. One year is equivalent to <u>365</u> days.

6. The U.S. Customary System measures temperature in degrees <u>Fahrenheit</u>.

8. To convert temperatures from degrees Fahrenheit to degrees Celsius, use the formula $\underline{C = \dfrac{5}{9}(F - 32)}$.

    To convert temperatures from degrees Celsius to degrees Fahrenheit, use the formula $\underline{F = \dfrac{9}{5}C + 32}$.

Guide Problems

10. Convert 25 years to decades.

    a. Write an appropriate unit ratio.
       Since there are 10 years in one decade
       and decades are the new unit, the unit ratio
       is

       $$\text{Unit ratio} = \frac{\text{New units}}{\text{Original units}}$$

       $$= \frac{1 \text{ decade}}{10 \text{ yr}}$$

    b. Multiply the original measure by
       the unit fraction.

       $$25 \text{ yr} \cdot \frac{1 \text{ decade}}{10 \text{ yr}}$$

       $$= 25 \text{ yr} \cdot \frac{1 \text{ decade}}{10 \text{ yr}}$$

       $$= \frac{25 \text{ decades}}{10} = 2.5 \text{ decades}$$

       Thus 25 years = $\underline{2.5}$ decades.

12. 416 weeks to years
    Unit ratio:

    $$\frac{\text{New units}}{\text{Original units}} = \frac{1 \text{ yr}}{52 \text{ wk}}$$

    Convert:

    $$416 \text{ wk} \cdot \frac{1 \text{ yr}}{52 \text{ wk}} = \frac{416}{52} \text{ yr}$$

    $$= 8 \text{ years.}$$

14. 66 months to quarters
    Unit ratio:

    $$\frac{\text{New units}}{\text{Original units}} = \frac{1 \text{ quarter}}{3 \text{ months}}$$

    Convert:

    $$66 \text{ months} \cdot \frac{1 \text{ quarter}}{3 \text{ months}} = \frac{66}{3} \text{ quarters}$$

    $$= 22 \text{ quarters}$$

16. 20 quarters to years

    Unit ratio: $\dfrac{1 \text{ yr}}{4 \text{ quarters}}$

    $$20 \text{ quarters} \cdot \frac{1 \text{ yr}}{4 \text{ quarters}}$$

    $$= 20 \text{ quarters} \cdot \frac{1 \text{ yr}}{4 \text{ quarters}}$$

    $$= \frac{20}{4} \text{ yr}$$

    $$= 5 \text{ years}$$

18. 8400 seconds to minutes

    Unit ratio: $\dfrac{1 \text{ min}}{60 \text{ sec}}$

    Convert:

    $$8400 \text{ sec} \cdot \frac{1 \text{ min}}{60 \text{ sec}}$$

    $$= \frac{8400}{60} \text{ min}$$

    $$= 140 \text{ minutes}$$

20. Converting 22 hours to minutes gives $22 \text{ hr} \cdot \dfrac{60 \text{ min}}{1 \text{ hr}} = 22 \cdot 60 \text{ min} = 1320 \text{ minutes.}$

22. If Albert works 1 more decade in addition to the 3 decades already worked, then he will have worked 4 decades total. Converting 4 decades to years tells us that Albert will have worked

    $$4 \text{ decades} \cdot \frac{10 \text{ yr}}{1 \text{ decade}} = 4 \cdot 10 \text{ yr} = 40 \text{ years.}$$

24. A 5 week trip is equivalent to $5 \text{ wk} \cdot \dfrac{7 \text{ days}}{1 \text{ wk}} = 5 \cdot 7 \text{ days} = 35 \text{ days}$.

Guide Problems

26. Convert 42 degrees Celsius to degrees Fahrenheit..

    a. What is the formula to convert Celsius to Fahrenheit?

    $$F = \frac{9}{5}C + 32$$

    b. Substitute the degrees Celsius in the formula and simplify.

    $$F = \frac{9}{5}C + 32 = \frac{9}{5} \cdot 42 + 32$$
    $$= 75.6 + 32 = 107.6$$

    Thus, $42^\circ\text{C} = \underline{107.6}\ ^\circ\text{F}.$

28. 20° Celsius to Fahrenheit
    $$F = \frac{9}{5}C + 32 = \frac{9}{5} \cdot 20 + 32$$
    $$= 36 + 32 = 68$$
    20° Celsius = 68° Fahrenheit

30. 52° Celsius to Fahrenheit
    $$F = \frac{9}{5}C + 32 = \frac{9}{5} \cdot 52 + 32$$
    $$= 93.6 + 32 = 125.6 \approx 126$$
    52° Celsius $\approx 126^\circ$ Fahrenheit

32. 40° Fahrenheit to Celsius
    $$C = \frac{5}{9}(F - 32) = \frac{5}{9}(40 - 32)$$
    $$= \frac{5}{9} \cdot 8 = 4.444... \approx 4$$
    40° Fahrenheit $\approx 4^\circ$ Celsius

34. 32° Fahrenheit to Celsius
    $$C = \frac{5}{9}(F - 32) = \frac{5}{9}(32 - 32)$$
    $$= \frac{5}{9} \cdot 0 = 0$$
    32° Fahrenheit $\approx 0^\circ$ Celsius

36. 64° Fahrenheit to Celsius
    $$C = \frac{5}{9}(F - 32) = \frac{5}{9}(64 - 32)$$
    $$= \frac{5}{9} \cdot 32 = 17.777... \approx 18$$
    64° Fahrenheit $\approx 18^\circ$ Celsius

38. 150° Fahrenheit to Celsius
    $$C = \frac{5}{9}(F - 32) = \frac{5}{9}(150 - 32)$$
    $$= \frac{5}{9} \cdot 118 = 65.555... \approx 66$$
    150° Fahrenheit $\approx 66^\circ$ Celsius

40. a. Using the formula, $C = \dfrac{5}{9}(F - 32) = \dfrac{5}{9}(300 - 32) = \dfrac{5}{9} \cdot 268 = 148.88 \approx 149$, and so the oil must be heated to 149° Celsius.

    b. A temperature of 100° Celsius is the same as $F = \dfrac{9}{5}C + 32 = \dfrac{9}{5} \cdot 100 + 32 = 180 + 32 = 212$ or 212° Fahrenheit.

42. Using the conversion formula, a temperature of 21° Celsius is the same as
    $$F = \frac{9}{5}C + 32 = \frac{9}{5} \cdot 21 + 32 = 37.8 + 32 = 69.8 \approx 70 \text{ or } 70^\circ \text{ Fahrenheit.}$$

Cumulative Skills Review

2. Using long division
   $$\frac{31}{80} = 0.3875$$

4. 35 sheep per 7 acres in fraction form is
   $$\frac{35 \text{ sheep}}{7 \text{ acres}} = \frac{\overset{5}{\cancel{35}} \text{ sheep}}{\underset{1}{\cancel{7}} \text{ acres}} = \frac{5 \text{ sheep}}{1 \text{ acre}}$$
   or 5 sheep per acre.

6. $\dfrac{15}{80} = \dfrac{3\cdot 5}{16\cdot 5} = \dfrac{3\cdot \cancel{5}}{16\cdot \cancel{5}} = \dfrac{3}{16}$

8. $2.48 + 10.5(1.24 - 0.54) - 3.1^2$

$= 2.48 + 10.5\cdot 0.7 - 3.1^2$

$= 2.48 + 10.5\cdot 0.7 - 9.61$

$= 2.48 + 7.35 - 9.61$

$= 9.83 - 9.61$

$= 0.22$

10. $8.5\% = \dfrac{8.5}{100} = \dfrac{8.5}{100}\cdot \dfrac{10}{10}$

$= \dfrac{85}{1000} = \dfrac{17\cdot 5}{200\cdot 5}$

$= \dfrac{17}{200}$

Chapter 6   Numerical Facts Of Life

a. To convert 0.002 cents to dollars, first write a unit fraction with the new units, dollars, in the numerator, and the original units, cents, in the denominator. Since 1 dollar = 100 cents, the unit fraction is

$\text{Unit ratio} = \dfrac{\text{New units}}{\text{Original units}} = \dfrac{1\ \text{dollar}}{100\ \text{cents}}$. Now multiply 0.002 cents by the unit fraction to obtain

$0.002\ \text{cents} = 0.002\ \text{cents}\cdot \dfrac{1\ \text{dollar}}{100\ \text{cents}} = \dfrac{0.002}{100}\ \text{dollars} = 0.00002\ \text{dollars}.$

b. Given usage of 35,893 kilobytes and an actual rate of 0.002 dollars per kilobyte, we have

$35{,}893\ \text{kilobytes}\cdot \dfrac{0.002\ \text{dollar}}{1\ \text{kilobyte}} = 35{,}893\cdot 0.002\ \text{dollars} = 71.786\ \text{dollars}.$ The customer was charged

$71.786 or $71.79.

c. With the incorrectly quoted rate of 0.002 cents per kilobyte, we have

$35{,}893\ \text{kilobytes}\cdot \dfrac{0.002\ \text{cents}}{1\ \text{kilobyte}} = 35{,}893\cdot 0.002\ \text{cents} = 71.786\ \text{cents}.$ The customer should have been

charged 71.786 cents or about 72¢.

Chapter 6 Review Exercises

1. 36 inches to feet
Unit ratio:
$$\frac{\text{New unit}}{\text{Old unit}} = \frac{1 \text{ ft}}{12 \text{ inches}}$$
Convert:
$$36 \text{ inches} \cdot \frac{1 \text{ ft}}{12 \text{ inches}}$$
$$= 36 \text{ \sout{inches}} \cdot \frac{1 \text{ ft}}{12 \text{ \sout{inches}}}$$
$$= \frac{36}{12} \text{ ft}$$
$$= 3 \text{ feet}$$

2. 2 miles to yards
Unit ratio:
$$\frac{\text{New unit}}{\text{Old unit}} = \frac{1760 \text{ yards}}{1 \text{ miles}}$$
Convert:
$$2 \text{ miles} \cdot \frac{1760 \text{ yards}}{1 \text{ miles}}$$
$$= 2 \text{ \sout{miles}} \cdot \frac{1760 \text{ yards}}{1 \text{ \sout{miles}}}$$
$$= 2 \cdot 1760 \text{ yards}$$
$$= 3520 \text{ yards}$$

3. 48 feet to yards
Unit ratio: $\frac{1 \text{ yard}}{3 \text{ feet}}$
Convert:
$$48 \text{ feet} \cdot \frac{1 \text{ yard}}{3 \text{ feet}}$$
$$= \frac{48}{3} \text{ yards}$$
$$= 16 \text{ yards}$$

4. 552 feet to yards
Unit ratio: $\frac{1 \text{ yard}}{3 \text{ feet}}$
Convert:
$$552 \text{ feet} \cdot \frac{1 \text{ yard}}{3 \text{ feet}}$$
$$= \frac{552}{3} \text{ yards}$$
$$= 184 \text{ yards}$$

5. 16,720 yards to miles
Unit ratio: $\frac{1 \text{ mile}}{1760 \text{ yards}}$
Convert:
$$16,720 \text{ miles} \cdot \frac{1 \text{ mile}}{1760 \text{ yards}}$$
$$= \frac{16,720}{1760} \text{ miles} = 9.5 \text{ miles}$$

6. 5 tons to ounces
First convert tons to pounds:
$$5 \text{ tons} \cdot \frac{2000 \text{ lb}}{1 \text{ tons}}$$
$$= 5 \cdot 2000 \text{ lb} = 10,000 \text{ lb}$$
Next convert pounds to ounces:
$$10,000 \text{ lb} \cdot \frac{16 \text{ ounces}}{1 \text{ lb}}$$
$$= 10,000 \cdot 16 \text{ ounces}$$
$$= 160,000 \text{ ounces.}$$

7. 3 tons to pounds
Unit ratio: $\frac{2000 \text{ lb}}{1 \text{ ton}}$
Convert:
$$3 \text{ ton} \cdot \frac{2000 \text{ lb}}{1 \text{ ton}}$$
$$= 3 \cdot 2000 \text{ lb}$$
$$= 6000 \text{ pounds}$$

8. 496 quarts to gallons
Unit ratio: $\frac{1 \text{ gal}}{4 \text{ qt}}$
Convert:
$$496 \text{ qt} \cdot \frac{1 \text{ gal}}{4 \text{ qt}}$$
$$= \frac{496}{4} \text{ gal}$$
$$= 124 \text{ gallons}$$

9. 42 cups to fluid ounces
Unit ratio: $\frac{8 \text{ fl oz}}{1 \text{ c}}$
Convert:
$$42 \text{ c} \cdot \frac{8 \text{ fl oz}}{1 \text{ c}}$$
$$= 42 \cdot 8 \text{ fl oz}$$
$$= 336 \text{ fluid ounces}$$

10. 399 teaspoons to tablespoons
Unit ratio: $\frac{1 \text{ tbs}}{3 \text{ tsp}}$
Convert:
$$399 \text{ tsp} \cdot \frac{1 \text{ tbs}}{3 \text{ tsp}}$$
$$= \frac{399}{3} \text{ tbs}$$
$$= 133 \text{ tablespoons}$$

11. 64 fluid ounces to cups
Unit ratio: $\frac{1 \text{ c}}{8 \text{ fl oz}}$
Convert:
$$64 \text{ fl oz} \cdot \frac{1 \text{ c}}{8 \text{ fl oz}}$$
$$= \frac{64}{8} \text{ c}$$
$$= 8 \text{ cups}$$

12. 52 pints to quarts
Unit ratio: $\frac{1 \text{ qt}}{2 \text{ pt}}$
Convert:
$$52 \text{ pt} \cdot \frac{1 \text{ qt}}{2 \text{ pt}}$$
$$= \frac{52}{2} \text{ qt}$$
$$= 26 \text{ quarts}$$

13. 12 in. = 1 ft
$$2 \text{ ft } 43 \text{ in.}$$
$$= 2 \text{ ft} + 43 \text{ in.}$$
$$= 2 \text{ ft} + 36 \text{ in.} + 7 \text{ in.}$$
$$= 2 \text{ ft} + 3 \text{ ft} + 7 \text{ in.}$$
$$= 5 \text{ ft} + 7 \text{ in.}$$
$$= 5 \text{ ft } 7 \text{ in.}$$

14. 3 ft = 1 yd
$$12 \text{ yd } 16 \text{ ft}$$
$$= 12 \text{ yd} + 16 \text{ ft}$$
$$= 12 \text{ yd} + 15 \text{ ft} + 1 \text{ ft}$$
$$= 12 \text{ yd} + 5 \text{ yd} + 1 \text{ ft}$$
$$= 17 \text{ yd} + 1 \text{ ft}$$
$$= 17 \text{ yd } 1 \text{ ft}$$

15. 16 fl oz = 1 pt
$$2 \text{ pt } 35 \text{ fl oz}$$
$$= 2 \text{ pt} + 35 \text{ fl oz}$$
$$= 2 \text{ pt} + 32 \text{ fl oz} + 3 \text{ fl oz}$$
$$= 2 \text{ pt} + 2 \text{ pt} + 3 \text{ fl oz}$$
$$= 4 \text{ pt} + 3 \text{ fl oz}$$
$$= 4 \text{ pt } 3 \text{ fl oz}$$

16. 12 in. = 1 ft
$$18 \text{ ft } 19 \text{ in.}$$
$$= 18 \text{ ft} + 19 \text{ in.}$$
$$= 18 \text{ ft} + 12 \text{ in.} + 7 \text{ in.}$$
$$= 18 \text{ ft} + 1 \text{ ft} + 7 \text{ in.}$$
$$= 19 \text{ ft} + 7 \text{ in.}$$
$$= 19 \text{ ft } 7 \text{ in.}$$

17. 4 qt = 1 gal
$$4 \text{ gal } 82 \text{ qt}$$
$$= 4 \text{ gal} + 82 \text{ qt}$$
$$= 4 \text{ gal} + 80 \text{ qt} + 2 \text{ qt}$$
$$= 4 \text{ gal} + 20 \text{ gal} + 2 \text{ qt}$$
$$= 24 \text{ gal} + 2 \text{ qt}$$
$$= 24 \text{ gal } 2 \text{ qt}$$

18. 16 oz = 1 lb
$$2 \text{ lb } 20 \text{ oz}$$
$$= 2 \text{ lb} + 20 \text{ oz}$$
$$= 2 \text{ lb} + 16 \text{ oz} + 4 \text{ oz}$$
$$= 2 \text{ lb} + 1 \text{ lb} + 4 \text{ oz}$$
$$= 3 \text{ lb} + 4 \text{ oz}$$
$$= 3 \text{ lb } 4 \text{ oz}$$

19.
$$\begin{array}{r} 12 \text{ ft } 10 \text{ in} \\ + \ 8 \text{ ft } \ 7 \text{ in} \\ \hline 20 \text{ ft } 17 \text{ in} \end{array}$$
$$= 20 \text{ ft} + 12 \text{ in.} + 5 \text{ in.}$$
$$= 20 \text{ ft} + 1 \text{ ft} + 5 \text{ in.}$$
$$= 21 \text{ ft } 5 \text{ in.}$$

20.
$$\begin{array}{r} 4 \text{ c } \ 7 \text{ fl oz} \\ 12 \text{ c } \ 6 \text{ fl oz} \\ + \ 16 \text{ c } \ 5 \text{ fl oz} \\ \hline 32 \text{ c } 18 \text{ fl oz} \end{array}$$
$$= 32 \text{ c} + 16 \text{ fl oz} + 2 \text{ fl oz}$$
$$= 32 \text{ c} + 2 \text{ c} + 2 \text{ fl oz}$$
$$= 34 \text{ c } 2 \text{ fl oz}$$

21.
$$\begin{array}{r} 18 \text{ lb } 12 \text{ oz} \\ + \ 26 \text{ lb } 15 \text{ oz} \\ \hline 44 \text{ lb } 27 \text{ oz} \end{array}$$
$$= 44 \text{ lb} + 16 \text{ oz} + 11 \text{ oz}$$
$$= 44 \text{ lb} + 1 \text{ lb} + 11 \text{ oz}$$
$$= 45 \text{ lb } 11 \text{ oz}$$

22.
$$\begin{array}{r} 3 \text{ t } 18 \text{ lb} \\ - \ 1 \text{ t } \ 2 \text{ lb} \\ \hline 2 \text{ t } 16 \text{ lb} \end{array}$$

23.
$$\begin{array}{r} 5 \text{ ft } 3 \text{ in.} \\ - \ 4 \text{ ft } 8 \text{ in.} \\ \hline \end{array}$$

$$\begin{array}{r} {}^{4 \text{ ft}}\ \ {}^{15 \text{ in.}} \\ \cancel{5 \text{ ft}} \ \cancel{3 \text{ in.}} \\ - \ 4 \text{ ft } \ 8 \text{ in.} \\ \hline 7 \text{ in.} \end{array}$$

24.
$$\begin{array}{r} 16 \text{ c } 3 \text{ fl oz} \\ - \ 12 \text{ c } 4 \text{ fl oz} \\ \hline \end{array}$$

$$\begin{array}{r} {}^{15 \text{ c}}\ \ {}^{11 \text{ fl oz}} \\ \cancel{16 \text{ c}} \ \cancel{3 \text{ fl oz}} \\ - \ 12 \text{ c } \ 4 \text{ fl oz} \\ \hline 3 \text{ c } \ 7 \text{ fl oz} \end{array}$$

25.
$$\begin{array}{r} 3 \text{ yd } 2 \text{ ft} \\ \times \qquad 3 \\ \hline 9 \text{ yd } 6 \text{ ft} \end{array}$$
$$= 9 \text{ yd} + 6 \text{ ft}$$
$$= 9 \text{ yd} + 2 \text{ yd}$$
$$= 11 \text{ yd}$$

26.
$$\begin{array}{r} 3 \text{ yd } 2 \text{ ft} \\ \times \qquad 8 \\ \hline 24 \text{ yd } 16 \text{ ft} \end{array}$$
$$= 24 \text{ yd} + 15 \text{ ft} + 1 \text{ ft}$$
$$= 24 \text{ yd} + 5 \text{ yd} + 1 \text{ ft}$$
$$= 29 \text{ yd } 1 \text{ ft}$$

27.
$$\begin{array}{r} 3 \text{ qt } 1 \text{ pt} \\ \times \qquad 5 \\ \hline 15 \text{ qt } 5 \text{ pt} \end{array}$$
$$= 15 \text{ qt} + 4 \text{ pt} + 1 \text{ pt}$$
$$= 15 \text{ qt} + 2 \text{ qt} + 1 \text{ pt}$$
$$= 17 \text{ qt } 1 \text{ pt}$$

28.
$$\begin{array}{r} 2 \text{ tbs } 1 \text{ tsp} \\ 2{\overline{\smash{)}\,4 \text{ tbs } 2 \text{ tsp}}} \\ \underline{4 \text{ tbs}} \\ 2 \text{ tsp} \end{array}$$

29.
$$\begin{array}{r} 2 \text{ ft } 11 \text{ in.} \\ 3{\overline{\smash{)}\,8 \text{ ft } 9 \text{ in.}}} \\ \underline{6 \text{ ft}} \\ 2 \text{ ft } \ 9 \text{ in.} \quad (= 33 \text{ in.}) \end{array}$$

30.
$$\begin{array}{r} 3 \text{ lb } 6 \text{ oz} \\ 6{\overline{\smash{)}\,20 \text{ lb } 4 \text{ oz}}} \\ \underline{18 \text{ lb}} \\ 2 \text{ lb } 4 \text{ oz} \quad (= 36 \text{ oz}) \end{array}$$

31. 65 meters to centimeters

 Unit ratio: $\dfrac{100 \text{ cm}}{1 \text{ m}}$

 Convert: $65 \text{ m} \cdot \dfrac{100 \text{ cm}}{1 \text{ m}} = 65 \cdot 100 \text{ cm}$

 $\qquad\qquad\qquad = 6500 \text{ cm}$

 65 meters $= 6500$ centimeters

32. 26 centimeters to meters

 Unit ratio: $\dfrac{1 \text{ m}}{100 \text{ cm}}$

 Convert: $26 \text{ cm} \cdot \dfrac{1 \text{ m}}{100 \text{ cm}} = \dfrac{26}{100} \text{ m}$

 $\qquad\qquad\qquad = 0.26 \text{ m}$

 26 centimeters $= 0.26$ meters

33. 37,498 millimeters to dekameters

 In the list

 $\qquad$ km hm <u>dam</u> m dm cm <u>mm</u>

 dam is four places to the *left* of mm so move the decimal four places to the left.

 $\qquad$ 37,498 millimeters $= 3.7498$ dekameters

34. 14,774 hectometers to meters

 Unit ratio: $\dfrac{100 \text{ m}}{1 \text{ hm}}$

 Convert: $14,774 \text{ hm} \cdot \dfrac{100 \text{ m}}{1 \text{ hm}} = 14,774 \cdot 100 \text{ m}$

 $\qquad\qquad\qquad = 1,477,400 \text{ m}$

 14,774 hectometers $= 1,477,400$ meters

35. 1.87 grams to centigrams

 Unit ratio: $\dfrac{100 \text{ cg}}{1 \text{ g}}$

 Convert: $1.87 \text{ g} \cdot \dfrac{100 \text{ cg}}{1 \text{ g}} = 1.87 \cdot 100 \text{ cg}$

 $\qquad\qquad\qquad = 187 \text{ cg}$

 1.87 grams $= 187$ centigrams

36. 8575 milligrams to grams

 Unit ratio: $\dfrac{1 \text{ g}}{1000 \text{ mg}}$

 Convert: $8575 \text{ mg} \cdot \dfrac{1 \text{ g}}{1000 \text{ mg}} = \dfrac{8575}{1000} \text{ g}$

 $\qquad\qquad\qquad = 8.575 \text{ g}$

 8575 milligrams $= 8.575$ grams

37. 199,836 grams to kilograms

 Unit ratio: $\dfrac{1 \text{ kg}}{1000 \text{ g}}$

 Convert: $199,836 \text{ g} \cdot \dfrac{1 \text{ kg}}{1000 \text{ g}} = \dfrac{199,836}{1000} \text{ kg}$

 $\qquad\qquad\qquad = 199.836 \text{ kg}$

 199,836 grams $= 199.836$ kilograms

38. 55 dekagrams to milligrams

 In the list

 $\qquad$ kg hg <u>dag</u> g dg cg <u>mg</u>

 mg is four places to the *right* of dag so move the decimal four places to the right.

 $\qquad$ 55 dekagrams $= 550,000$ milligrams

39. 37,345 milligrams to kilograms

 In the list

 $\qquad$ <u>kg</u> hg dag g dg cg <u>mg</u>

 kg is six places to the *left* of mg so move the decimal six places to the left.

 $\qquad$ 37,345 milligrams $= 0.037345$ kilograms

40. 7000 liters to kiloliters

 Unit ratio: $\dfrac{1 \text{ kL}}{1000 \text{ L}}$

 Convert: $7000 \text{ L} \cdot \dfrac{1 \text{ kL}}{1000 \text{ L}} = \dfrac{7000}{1000} \text{ kL}$

 $\qquad\qquad\qquad = 7 \text{ kL}$

 7000 liters $= 7$ kiloliters

41. 58 liters to deciliters

 Unit ratio: $\dfrac{10 \text{ dL}}{1 \text{ L}}$

 Convert: $58 \text{ L} \cdot \dfrac{10 \text{ dL}}{1 \text{ L}} = 58 \cdot 10 \text{ dL}$

 $\qquad\qquad\qquad = 580 \text{ dL}$

 58 liters $= 580$ deciliters

42. 128 deciliters to liters

 Unit ratio: $\dfrac{1 \text{ L}}{10 \text{ dL}}$

 Convert: $128 \text{ dL} \cdot \dfrac{1 \text{ L}}{10 \text{ dL}} = \dfrac{128}{10} \text{ L}$

 $\qquad\qquad\qquad = 12.8 \text{ L}$

 128 deciliters $= 12.8$ liters

43. 88 kilometers to dekameters
    In the list
            <u>km</u> hm <u>dam</u> m dm cm mm
    dam is two places to the *right* of km so move the
    decimal two places to the right.
            88 kilometers = 8800 dekameters

44. 10 deciliters to milliliters
    In the list
            kL hL daL L <u>dL</u> cL <u>mL</u>
    mL is two places to the *right* of dL so move the
    decimal two places to the right.
            10 deciliters = 1000 milliliters

45. 4697 dekaliters to hectoliters
    In the list
            kL <u>hL</u> <u>daL</u> L dL cL mL
    hL is one place to the *left* of daL so move the decimal one place to the left.
    4697 dekaliters = 469.7 hectoliters

46. 4 meters to feet

    Unit ratio: $\dfrac{3.3 \text{ ft}}{1 \text{ m}}$

    Convert:

    $4 \text{ m} \cdot \dfrac{3.3 \text{ ft}}{1 \text{ m}} = 4 \cdot 3.3 \text{ ft}$

    $= 13.2 \text{ ft}$

    4 meters ≈ 13.2 feet

47. 12 miles to kilometers

    Unit ratio: $\dfrac{1.61 \text{ km}}{1 \text{ mi}}$

    Convert:

    $12 \text{ mi} \cdot \dfrac{1.61 \text{ km}}{1 \text{ mi}} = 12 \cdot 1.61 \text{ km}$

    $= 19.32 \text{ km}$

    12 miles ≈ 19.32 kilometers

48. 14 inches to centimeters

    Unit ratio: $\dfrac{2.54 \text{ cm}}{1 \text{ in}}$

    Convert:

    $14 \text{ in} \cdot \dfrac{2.54 \text{ cm}}{1 \text{ in}} = 14 \cdot 2.54 \text{ cm}$

    $= 35.56 \text{ cm}$

    14 inches = 35.56 centimeters

49. 90 yards to meters

    Unit ratio: $\dfrac{0.91 \text{ m}}{1 \text{ yd}}$

    Convert:

    $90 \text{ yd} \cdot \dfrac{0.91 \text{ m}}{1 \text{ yd}} = 90 \cdot 0.91 \text{ m}$

    $= 81.9 \text{ m}$

    90 yards ≈ 81.9 meters

50. 60 kilograms to pounds

    Unit ratio: $\dfrac{2.2 \text{ lb}}{1 \text{ kg}}$

    Convert:

    $60 \text{ kg} \cdot \dfrac{2.2 \text{ lb}}{1 \text{ kg}} = 60 \cdot 2.2 \text{ lb}$

    $= 132 \text{ lb}$

    60 kilograms ≈ 132 pounds

51. 250 pounds to kilograms

    Unit ratio: $\dfrac{0.45 \text{ kg}}{1 \text{ lb}}$

    Convert:

    $250 \text{ lb} \cdot \dfrac{0.45 \text{ kg}}{1 \text{ lb}} = 250 \cdot 0.45 \text{ kg}$

    $= 112.5 \text{ kg}$

    250 pounds ≈ 112.5 kilograms

52. 16 ounces to grams

    Unit ratio: $\dfrac{28.35 \text{ g}}{1 \text{ oz}}$

    Convert:

    $16 \text{ oz} \cdot \dfrac{28.35 \text{ g}}{1 \text{ oz}} = 16 \cdot 28.35 \text{ g}$

    $= 453.6 \text{ g}$

    16 ounces ≈ 453.6 grams

53. 500 fluid ounces to liters

    Unit ratio: $\dfrac{0.03 \text{ liters}}{1 \text{ fl oz}}$

    Convert:

    $500 \text{ fl oz} \cdot \dfrac{0.03 \text{ liters}}{1 \text{ fl oz}}$

    $= 500 \cdot 0.03 \text{ liters}$

    $= 15 \text{ liters}$

    500 fluid ounces ≈ 15 liters

54. 32 quarts to liters

    Unit ratio: $\dfrac{0.95 \text{ liters}}{1 \text{ qt}}$

    Convert:

    $32 \text{ qt} \cdot \dfrac{0.95 \text{ liters}}{1 \text{ qt}} = 32 \cdot 0.95 \text{ liter}$

    $= 30.4 \text{ liter}$

    32 quarts ≈ 30.4 liters

55. 105 liters to gallons

Unit ratio: $\dfrac{0.26 \text{ gal}}{1 \text{ liter}}$

Convert:

$105 \text{ liters} \cdot \dfrac{0.26 \text{ gal}}{1 \text{ liter}} = 105 \cdot 0.26 \text{ gal}$

$= 27.3 \text{ gal}$

$105 \text{ liters} \approx 27.3 \text{ gallons}$

56. 8 liters to pints

Unit ratio: $\dfrac{2.11 \text{ pt}}{1 \text{ liter}}$

Convert:

$8 \text{ liters} \cdot \dfrac{2.11 \text{ pt}}{1 \text{ liter}} = 8 \cdot 2.11 \text{ pt}$

$= 16.88 \text{ pt}$

$8 \text{ liters} \approx 16.88 \text{ pints}$

57. 18 gallons to liters

Unit ratio: $\dfrac{3.78 \text{ liters}}{1 \text{ gal}}$

Convert:

$18 \text{ gal} \cdot \dfrac{3.78 \text{ liters}}{1 \text{ gal}} = 18 \cdot 3.78 \text{ liters}$

$= 68.04 \text{ liters}$

$18 \text{ gallons} \approx 68.04 \text{ liters}$

58. 12 minutes to seconds

Unit ratio: $\dfrac{60 \text{ sec}}{1 \text{ min}}$

Convert:

$12 \text{ min} \cdot \dfrac{60 \text{ sec}}{1 \text{ min}}$

$= 12 \cdot 60 \text{ sec}$

$= 720 \text{ seconds}$

59. 52 weeks to days

Unit ratio: $\dfrac{7 \text{ days}}{1 \text{ week}}$

Convert:

$52 \text{ weeks} \cdot \dfrac{7 \text{ days}}{1 \text{ week}}$

$= 52 \cdot 7 \text{ days}$

$= 364 \text{ days}$

60. 3 centuries to years

Unit ratio: $\dfrac{100 \text{ yr}}{1 \text{ century}}$

Convert:

$3 \text{ centuries} \cdot \dfrac{100 \text{ yr}}{1 \text{ century}}$

$= 3 \cdot 100 \text{ yr}$

$= 300 \text{ years}$

61. 88° Fahrenheit to Celsius

$C = \dfrac{5}{9}(F - 32) = \dfrac{5}{9}(88 - 32)$

$= \dfrac{5}{9} \cdot 56 = 31.111... \approx 31$

$88° \text{ F} \approx 31° \text{ C}$

62. 50° Celsius to Fahrenheit

$F = \dfrac{9}{5}C + 32 = \dfrac{9}{5} \cdot 50 + 32$

$= 90 + 32 = 122$

$50° \text{ C} = 122° \text{ F}$

63. 100° Fahrenheit to Celsius

$C = \dfrac{5}{9}(F - 32) = \dfrac{5}{9}(100 - 32)$

$= \dfrac{5}{9} \cdot 68 = 37.777... \approx 38$

$100° \text{ F} \approx 38° \text{ C}$

64. First, express 3 yards as the equivalent 9 feet. Then subtract 3 feet 8 inches from 9 feet.

$$
\begin{array}{r}
\overset{8 \text{ ft}}{\cancel{9 \text{ ft}}} \quad 12 \text{ in.} \\
- \quad 3 \text{ ft} \quad 8 \text{ in.} \\
\hline
5 \text{ ft} \quad 4 \text{ in.}
\end{array}
$$

There is 5 feet 4 inches left of the stock piece.

65. Convert two quarters to months:

$2 \text{ quarters} \cdot \dfrac{3 \text{ months}}{1 \text{ quarter}}$

$= 2 \cdot 3 \text{ months}$

$= 6 \text{ months}$

and so 6 months have passed.

66. a. Convert 6000 feet to meters

$6000 \text{ ft} \cdot \dfrac{0.31 \text{ m}}{1 \text{ ft}} = 6000 \cdot 0.31 \text{ ft}$

$= 1860 \text{ m}$

Anthony runs roughly 1860 meters.

b. From part a., Anthony will run $4 \cdot 1860 = 7440$ meters per week. Converting to kilometers

$7440 \text{ m} \cdot \dfrac{1 \text{ km}}{1000 \text{ m}} = \dfrac{7440}{1000} \text{ km}$

$= 7.44 \text{ km}$

Anthony will run about 7.44 kilometers in a week.

c. Convert the answer from b. to miles:

$7.44 \text{ km} \cdot \dfrac{0.62 \text{ mi}}{1 \text{ km}} = 7.44 \cdot 0.62 \text{ mi}$

$\approx 4.6 \text{ mi}$

Anthony runs about 4.6 miles.
Note that Anthony runs 6000 feet per day so in 4 days, Anthony runs 24,000 feet. Converting this number to miles gives

$24,000 \text{ ft} \cdot \dfrac{1 \text{ mi}}{5280 \text{ ft}} = \dfrac{24,000}{5280} \text{ mi}$

$\approx 4.5 \text{ mi}$

The answers differ slightly because of the approximate conversion factors used in U.S. metric conversions.

67. Using the Celsius to Fahrenheit formula with
    $C = 15$, we have
    $$F = \frac{9}{5}C + 32 = \frac{9}{5} \cdot 15 + 32$$
    $$= 27 + 32 = 59$$
    The temperature at Heathrow is 59° Fahrenheit.

68. Use unit ratios to convert 3 days per week to a
    rate involving quarters.
    $$\frac{3 \text{ days}}{1 \text{ week}} \cdot \frac{52 \text{ weeks}}{1 \text{ yr}} \cdot \frac{1 \text{ yr}}{4 \text{ quarters}}$$
    $$= \frac{3 \text{ days}}{1 \text{ week}} \cdot \frac{\overset{13}{\cancel{52}} \text{ weeks}}{1 \text{ yr}} \cdot \frac{1 \text{ yr}}{\underset{1}{\cancel{4}} \text{ quarters}}$$
    $$= \frac{3 \cdot 13 \text{ days}}{\text{quarter}} = \frac{39 \text{ days}}{\text{quarter}}$$
    Firefighters get 39 days off each quarter.

69. a. 30 years is equivalent to
    $$30 \text{ yr} \cdot \frac{1 \text{ decade}}{10 \text{ yr}} = \frac{30}{10} \text{ decade} = 3 \text{ decades.}$$
    The 30-year reunion attendees went to school 3
    decades ago.

    b. 10 years is equivalent to
    $$10 \text{ yr} \cdot \frac{12 \text{ months}}{1 \text{ yr}} = 10 \cdot 12 \text{ months}$$
    $$= 120 \text{ months.}$$
    The 10-year reunion attendees went to school
    120 months ago.

    c. Convert 20 years to quarters.
    $$20 \text{ yr} \cdot \frac{4 \text{ quarters}}{1 \text{ yr}} = 20 \cdot 4 \text{ quarters}$$
    $$= 80 \text{ quarters}$$
    The 20-year reunion attendees went to school
    80 quarters ago.

70. If one pill contains 500 milligrams, then four pills
    contain $4 \cdot 500 = 2000$ milligrams. Convert this
    amount to grams.
    $$2000 \text{ mg} \cdot \frac{1 \text{ g}}{1000 \text{ mg}} = \frac{2000}{1000} \text{ g} = 2 \text{ g}$$
    Four tablets contain 2 grams of medication.

71. If each tank holds 1000 gallons then three tanks
    hold 3000 gallons. Convert this amount to liters.
    $$3000 \text{ gal} \cdot \frac{3.78 \text{ L}}{1 \text{ gal}} = 3000 \cdot 3.78 \text{ L}$$
    $$= 11,340 \text{ L}$$
    The tanks can hold roughly 11,340 liters.

72. To convert 100 milligrams to centigrams, note
    that in the list
        kg hg dag g dg <u>cg</u> <u>mg</u>
    cg is one place to the left of mg, so move the
    decimal point one place to the left to find
    100 milligrams = 10 centigrams.
    Thus tablets contain 20 centigrams.

73. Convert 1.5 tablespoons to teaspoons.
    $$1.5 \text{ tbs} \cdot \frac{3 \text{ tsp}}{1 \text{ tbs}} = 1.5 \cdot 3 \text{ tsp} = 4.5 \text{ tsp}$$
    The patient takes 4.5 teaspoons of fiber.

74. First multiply the rate, 30 milliliters per hour, by
    the time, 24 hours.
    $$24 \text{ hr} \cdot \frac{30 \text{ mL}}{1 \text{ hr}} = 720 \text{ mL}$$
    Next, convert this amount to liters.
    $$720 \text{ mL} \cdot \frac{1 \text{ L}}{1000 \text{ mL}} = \frac{720}{1000} \text{ L} = 0.72 \text{ L}$$
    The patient receives 0.72 liters in 24 hours.

75. a. Compute 239° Fahrenheit to degrees Celsius.
    $$C = \frac{5}{9}(F - 32) = \frac{5}{9}(239 - 32) = \frac{5}{9} \cdot 207 = 115$$
    The solution boils at 115° Celsius.

    b. Convert 4.5 minutes to seconds.
    $$4.5 \text{ min} \cdot \frac{60 \text{ sec}}{1 \text{ min}} = 4.5 \cdot 60 \text{ sec} = 270 \text{ sec}$$
    The solution boils in 270 seconds.

76. The time increased from 3 hours, 19 minutes, 5 seconds in 1970 to 3 hours, 42 minutes, 42 seconds in
    1980. Subtracting hours: $3 - 3 = 0$, minutes: $42 - 19 = 23$, and seconds: $42 - 5 = 37$ gives an increase of 23
    minutes 37 seconds.

77. The time increased from 4 hours, 12 minutes, 3 seconds in 1990 to 4 hours, 21 minutes, 32 seconds. Subtracting hours: $4 - 4 = 0$, minutes: $21 - 12 = 9$, and seconds: $32 - 3 = 29$ gives an increase of 9 minutes 29 seconds.

78. The time increased from 3 hours, 19 minutes, 5 seconds in 1970 to 4 hours, 21 minutes, 32 seconds. Subtracting hours: $4 - 3 = 1$, minutes: $21 - 19 = 2$, and seconds: $32 - 5 = 27$ gives an increase of 1hour 2 minutes 27 seconds.

79. The average increase over the thirty year period is found by dividing 30 into the total increase found in exercise 78 which was 1 hour 2 minutes 27 seconds. The division is shown below. Since 30 does not divide 1, convert 1 hour to 60 minutes and write the dividend as 62 minutes 27 seconds.

$$
\begin{array}{r}
2 \text{ min} \\
30\overline{)62 \text{ min} \quad 27 \text{ sec}} \\
\underline{60 \text{ min}} \\
2 \text{ min} \quad 27 \text{ sec} \quad (=147 \text{ sec})
\end{array}
$$

Dividing 147 seconds by 30 gives 4.9 seconds, so, to the nearest second, the average increase was 2 minutes 5 seconds.

Chapter 6 Assessment Test

1. 938 yards to feet
   Unit ratio:
   $$\frac{\text{New unit}}{\text{Old unit}} = \frac{3 \text{ ft}}{1 \text{ yd}}$$
   Convert:
   $$938 \text{ yd} \cdot \frac{3 \text{ ft}}{1 \text{ yd}}$$
   $$= 938 \text{ yd} \cdot \frac{3 \text{ ft}}{1 \text{ yd}}$$
   $$= 938 \cdot 3 \text{ ft}$$
   $$= 2814 \text{ feet}$$

2. 272 quarts to gallons
   Unit ratio:
   $$\frac{\text{New unit}}{\text{Old unit}} = \frac{1 \text{ gal}}{4 \text{ qt}}$$
   Convert:
   $$272 \text{ qt} \cdot \frac{1 \text{ gal}}{4 \text{ qt}}$$
   $$= 272 \text{ qt} \cdot \frac{1 \text{ gal}}{4 \text{ qt}}$$
   $$= \frac{272}{4} \text{ gal}$$
   $$= 68 \text{ gallons}$$

3. 3 pounds to ounces
   Unit ratio:
   $$\frac{\text{New unit}}{\text{Old unit}} = \frac{16 \text{ oz}}{1 \text{ lb}}$$
   Convert:
   $$3 \text{ lb} \cdot \frac{16 \text{ oz}}{1 \text{ lb}}$$
   $$= 3 \text{ lb} \cdot \frac{16 \text{ oz}}{1 \text{ lb}}$$
   $$= 3 \cdot 16 \text{ oz}$$
   $$= 48 \text{ ounces}$$

4. 160 fluid ounces to cups
   Unit ratio:
   $$\frac{\text{New unit}}{\text{Old unit}} = \frac{1 \text{ c}}{8 \text{ fl oz}}$$
   Convert:
   $$160 \text{ fl oz} \cdot \frac{1 \text{ c}}{8 \text{ fl oz}}$$
   $$= 160 \text{ fl oz} \cdot \frac{1 \text{ c}}{8 \text{ fl oz}}$$
   $$= \frac{160}{8} \text{ c}$$
   $$= 20 \text{ cups}$$

5. There are 4 quarts in a gallon so divide 15 by 4.

   $$
   \begin{array}{r}
   3 \quad R \ 3 \\
   4\overline{)15} \\
   \underline{12} \\
   3
   \end{array}
   $$

   15 qt = 3 gal 3 qt

6. There are 3 feet in a yard so divide 74 by 3.

   $$
   \begin{array}{r}
   24 \quad R \ 2 \\
   3\overline{)74} \\
   \underline{6} \\
   14 \\
   \underline{12} \\
   2
   \end{array}
   $$

   74 ft = 24 yd 2 ft

7.   2 cups = 1 pint
         15 pints 3 cups = 15 pints + 2 cups + 1 cup
                        = 15 pints + 1 pint + 1 cup
                        = 16 pt 1 c

8.   5280 feet = 1 mile
      3 miles 6700 feet
          = 3 miles + 5280 feet + 1420 feet
          = 3 miles + 1 mile + 1420 feet
          = 4 mi 1420 ft

9.   15 ft 10 in.
      20 ft   2 in.
    + 1 ft   8 in.
    ───────────────
      36 ft 20 in.
              = 36 ft + 12 in. + 8 in.
              = 36 ft + 1 ft + 8 in.
              = 37 ft 8 in.

10.   80 t 100 lb
       − 26 t 500 lb

            79 t   2100 lb
            8̶0̶ t̶   1̶0̶0̶ l̶b̶
          − 26 t   500 lb
          ─────────────────
            53 t   1600 lb

11.   12 ft   5 in.
     ×   4
     ───────────────
       48 ft 20 in.
               = 48 ft + 12 in. + 8 in.
               = 48 ft + 1 ft + 8 in.
               = 49 ft 8 in.

12.   1 lb 12 oz
       ───────────────
     7)12 lb   4 oz
        7 lb
       ───────────────
        5 lb   4 oz   (= 84 oz)

13. 987 centiliters to milliliters
     In the list
            kL hL daL L dL cL mL
     mL is one place to the *right* of cL so move the
     decimal one place to the right.
            987 centiliters = 9870 milliliters

14. 84 grams to decigrams
     Unit ratio: $\dfrac{10 \text{ dg}}{1 \text{ g}}$
     Convert: $84 \text{ g} \cdot \dfrac{10 \text{ dg}}{1 \text{ g}} = 84 \cdot 10 \text{ dg}$
                                     $= 840 \text{ dg}$
     84 grams = 840 decigrams

15. 32 hectometers to centimeters
     In the list
            km hm dam m dm cm mm
     cm is four places to the *right* of hm so move the
     decimal four places to the right.
            32 hectometers = 320,000 centimeters

16. 3155 centigrams to dekagrams
     In the list
            kg hg dag g dg cg mg
     dag is three places to the *left* of cg so move the
     decimal three places to the left.
            3155 centigrams = 3.155 dekagrams

17. 64 feet to meters
     Unit ratio: $\dfrac{0.31 \text{ m}}{1 \text{ ft}}$
     Convert:
       $64 \text{ ft} \cdot \dfrac{0.31 \text{ m}}{1 \text{ ft}} = 64 \cdot 0.31 \text{ m}$
                              $= 19.84 \text{ m}$

     64 feet ≈ 19.84 meters

18. 3 kilometers to miles
     Unit ratio: $\dfrac{0.62 \text{ mi}}{1 \text{ km}}$
     Convert:
       $3 \text{ km} \cdot \dfrac{0.62 \text{ mi}}{1 \text{ km}} = 3 \cdot 0.62 \text{ mi}$
                              $= 1.86 \text{ mi}$

     3 kilometers ≈ 1.86 miles

19. 290 pounds to kilograms

Unit ratio: $\dfrac{0.45 \text{ kg}}{1 \text{ lb}}$

Convert:

$290 \text{ lb} \cdot \dfrac{0.45 \text{ kg}}{1 \text{ lb}} = 290 \cdot 0.45 \text{ kg}$

$= 130.5 \text{ kg}$

290 pounds $\approx$ 130.5 kilograms

20. 85 fluid ounces to liters

Unit ratio: $\dfrac{0.03 \text{ liters}}{1 \text{ fl oz}}$

Convert:

$85 \text{ fl oz} \cdot \dfrac{0.03 \text{ liters}}{1 \text{ fl oz}}$

$= 85 \cdot 0.03 \text{ liters}$

$= 2.55 \text{ liters}$

85 fluid ounces $\approx$ 2.55 liters

21. 3 millenniums to years

Unit ratio: $\dfrac{1000 \text{ yr}}{1 \text{ millennium}}$

Convert:

$3 \text{ millenniums} \cdot \dfrac{1000 \text{ yr}}{1 \text{ millennium}}$

$= 3 \cdot 1000 \text{ yr}$

$= 3000 \text{ years}$

22. 365 days to minutes
Multiply by a sequence of unit ratios.
Convert:

$365 \text{ days} \cdot \dfrac{24 \text{ hr}}{1 \text{ day}} \cdot \dfrac{60 \text{ min}}{1 \text{ hr}}$

$= 365 \; \cancel{\text{days}} \cdot \dfrac{24 \; \cancel{\text{hr}}}{1 \; \cancel{\text{day}}} \cdot \dfrac{60 \text{ min}}{1 \; \cancel{\text{hr}}}$

$= 365 \cdot 24 \cdot 60 \text{ min}$

$= 525,600 \text{ minutes}$

23. 300° Fahrenheit to Celsius

$C = \dfrac{5}{9}(F - 32) = \dfrac{5}{9}(300 - 32)$

$= \dfrac{5}{9} \cdot 268 = 148.888... \approx 149$

300° Fahrenheit $\approx 149^{\circ}$ Celsius

24. 8° Celsius to Fahrenheit

$F = \dfrac{9}{5}C + 32 = \dfrac{9}{5} \cdot 8 + 32$

$= 14.4 + 32 = 46.4 \approx 46$

8° Celsius $\approx 46^{\circ}$ Fahrenheit

25. $\begin{array}{r} 46 \text{ ft } 11 \text{ in.} \\ + \; 29 \text{ ft } 7 \text{ in.} \\ \hline 75 \text{ ft } 18 \text{ in.} \end{array}$

$= 75 \text{ ft} + 12 \text{ in.} + 6 \text{ in.}$

$= 75 \text{ ft} + 1 \text{ ft} + 6 \text{ in.}$

$= 76 \text{ ft } 6 \text{ in.}$

The total length of the slabs is 76 feet 6 inches.

26. Convert 15 pounds to kilograms

$15 \text{ lb} \cdot \dfrac{0.45 \text{ kg}}{1 \text{ lb}} = 15 \cdot 0.45 \text{ kg}$

$= 6.75 \text{ kg}$

Mark lost roughly 6.75 kilograms.

27. 300 milligrams at a rate of 50 milligrams per teaspoon is

$300 \text{ mg} \cdot \dfrac{1 \text{ tsp}}{50 \text{ mg}} = \dfrac{300}{50} \text{ tsp}$

$= 6 \text{ tsp}$

The patient takes 6 teaspoons.

28. Convert 1.5 pints to liters

$1.5 \text{ pt} \cdot \dfrac{0.47 \text{ liters}}{1 \text{ pt}}$

$= 1.5 \cdot 0.47 \text{ liters}$

$= 0.705 \text{ liters}$

The patient drinks 0.705 liters of juice.

29. There are 60 minutes in an hour so divide 315 by 60

$$
\begin{array}{r}
5 \ R \ 15 \\
60\overline{)315} \\
\underline{300} \\
15
\end{array}
$$

so 315 minutes is 5 hours 15 minutes.

30. Convert $102°$ Fahrenheit to Celsius

$$C = \frac{5}{9}(F-32) = \frac{5}{9}(102-32)$$

$$= \frac{5}{9} \cdot 70 = 38.888... \approx 38.9$$

To the nearest tenth of a degree, Henry's body temperature is $38.9°$ C.

Chapter 7 Geometry

Section 7.1   Lines and Angles

Concept Check

2. A _plane_ is a flat surface that has infinite length, infinite width, and no depth.

4. _Space_ is the expanse that has infinite length, infinite width, and infinite depth.

6. A _point_ is an exact location or position in space.

8. Lines that lie in the same plane but never cross are known as _parallel_ lines.

10. A finite portion of a line with a point at each end is called a/an _line_ _segment_ .

12. A portion of a line that has one endpoint and extends forever in one direction is called a/an _ray_ .

14. The common endpoint of the two rays that form an angle is known as the _vertex_ of the angle, and the two rays that form an angle are known as the _sides_ of the angle.

16. A _protractor_ is a device used to measure an angle.

18. Two angles, the sum of whose degree measure is $90°$, are called _complementary_ angles. Two angles, the sum of whose degree measure is $180°$, are called _supplementary_ angles.

Guide Problems

20. A line is named using the letters of any two points on the line with an arrowhead above each of the letters.

    a. Label the points on the line with the letters F and G.

    $\overset{\bullet}{F} \qquad \overset{\bullet}{G}$

    b. Name the line appropriately: $\overleftrightarrow{FG}$ or $\overleftrightarrow{GF}$

22. A ray is named using its endpoint and one other point of the ray. The endpoint is always written first.

    a. Label the endpoint of the ray with the letter L. Label the other point B.

    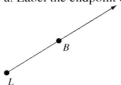

    b. Name the ray appropriately: $\overrightarrow{LB}$

In Problems 24 through 30, identify each figure using the definitions of plane figures and according to the guidelines in Guide Problems 18 through 22.

24. The figure shown is a line because it extends forever in either direction. It is named $\overleftrightarrow{TX}$ or $\overleftrightarrow{XT}$.

26. The figure shown is a line because it extends forever in either direction. It is named $\overleftrightarrow{FQ}$ or $\overleftrightarrow{QF}$.

28. The figure shown is a ray because it begins at one point and extends forever in one direction. It is named $\overrightarrow{LA}$.

30. The figure shown is a line because it extends forever in either direction. It is named $\overleftrightarrow{NZ}$ or $\overleftrightarrow{ZN}$.

Guide Problems

32. An angle is named by its vertex alone, or by using the vertex and a point on each side of the angle. Name each angle in all possible ways.

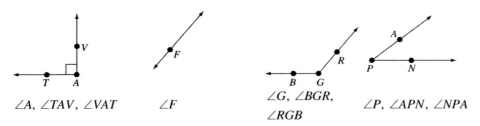

$\angle A$, $\angle TAV$, $\angle VAT$ $\angle F$ $\angle G$, $\angle BGR$, $\angle RGB$ $\angle P$, $\angle APN$, $\angle NPA$

In Problems 34 through 42, name and classify each angle using the definitions of acute, right, obtuse, or straight angles as shown in Guide Problems 32 and 33.

34. $\angle G$, $\angle CGE$, $\angle EGC$; this angle is acute because its measure is greater than $0°$ and less than $90°$.

36. $\angle I$, $\angle KIZ$, $\angle ZIK$; this angle is obtuse because its measure is greater than $90°$ and less than $180°$.

38. $\angle D$, $\angle BDW$, $\angle WDB$; this angle is acute because its measure is greater than $0°$ and less than $90°$.

40. $\angle L$, $\angle KLO$, $\angle OLK$; this angle is obtuse because its measure is greater than $90°$ and less than $180°$.

42. $\angle Y$, $\angle UYQ$, $\angle QYU$; this angle is obtuse because its measure is greater than $90°$ and less than $180°$.

Guide Problems

44. Supplementary angles are two angles whose degree measures is $180°$. To find the supplement of an angle, subtract the measure of the angle from $180°$. Find the measure of the supplement of an angle measuring $110°$.
$180° - 110° = \underline{70°}$

In Exercises 46 through 50 find the measure of the complement or supplement of each angle with the given measure using the definitions of complementary and supplementary angles.

46. $90° - 10° = 80°$ 48. $180° - 117° = 63°$ 50. $90° - 84° = 6°$

52. $\angle Z$ and the $130°$ angle form a straight angle, so the angles are supplementary.
$m\angle Z = 180° - 130° = 50°$

54. $\angle T$ and the $25°$ angle form a right angle, so the angles are complementary.
$m\angle T = 90° - 25° = 65°$

56. $\angle ION$, the $25°$ angle, and the $95°$ angle form a straight angle, so the angles are supplementary.
$m\angle ION = 180° - 25° - 95° = 60°$

Cumulative Skills Review

2. Set up the ratio, 120 shares for $3018, as a rate in fraction notation. Use the price as the numerator and the number of shares as the denominator.

$$\frac{\$3018}{120}$$

Divide the numerator by the denominator and write the unit price in fraction notation.

$$\frac{\$25.15}{1 \text{ share}}$$

Daniel paid $25.15 per share.

4. Convert the fraction $\frac{43}{50}$ to a decimal: $\frac{43}{50} = 0.86$

Convert the decimal to a percent by multiplying by 100%: $0.86 \cdot 100\% = 86\%$

6. Substitute the known amounts into the formula to find the interest.
$\$45,000 \cdot 2.5\% \cdot 5 = \$5,625$

8. Write an appropriate unit ratio.

$$\text{Unit ratio} = \frac{\text{New units}}{\text{Original units}} = \frac{5280 \text{ ft}}{1 \text{ mi}}$$

Multiply the original measure by the unit fraction.

$$8 \text{ mi} \cdot \frac{5280 \text{ ft}}{1 \text{ mi}} = 42,240 \text{ ft}$$

10.
$$\begin{array}{r} 8.33 \\ \times 9.21 \\ \hline 833 \\ 16660 \\ \underline{749700} \\ 76.7193 \end{array}$$

Section 7.2   Plane and Solid Geometric Figures

Concept Check

2. A three-sided polygon is called a _triangle_.

4. A triangle with at least two sides of equal length in which the angles opposite these sides have equal measure is called an _isosceles_ triangle.

6. An _acute_ triangle is a triangle that has three acute angles.

8. An _obtuse_ triangle is a triangle that has an obtuse angle.

10. A quadrilateral whose opposite sides are parallel and equal in length is known as a _parallelogram_.

12. A parallelogram in which all sides are of equal length is called a _rhombus_.

14. A quadrilateral that has one pair of parallel sides is called a _trapezoid_.

16. The fixed point that defines a circle is known as the _center_ of the circle.

18. The length of a line segment that passes through the center of a circle and whose endpoints lie on the circle is called the _diameter_ of the circle.

20. The diameter is _two_ times the radius.

22. A _cube_ is a rectangular solid in which all six faces are squares.

24. A solid that consists of all points in space that lie the same distance from some fixed point is called a _sphere_.

26. A solid with a circular base in which all points of the base are joined by line segments to a single point in a different plane is known as a _cone_.

Guide Problems

28. Classify each triangle as acute, right, or obtuse.

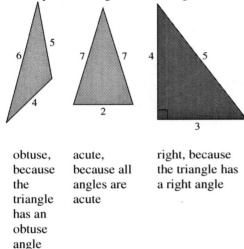

| obtuse, because the triangle has an obtuse angle | acute, because all angles are acute | right, because the triangle has a right angle |

In problems 30 through 36, classify each triangle as equilateral, isosceles, or scalene using the definitions of these triangles. Also, classify each triangle as acute, right, or obtuse using the definitions of these triangles.

30. The triangle shown is a scalene triangle because all sides have different lengths. The triangle is also an obtuse triangle because the triangle has an obtuse angle.

32. The triangle shown is a scalene triangle because all sides have different lengths. The triangle is also a right triangle because the triangle has a right angle.

34. The triangle shown is an equilateral or isosceles triangle because all sides have equal length. The triangle is also an acute triangle because all angles are acute.

36. The triangle shown is an equilateral or isosceles triangle because all sides have equal length. The triangle is also an acute triangle because all angles are acute.

Guide Problems

38. The sum of the measures of the three angles of a triangle is 180°. Find the measure of the unknown angle.

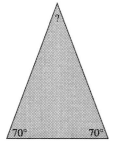

    a.   Find the sum of the two given angles.
          $70° + 70° = 140°$

    b.   Subtract the sum from 180°.
          $180° - 140° = 40°$
          The measure of the unknown angle is 40°.

For problems 40 through 48, find the measure of the unknown angle of each triangle by first finding the sum of the two given angles and subtracting the sum from 180°.

40. $64° + 58° = 122°$, so $180° - 122° = 58°$.   42. $48° + 20° = 68°$, so $180° - 68° = 112°$.

44. $33° + 33° = 66°$, so $180° - 66° = 114°$.   46. $22° + 120° = 142°$, so $180° - 142° = 38°$.

48. $74° + 58° = 132°$, so $180° - 132° = 48°$.

Guide Problems

50. Label each figure according to the number of sides: triangle (3 sides), quadrilateral (4 sides), pentagon (5 sides), hexagon (6 sides), or octagon (8 sides).

  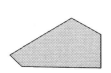 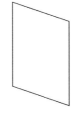 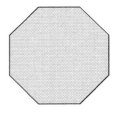

hexagon,   triangle,   pentagon, because   quadrilateral,   octagon, because
because   because   there are 5 sides   because   there are 8 sides
there are 6   there are 3   there are 4
sides   sides   sides

For problems 52 through 58, identify each quadrilateral as a rectangle, square, trapezoid, or rhombus using the definitions of each figure.

52. This figure is a square, rectangle, or rhombus because all sides have equal length and there are four right angles.

54. This figure is a rhombus because all sides have equal length.

56. This figure is a square, rectangle, or rhombus because all sides have equal length and there are four right angles.

58. This figure is a rectangle because there are four right angles.

For problems 60 through 70, identify each polygon as a triangle, quadrilateral, pentagon, hexagon, or octagon according to the number of sides of the figure.

60. The figure is a quadrilateral because it has 4 sides.

62. The figure is a pentagon because it has 5 sides.

64. The figure is a quadrilateral because it has 4 sides.

66. The figure is an octagon because it has 8 sides.

68. The figure is a quadrilateral because it has 4 sides.

70. The figure is a hexagon because it has 6 sides.

Guide Problems

72. To find the radius of a circle, divide the diameter by 2.

$$\text{Radius} = \frac{\text{Diameter}}{2}$$

What is the radius of a circle with diameter of 12 feet?

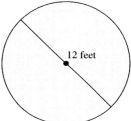

Divide the diameter by 2.

$\dfrac{12 \text{ ft}}{2} = 6$ ft, so the radius is 6 feet.

For problems 74 through 78, find the radius or diameter using the given information. If the diameter is given divide by 2 to find the radius. If the radius is given, multiply by 2 to find the diameter.

74. $\dfrac{6 \text{ in.}}{2} = 3$ in.

76. $\dfrac{9 \text{ km}}{2} = 4.5$ km

78. $\dfrac{10 \text{ ft}}{2} = 5$ ft

Guide Problems

80. Identify each solid as a rectangular solid, a cube, or a pyramid.

  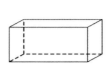

cube, because there are six square faces

pyramid, because there are four triangular-shaped faces with a common vertex

rectangular solid, because there are six rectangular faces

For problems 82 through 92, identify each solid using the definitions of the solids.

82. The solid is a rectangular solid because there are six rectangular faces.

84. The solid is a pyramid because there are four triangular-shaped faces with a common vertex.

86. The solid is a sphere because the solid consists of all points that lie the same distance from some fixed point.

88. The solid is a cylinder because the solid has two identical circular bases joined by line segments perpendicular to these bases.

90. The solid is a cone because the solid has a circular base and a common vertex.

92. The solid is a cube because there are six square faces.

Cumulative Skills Review

2. Check all possible factors until a repeat is found.

$33 \div 1 = 33$

$33 \div 2$ Does not divide evenly.

$33 \div 3 = 11$

$33 \div 4$ Does not divide evenly.

$33 \div 5$ Does not divide evenly.

$33 \div 6$ Does not divide evenly.

$33 \div 7$ Does not divide evenly.

$33 \div 8$ Does not divide evenly.

$33 \div 9$ Does not divide evenly.

$33 \div 10$ Does not divide evenly.

$33 \div 11 = 3$

The factors of 33 are 1, 3, 11, and 33.

4.   The formula to convert Celsius to Fahrenheit is $F = \dfrac{9}{5}C + 32$. Substitute the degrees Celsius in the formula and simplify.

$$F = \frac{9}{5} \cdot 55 + 32 = 99 + 32 = 131$$

Thus, $55°$ Celsius $= 131°$ Fahrenheit.

6.   The figure shown is a ray because it begins at one point and extends forever in one direction. It is named $\overrightarrow{HA}$.

8.   To convert a decimal to a percent, multiply by 100%.
$0.80 \cdot 100\% = 80\%$

10.   To find the amount of the down payment, find 15% of $250,000. Convert the percent, 15%, to a decimal, 0.15, and multiply by $250,000.
$0.15 \cdot \$250,000 = \$37,500$
A down payment of $37,500 is needed.

Section 7.3   Perimeter and Circumference

Concept Check

2.   The perimeter of a polygon is the __sum__ of the lengths of its sides.

4.   To find the perimeter of a square, we find the sum of all sides or use the formula $P = $ __$4s$__ .

6.   For any circle, if we divide the circumference, C, by the diameter, we get a constant whose value is approximately equal to __3.14__ . We represent it by the Greek letter __π__ .

8.   When r represents the radius of a circle, then the circumference C is found using the formula $C = $ __$2\pi r$__ .

Guide Problems

10.   What is the perimeter of the polygon?

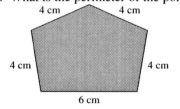

Add the lengths of the sides.
$4 \text{ cm} + 4 \text{ cm} + 4 \text{ cm} + 4 \text{ cm} + 6 \text{ cm} = \underline{22 \text{ cm}}$

12.   What is the perimeter of the square?

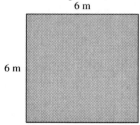

Use the formula $P = 4s$, where $s = 6$ meters.
$P = 4 \cdot 6 \text{ m} = 24 \text{ m}$

For problems 14 through 20, find the perimeter of each polygon. Add all sides or use a perimeter formula.

14. $P = 5.5 \text{ mm} + 3 \text{ mm} + 5.5 \text{ mm} + 3 \text{ mm} = 17 \text{ mm}$

16. $P = 3.9 \text{ mm} + 6.5 \text{ mm} + 3.9 \text{ mm} = 14.3 \text{ mm}$

18. $P = 5 \text{ ft} + 5 \text{ ft} + 5 \text{ ft} + 5 \text{ ft} + 5 \text{ ft} = 25 \text{ ft}$

20. $P = 1.5 \text{ yd} + 1.5 \text{ yd} + 1.5 \text{ yd} = 4.5 \text{ yd}$

Guide Problems

22. What is the circumference of a circle with diameter of 18 meters? Use 3.14 for π. Round to the nearest whole meter.

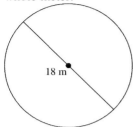

$C = \pi d$

$\approx (3.14)(18 \text{ m})$

$\approx \underline{57 \text{ m}}$

For problems 24 through 32, find the circumference of each circle. Use 3.14 for π. Round to the nearest hundredth. Use the formula $C = \pi d$ if the diameter is given or the formula $C = 2\pi r$ if the radius is given.

24. The diameter is 8 ft.
    $C = \pi d$

    $\approx (3.14)(8 \text{ ft})$

    $\approx 25.12 \text{ ft}$

26. The diameter is 9 m.
    $C = \pi d$

    $\approx (3.14)(9 \text{ m})$

    $\approx 28.26 \text{ m}$

28. The radius is 3 yd.
    $C = 2\pi r$

    $\approx (2)(3.14)(3 \text{ yd})$

    $\approx 18.84 \text{ yd}$

30. The radius is 6 in.
    $C = 2\pi r$

    $\approx (2)(3.14)(6 \text{ in.})$

    $\approx 37.68 \text{ in.}$

32. The radius is 8 mm.
    $C = 2\pi r$

    $\approx (2)(3.14)(8 \text{ mm})$

    $\approx 50.24 \text{ mm}$

For problems 34 through 36, solve each problem by finding the perimeter using the methods practiced in this section.

34. a. $P = 4s = 4 \cdot 4.5 \text{ m} = 18 \text{ m}$

    b. Multiply the perimeter by the cost per meter.

    $18 \text{ m} \cdot \dfrac{\$20}{\text{meter}} = \$360$

    It will cost $360 to fence in the pool area.

36. Find the perimeter of the kite, then divide the result by 2 to find the length of the tail.
    $P = 3.5 \text{ ft} + 3.5 \text{ ft} + 6.5 \text{ ft} + 6.5 \text{ ft} = 20 \text{ ft}$

    $\dfrac{20 \text{ ft}}{2} = 10 \text{ ft}$

    The tail will be 10 feet long.

Cumulative Skills Review

2. The similar figures yield the following proportion.

$$\frac{6}{k} = \frac{5}{10}$$

Separate the cross products with an equal sign to form an equation, and solve the proportion.

$$k \cdot 5 = 6 \cdot 10$$
$$5k = 60$$
$$\frac{5k}{5} = \frac{60}{5}$$
$$k = 12$$

4. The least common denominator of the fractions $\frac{1}{2}$, $\frac{5}{8}$, and $\frac{4}{5}$ is the least common multiple of the denominators 2, 8, and 5.

$$2 = 2$$
$$8 = 2 \cdot 2 \cdot 2$$
$$5 = 5$$
$$2 \cdot 2 \cdot 2 \cdot 5 = 40$$

The least common denominator is 40.

6. To convert milliliters to liters, write an appropriate unit ratio.

$$\text{Unit ratio} = \frac{\text{New units}}{\text{Original units}} = \frac{1 \text{ L}}{1000 \text{ mL}}$$

Multiply the original measure by the unit fraction.

$$23,450 \text{ mL} \cdot \frac{1 \text{ L}}{1000 \text{ mL}} = 23.45 \text{ L}$$

8. Identify the parts of the percent problem.
Amount: 25
Percent: unknown, p
Base: 355
Write the problem as a percent equation.

$$355 \cdot p = 25$$

Solve the equation.

$$\frac{355p}{355} = \frac{25}{355}$$
$$p \approx 0.07$$

Convert the answer to a percent: 7%

10. To solve $\dfrac{12.5}{42} = \dfrac{7}{w}$, cross multiply to find the cross products.

$42 \cdot 7 = 294$

$12.5 \cdot w = 12.5w$

Separate the cross products by an equal sign to form an equation.

$294 = 12.5w$

Divide both sides of the equation by the number on the side with the unknown.

$\dfrac{294}{12.5} = \dfrac{12.5w}{12.5}$

Simplify.

$w = 23.52$

Section 7.4   Area

Concept Check

2. Area is measured in __square__ units.

4. The formula for the area of a square is $\underline{A = s^2}$.

6. The formula for the area of a triangle is $\underline{A = \dfrac{1}{2}bh}$.

8. The formula for the area of a circle is $\underline{A = \pi r^2}$.

Guide Problems

10. Find the area of the square.

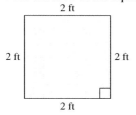

2 ft

2 ft   2 ft

2 ft

$A = s^2$

$A = \left(\underline{2\ \text{ft}}\right)^2$

$A = \underline{4\ \text{ft}^2}$

For problems 12 through 28, use the formulas for the area of a rectangle and the area of a square to find the area of each figure. The formula for the area of a rectangle is A = lw and the formula for the area of a square is A = s².

12. The figure is a rectangle with l = 120 yd and w = 85 yd.

$A = lw$

$A = \left(120\ \text{yd}\right)\left(85\ \text{yd}\right)$

$A = 10{,}200\ \text{yd}^2$

14. The figure is a square with $s = 22$ ft.

$A = s^2$

$A = (22 \text{ ft})^2$

$A = 484 \text{ ft}^2$

16. The figure is a rectangle with $l = 6$ m and $w = 2.8$ m.

$A = lw$

$A = (6 \text{ m})(2.8 \text{ m})$

$A = 16.8 \text{ m}^2$

18. The figure is a square with $s = 3$ in.

$A = s^2$

$A = (3 \text{ in.})^2$

$A = 9 \text{ in.}^2$

20. The figure is a rectangle with $l = 15$ cm and $w = 9$ cm.

$A = lw$

$A = (15 \text{ cm})(9 \text{ cm})$

$A = 135 \text{ cm}^2$

22. The figure is a square with $s = 12$ mi.

$A = s^2$

$A = (12 \text{ mi})^2$

$A = 144 \text{ mi}^2$

24. The figure is a rectangle with $l = 9.5$ yd and $w = 4$ yd.

$A = lw$

$A = (9.5 \text{ yd})(4 \text{ yd})$

$A = 38 \text{ yd}^2$

26. The figure is a square with $s = 15$ mm.

$A = s^2$

$A = (15 \text{ mm})^2$

$A = 225 \text{ mm}^2$

28. The figure is a square with $s = 3.5$ mi.

$A = s^2$

$A = (3.5 \text{ mi})^2$

$A = 12.25 \text{ mi}^2$

Guide Problems

30. Find the area of the triangle.

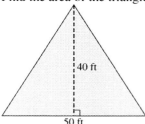

$$A = \frac{1}{2}bh$$

$$A = \frac{1}{2}(50 \text{ ft})(\underline{40 \text{ ft}})$$

$$A = \underline{1000 \text{ ft}^2}$$

32. Find the area of the circle. Use 3.14 for π.

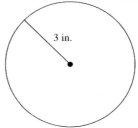

$$A = \pi r^2$$

$$A \approx (3.14)(\underline{3 \text{ in.}})^2$$

$$A = \underline{28.26 \text{ in.}^2}$$

For problems 34 through 48 use the formulas for the area of a triangle, the area of a parallelogram, the area of a trapezoid, and the area of a circle to find the area of each figure. Use 3.14 for π.

34. The figure is a triangle with $b = 27$ cm and $h = 17$ cm.

$$A = \frac{1}{2}bh$$

$$A = \frac{1}{2}(27 \text{ cm})(17 \text{ cm})$$

$$A = 229.5 \text{ cm}^2$$

36. The figure is a triangle with $b = 14$ yd and $h = 9$ yd.

$$A = \frac{1}{2}bh$$

$$A = \frac{1}{2}(14 \text{ yd})(9 \text{ yd})$$

$$A = 63 \text{ yd}^2$$

38. The figure is a parallelogram with $b = 13$ yd and $h = 5.5$ yd.

$$A = bh$$

$$A = (13 \text{ yd})(5.5 \text{ yd})$$

$$A = 71.5 \text{ yd}^2$$

40. The figure is a parallelogram with $b = 27$ in. and $h = 12$ in.

$$A = bh$$

$$A = (27 \text{ in.})(12 \text{ in.})$$

$$A = 324 \text{ in.}^2$$

42. The figure is a trapezoid with $a = 10$ mi, $b = 3$ mi, and $h = 4$ mi.

$$A = \frac{1}{2}(a+b)h$$

$$A = \frac{1}{2}(10 \text{ mi} + 3 \text{ mi})4 \text{ mi}$$

$$A = 26 \text{ mi}^2$$

44. The figure is a trapezoid with $a = 2$ m, $b = 5$ m, and $h = 3.5$ m.

$$A = \frac{1}{2}(a+b)h$$

$$A = \frac{1}{2}(2 \text{ m} + 5 \text{ m})3.5 \text{ m}$$

$$A = 12.25 \text{ m}^2$$

46. The figure is a circle with $r = 15$ mm.

$$A = \pi r^2$$

$$A \approx (3.14)(15 \text{ mm})^2$$

$$A = 706.5 \text{ mm}^2$$

48. The figure is a circle with $r = 5$ in.

$$A = \pi r^2$$

$$A \approx (3.14)(5 \text{ in.})^2$$

$$A = 78.5 \text{ in.}^2$$

For problems 50 through 56, apply your knowledge of the area formulas to solve each problem.

50. Use the formula for the area of a square with $s = 17$ cm.

$$A = s^2$$

$$A = (17 \text{ cm})^2$$

$$A = 289 \text{ cm}^2$$

52. Use the formula for the area of a rectangle with $A = 176$ in.^{2} and $l = 16$ in. and find the value of w.

$$A = lw$$

$$176 \text{ in.}^2 = (16 \text{ in.})w$$

$$\frac{176 \text{ in.}^2}{16 \text{ in.}} = \frac{(16 \text{ in.})w}{16 \text{ in.}}$$

$$w = 11 \text{ in.}$$

The air duct can be 11 in. wide.

54. Use the formulas for the area of a circle and the area of a square.

Burger King:

$$r = \frac{1}{2}d$$

$$r = \frac{1}{2}(3.5 \text{ in.})$$

$$r = 1.75 \text{ in.}$$

$$A = \pi r^2$$

$$A \approx (3.14)(1.75 \text{ in.})^2$$

$$A \approx 9.6 \text{ in.}^2$$

Wendy's:

$$A = s^2$$

$$A = (3 \text{ in.})^2$$

$$A = 9 \text{ in.}^2$$

The Burger King hamburger has a larger area. It is $9.6 \text{ in.}^2 - 9 \text{ in.}^2 = 0.6 \text{ in.}^2$ larger.

56. Use the formula for the area of a triangle with $b = 1032$ mi and $h = 895$ mi.

$$A = \frac{1}{2}bh$$

$$A = \frac{1}{2}(1032 \text{ mi})(895 \text{ mi})$$

$$A = 461,820 \text{ mi}^2$$

Cumulative Skills Review

2. $$\begin{array}{r} \overset{\overset{11 \text{ yd}}{\cancel{12}}\,\overset{4 \text{ ft}}{\cancel{1}}}{\cancel{12} \text{ yd} \quad \cancel{1} \text{ ft}} \\ -\,9 \text{ yd} \quad 2 \text{ ft} \\ \hline 2 \text{ yd} \quad 2 \text{ ft} \end{array}$$

4. Write an equivalent division problem in which the divisor is a whole number, then divide.

$$\begin{array}{r} 5.12 \\ 1662\overline{)8512.00} \\ \underline{-8310} \\ 2020 \\ \underline{-1662} \\ 3580 \\ \underline{-3324} \\ 256 \end{array}$$

Rounding to the nearest tenth, the result is 5.1.

6. The solid is a cylinder because the solid has two identical circular bases joined by line segments perpendicular to these bases.

8. Multiply the radius by 2.
   8 ft $\cdot 2 = 16$ ft, so the diameter is 16 feet.

10. The earnings from the tickets sold are $112 \cdot \$35 = \$3920$.
   The earnings from the minimum number of sodas each participant must purchase are

$$\begin{array}{r} \$4.75 \\ \times 112 \\ \hline 950 \\ 4750 \\ \underline{+47500} \\ \$532.00 \end{array}$$

   The total earnings are $\$3920 + \$532.00 = \$4452.00$.

Section 7.5   Square Roots and the Pythagorean Theorem

Concept Check

2. The _principal_ _square_ _root_ of a number n is a number whose square is n.

4. The number underneath the radical sign is called the _radicand_.

6. In a right triangle, the side opposite the right angle is called the _hypotenuse_.

8. If a right triangle has legs of lengths a and b units and a hypotenuse of length c units, then $\underline{a^2 + b^2} = c^2$. This result is known as the _Pythagorean_ Theorem.

Guide Problems

10. Find the principal square root of 144.
$$12^2 = 144$$
$$\sqrt{144} = \underline{12}$$

For problems 12 through 34, find each principal square root by identifying the number that must be squared to obtain the radicand.

12. $10^2 = 100$ so $\sqrt{100} = 10$.

14. $8^2 = 64$ so $\sqrt{64} = 8$.

16. $14^2 = 196$ so $\sqrt{196} = 14$.

18. $20^2 = 400$ so $\sqrt{400} = 20$.

20. $2^2 = 4$ so $\sqrt{4} = 2$.

22. $12^2 = 144$ so $\sqrt{144} = 12$.

24. $6^2 = 36$ so $\sqrt{36} = 6$.

26. $16^2 = 256$ so $\sqrt{256} = 16$.

28. $18^2 = 324$ so $\sqrt{324} = 18$.

30. $4^2 = 16$ so $\sqrt{16} = 4$.

32. $22^2 = 484$ so $\sqrt{484} = 22$.

34. $24^2 = 576$ so $\sqrt{576} = 24$.

Guide Problems

36. Approximate the principal square root of 879 using Appendix D or a calculator. Round to the nearest hundredth.
$$\sqrt{879} \approx \underline{29.65}$$

For problems 38 through 52, approximate each principal square root using Appendix D or a calculator. Round to the nearest hundredth.

38. $\sqrt{54} \approx 7.35$

40. $\sqrt{78} \approx 8.83$

42. $\sqrt{48} \approx 6.93$

44. $\sqrt{70} \approx 8.37$

46. $\sqrt{93} \approx 9.64$

48. $\sqrt{38} \approx 6.16$

50. $\sqrt{535} \approx 23.13$

52. $\sqrt{908} \approx 30.13$

Guide Problems

54. Find the unknown length in the right triangle. Round to the nearest hundredth of an inch.

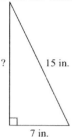

$$b = \sqrt{c^2 - a^2}$$

$$b = \sqrt{(15 \text{ in.})^2 - (7 \text{ in.})^2}$$

$$b = \sqrt{225 \text{ in.}^2 - 49 \text{ in.}^2}$$

$$b = \sqrt{176 \text{ in.}^2}$$

$$b \approx \underline{13.27 \text{ in.}}$$

For problems 56 through 72, find the unknown length in each triangle using the Pythagorean Theorem in an appropriate form. Round to the nearest hundredth, if necessary.

56. $c = \sqrt{a^2 + b^2}$

$c = \sqrt{(3 \text{ mi})^2 + (4 \text{ mi})^2}$

$c = \sqrt{9 \text{ mi}^2 + 16 \text{ mi}^2}$

$c = \sqrt{25 \text{ mi}^2}$

$c = 5 \text{ mi}$

58. $b = \sqrt{c^2 - a^2}$

$b = \sqrt{(62 \text{ mm})^2 - (45 \text{ mm})^2}$

$b = \sqrt{3844 \text{ mm}^2 - 2025 \text{ mm}^2}$

$b = \sqrt{1819 \text{ mm}^2}$

$b \approx 42.65 \text{ mm}$

60. $c = \sqrt{a^2 + b^2}$

$c = \sqrt{(12 \text{ ft})^2 + (6.5 \text{ ft})^2}$

$c = \sqrt{144 \text{ ft}^2 + 42.25 \text{ ft}^2}$

$c = \sqrt{186.25 \text{ ft}^2}$

$c \approx 13.65 \text{ ft}$

62. $b = \sqrt{c^2 - a^2}$

$b = \sqrt{(7 \text{ m})^2 - (3 \text{ m})^2}$

$b = \sqrt{49 \text{ m}^2 - 9 \text{ m}^2}$

$b = \sqrt{40 \text{ m}^2}$

$b \approx 6.32 \text{ m}$

64. $c = \sqrt{a^2 + b^2}$

$c = \sqrt{(1.5 \text{ cm})^2 + (2.5 \text{ cm})^2}$

$c = \sqrt{2.25 \text{ cm}^2 + 6.25 \text{ cm}^2}$

$c = \sqrt{8.5 \text{ cm}^2}$

$c \approx 2.92 \text{ cm}$

66. $b = \sqrt{c^2 - a^2}$

$b = \sqrt{(15 \text{ yd})^2 - (10.5 \text{ yd})^2}$

$b = \sqrt{225 \text{ yd}^2 - 110.25 \text{ yd}^2}$

$b = \sqrt{114.75 \text{ yd}^2}$

$b \approx 10.71 \text{ yd}$

68. $b = \sqrt{c^2 - a^2}$

$b = \sqrt{(21 \text{ in.})^2 - (17 \text{ in.})^2}$

$b = \sqrt{441 \text{ in.}^2 - 289 \text{ in.}^2}$

$b = \sqrt{152 \text{ in.}^2}$

$b \approx 12.33 \text{ in.}$

70. $b = \sqrt{c^2 - a^2}$

$b = \sqrt{(90 \text{ ft})^2 - (40 \text{ ft})^2}$

$b = \sqrt{8100 \text{ ft}^2 - 1600 \text{ ft}^2}$

$b = \sqrt{6500 \text{ ft}^2}$

$b \approx 80.62 \text{ ft}$

72. $b = \sqrt{c^2 - a^2}$

$b = \sqrt{(8 \text{ m})^2 - (7 \text{ m})^2}$

$b = \sqrt{64 \text{ m}^2 - 49 \text{ m}^2}$

$b = \sqrt{15 \text{ m}^2}$

$b \approx 3.87 \text{ m}$

74. Use the Pythagorean Theorem to find the length of the diagonal of the TV.

$$c = \sqrt{a^2 + b^2}$$

$$c = \sqrt{(21 \text{ in.})^2 + (24 \text{ in.})^2}$$

$$c = \sqrt{441 \text{ in.}^2 + 576 \text{ in.}^2}$$

$$c = \sqrt{1017 \text{ in.}^2}$$

$$c \approx 32 \text{ in.}$$

The TV is advertised as a 32-inch TV.

Cumulative Skills Review

2. 12 to 35, 12:35, or $\dfrac{12}{35}$

4. The diameter is 40 ft.

$$C = \pi d$$
$$\approx (3.14)(40 \text{ ft})$$
$$\approx 125.6 \text{ ft}$$

6. Reduce $\dfrac{60}{135}$ to lowest terms by dividing out the GCF, 15.

$$\dfrac{\overset{4}{\cancel{60}}}{\underset{9}{\cancel{135}}} = \dfrac{4}{9}$$

8. The figure consists of 5 equal triangles. 4 triangles are shaded. The fraction $\dfrac{4}{5}$ represents the shaded portion.

10. Write an appropriate unit ratio.

$$\text{Unit ratio} = \dfrac{\text{New units}}{\text{Original units}} \approx \dfrac{1 \text{ km}}{0.62 \text{ mi}}$$

Multiply the original measure by the unit fraction.

$$30 \text{ mi} \cdot \dfrac{1 \text{ km}}{0.62 \text{ mi}} \approx 48.3 \text{ km}$$

Section 7.6   Volume

Concept Check

2. Volume is measured in __cubic__ units.

4. If s represents the common length, width, and height of a cube, then the formula for the volume is __$V = s^3$__.

6. The formula for the volume of a cone is __$V = \dfrac{1}{3}\pi r^2 h$__.

8. The formula for the volume of a sphere is __$V = \dfrac{4}{3}\pi r^3$__.

Guide Problems

10. Find the volume of the cube.

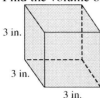

3 in.

3 in.

3 in.

$V = s^3$

$V = (\underline{3 \text{ in.}})^3$

$V = \underline{27 \text{ in.}}^3$

For problems 12 through 24, find the volume of each rectangular solid. Use the formula V = lwh for a rectangular solid or V = s³ for a cube.

12. The figure is a rectangular solid with *l* = 6 mi, *w* = 4 mi, and *h* = 12 mi.
    $V = lwh$

    $V = (6 \text{ mi})(4 \text{ mi})(12 \text{ mi})$

    $V = 288 \text{ mi}^3$

14. The figure is a rectangular solid with *l* = 6 mi, *w* = 7 mi, and *h* = 9 mi.
    $V = lwh$

    $V = (6 \text{ mi})(7 \text{ mi})(9 \text{ mi})$

    $V = 378 \text{ mi}^3$

16. The figure is a rectangular solid with *l* = 66 cm, *w* = 10 cm, and *h* = 12 cm.
    $V = lwh$

    $V = (66 \text{ cm})(10 \text{ cm})(12 \text{ cm})$

    $V = 7920 \text{ cm}^3$

18. The figure is a cube with *s* = 25 mm.
    $V = s^3$

    $V = (25 \text{ mm})^3$

    $V = 15,625 \text{ mm}^3$

20. The figure is a rectangular solid with *l* = 3.0 yd, *w* = 2.2 yd, and *h* = 5.4 yd.
    $V = lwh$

    $V = (3.0 \text{ yd})(2.2 \text{ yd})(5.4 \text{ yd})$

    $V = 35.64 \text{ yd}^3$

22. The figure is a rectangular solid with *l* = 7.5 ft, *w* = 10 ft, and *h* = 7 ft.
    $V = lwh$

    $V = (7.5 \text{ ft})(10 \text{ ft})(7 \text{ ft})$

    $V = 525 \text{ ft}^3$

24. The figure is a rectangular solid with $l = 9$ ft, $w = 13.2$ ft, and $h = 22$ ft.

$V = lwh$

$V = (9 \text{ ft})(13.2 \text{ ft})(22 \text{ ft})$

$V = 2613.6 \text{ ft}^3$

Guide Problems

26. Find the volume of the pyramid. Round to the nearest hundredth.

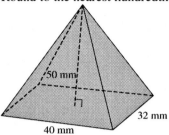

$V = \dfrac{1}{3}Bh$

$V = \dfrac{1}{3}(40 \text{ mm})(32 \text{ mm})(50 \text{ mm})$

$= \dfrac{1}{3}(1280 \text{ mm}^2)(50 \text{ mm})$

$\approx \underline{21,333.33 \text{ mm}^3}$

28. Find the volume of the sphere. Use 3.14 for π. Round to the nearest hundredth.

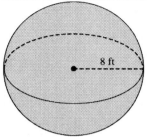

8 ft

$V = \dfrac{4}{3}\pi r^3$

$V \approx \dfrac{4}{3}(3.14)(\underline{8 \text{ ft}})^3$

$\approx \underline{2143.57 \text{ ft}^3}$

For problems 30 through 60, find the volume of each solid using the appropriate formula. Use 3.14 for π. Round to the nearest hundredth, if necessary.

30. The figure is a cylinder with $r = 5$ mm and $h = 20$ mm.

$V = \pi r^2 h$

$V \approx (3.14)(5 \text{ mm})^2 (20 \text{ mm})$

$= (3.14)(25 \text{ mm}^2)(20 \text{ mm})$

$= 1570 \text{ mm}^3$

32. The figure is a cone with $r = 4$ mi and $h = 10$ mi.

$V = \dfrac{1}{3}\pi r^2 h$

$V \approx \dfrac{1}{3}(3.14)(4 \text{ mi})^2 (10 \text{ mi})$

$= \dfrac{1}{3}(3.14)(16 \text{ mi}^2)(10 \text{ mi})$

$\approx 167.47 \text{ mi}^3$

34. The figure is a pyramid with $B = (5 \text{ mi})(7 \text{ mi}) = 35 \text{ mi}^2$ and $h = 13$ mi.

$$V = \frac{1}{3}Bh$$

$$V = \frac{1}{3}\left(35 \text{ mi}^2\right)(13 \text{ mi})$$

$$\approx 151.67 \text{ mi}^3$$

36. The figure is a sphere with $r = 3$ mi.

$$V = \frac{4}{3}\pi r^3$$

$$V \approx \frac{4}{3}(3.14)(3 \text{ mi})^3$$

$$= \frac{4}{3}(3.14)\left(27 \text{ mi}^3\right)$$

$$= 113.04 \text{ mi}^3$$

38. The figure is a cylinder with $r = 6$ ft and $h = 15$ ft.

$$V = \pi r^2 h$$

$$V \approx (3.14)(6 \text{ ft})^2 (15 \text{ ft})$$

$$= (3.14)\left(36 \text{ ft}^2\right)(15 \text{ ft})$$

$$= 1695.6 \text{ ft}^3$$

40. The figure is a cone with $r = 16$ mm and $h = 29$ mm.

$$V = \frac{1}{3}\pi r^2 h$$

$$V \approx \frac{1}{3}(3.14)(16 \text{ mm})^2 (29 \text{ mm})$$

$$= \frac{1}{3}(3.14)\left(256 \text{ mm}^2\right)(29 \text{ mm})$$

$$\approx 7770.45 \text{ mm}^3$$

42. The figure is a pyramid with $B = (10 \text{ ft})(13.5 \text{ ft}) = 135 \text{ ft}^2$ and $h = 18$ ft.

$$V = \frac{1}{3}Bh$$

$$V = \frac{1}{3}\left(135 \text{ ft}^2\right)(18 \text{ ft})$$

$$= 810 \text{ ft}^3$$

44. The figure is a sphere with $r = 60$ mm.

$$V = \frac{4}{3}\pi r^3$$

$$V \approx \frac{4}{3}(3.14)(60 \text{ mm})^3$$

$$= \frac{4}{3}(3.14)\left(216{,}000 \text{ mm}^3\right)$$

$$= 904{,}320 \text{ mm}^3$$

46. The figure is a cylinder with $r = 1$ m and $h = 7$ m.

$$V = \pi r^2 h$$

$$V \approx (3.14)(1 \text{ m})^2 (7 \text{ m})$$

$$= (3.14)\left(1 \text{ m}^2\right)(7 \text{ m})$$

$$= 21.98 \text{ m}^3$$

48. The figure is a cone with $r = 4$ ft and $h = 18$ ft.

$$V = \frac{1}{3}\pi r^2 h$$

$$V \approx \frac{1}{3}(3.14)(4 \text{ ft})^2 (18 \text{ ft})$$

$$= \frac{1}{3}(3.14)(16 \text{ ft}^2)(18 \text{ ft})$$

$$= 301.44 \text{ ft}^3$$

50. The figure is a pyramid with $B = (9 \text{ m})(6 \text{ m}) = 54 \text{ m}^2$ and $h = 14$ m.

$$V = \frac{1}{3}Bh$$

$$V = \frac{1}{3}(54 \text{ m}^2)(14 \text{ m})$$

$$= 252 \text{ m}^3$$

52. The figure is a sphere with $r = 13$ ft.

$$V = \frac{4}{3}\pi r^3$$

$$V \approx \frac{4}{3}(3.14)(13 \text{ ft})^3$$

$$= \frac{4}{3}(3.14)(2197 \text{ ft}^3)$$

$$\approx 9198.11 \text{ ft}^3$$

54. The figure is a cylinder with $r = 4$ cm and $h = 5$ cm.

$$V = \pi r^2 h$$

$$V \approx (3.14)(4 \text{ cm})^2 (5 \text{ cm})$$

$$= (3.14)(16 \text{ cm}^2)(5 \text{ cm})$$

$$= 251.2 \text{ cm}^3$$

56. The figure is a cone with $r = 3.5$ m and $h = 9$ m.

$$V = \frac{1}{3}\pi r^2 h$$

$$V \approx \frac{1}{3}(3.14)(3.5 \text{ m})^2 (9 \text{ m})$$

$$= \frac{1}{3}(3.14)(12.25 \text{ m}^2)(9 \text{ m})$$

$$\approx 115.40 \text{ m}^3$$

58. The figure is a pyramid with $B = (6 \text{ in.})(8 \text{ in.}) = 48 \text{ in.}^2$ and $h = 19$ in.

$$V = \frac{1}{3}Bh$$

$$V = \frac{1}{3}(48 \text{ in.}^2)(19 \text{ in.})$$

$$= 304 \text{ in.}^3$$

60. The figure is a sphere with $r = 9.5$ in.

$$V = \frac{4}{3}\pi r^3$$

$$V \approx \frac{4}{3}(3.14)(9.5 \text{ in.})^3$$

$$= \frac{4}{3}(3.14)(857.375 \text{ in.}^3)$$

$$\approx 3589.54 \text{ in.}^3$$

62. The silo is a cylinder with $r = 12.5$ ft and $h = 40$ ft.

$$V = \pi r^2 h$$

$$V \approx (3.14)(12.5 \text{ ft})^2(40 \text{ ft})$$

$$= (3.14)(156.25 \text{ ft}^2)(40 \text{ ft})$$

$$= 19{,}625 \text{ ft}^3$$

Cumulative Skills Review

2. Identify the parts of the percent problem.
   Amount: 22.5
   Part: 90
   Base: unknown, b
   Substitute the values of the amount, base, and part into the proportion.

   $$\frac{22.5}{b} = \frac{90}{100}$$

   Cross multiply and set the products equal.
   $$b \cdot 90 = 22.5 \cdot 100$$

   $$90b = 2250$$
   Divide both sides of the equation by the number on the side with the unknown.

   $$\frac{90b}{90} = \frac{2250}{90}$$

   $$b = 25$$

4. The figure is a rectangle with $l = 12$ mi and $w = 5$ mi.
   $$A = lw$$

   $$A = (12 \text{ mi})(5 \text{ mi})$$

   $$A = 60 \text{ mi}^2$$

6. Change each mixed number to an improper fraction.

   $$5\frac{2}{7} = \frac{37}{7}, \quad 3\frac{4}{5} = \frac{19}{5}$$

   Multiply the fractions.

   $$\frac{37}{7} \times \frac{19}{5} = \frac{703}{35} = 20\frac{3}{35}$$

8. Convert the mixed number to a decimal.

   $$2\frac{4}{5} = 2.8$$

   Convert the decimal to a percent by multiplying by 100%.
   $$2.8 \cdot 100\% = 280\%$$

10. The figure is a hexagon because it has 6 sides.

Numerical Facts of Life

2. Write a proportion to find the number of BTUs per hour, x, are required.
$$\frac{5000 \text{ BTUs per hour}}{100 \text{ ft}^2} = \frac{x \text{ BTUs per hour}}{20{,}000 \text{ ft}^2}$$
    Cross multiply and set the products equal.
    $$(x \text{ BTUs per hour}) \cdot (100 \text{ ft}^2) = (5000 \text{ BTUs per hour}) \cdot (20{,}000 \text{ ft}^2)$$
    Divide both sides of the equation by the number on the side with the unknown.
    $$\frac{(x \text{ BTUs per hour}) \cdot (100 \text{ ft}^2)}{(100 \text{ ft}^2)} = \frac{(5000 \text{ BTUs per hour}) \cdot (20{,}000 \text{ ft}^2)}{(100 \text{ ft}^2)}$$
    $$x = 1{,}000{,}000 \text{ BTUs per hour}$$

4. The tank is a cylinder with $r = 10$ ft and $h = 6$ ft.
    $$V = \pi r^2 h$$
    $$V \approx (3.14)(10 \text{ ft})^2 (6 \text{ ft})$$
    $$= (3.14)(100 \text{ ft}^2)(6 \text{ ft})$$
    $$= 1884 \text{ ft}^3$$

Chapter 7 Review Exercises

1. The figure shown consists of point C, point B, and point S.

2. The figure shown is a line because it extends forever in either direction. It is named $\overleftrightarrow{BD}$ or $\overleftrightarrow{DB}$.

3. The figure shown is a line segment because it has two endpoints. It is named $\overline{GK}$ or $\overline{KG}$.

4. The figure shown is a ray because it begins at one point and extends forever in one direction. It is named $\overrightarrow{CN}$.

5. $\angle K$, $\angle DKX$, $\angle XKD$; this angle is right because its measure is $90°$.

6. $\angle W$; this angle is straight because its measure is $180°$.

7. $\angle L$, $\angle SLE$, $\angle ELS$; this angle is obtuse because its measure is greater than $90°$ and less than $180°$.

8. $\angle H$, $\angle OHM$, $\angle MHO$; this angle is acute because its measure is greater than $0°$ and less than $90°$.

9. Complementary angles are two angles, the sum of whose degree measure is $90°$. To find the complement of an angle, subtract the measure of the angle from $90°$.
    $$90° - 25° = 65°$$

10. Supplementary angles are two angles, the sum of whose degree measures is $180°$. To find the supplement of an angle, subtract the measure of the angle from $180°$.
    $$180° - 130° = 50°$$

11. Supplementary angles are two angles, the sum of whose degree measures is $180°$. To find the supplement of an angle, subtract the measure of the angle from $180°$.
    $$180° - 18° = 162°$$

12. Complementary angles are two angles, the sum of whose degree measure is $90°$. To find the complement of an angle, subtract the measure of the angle from $90°$.

    $90° - 47° = 43°$

13. Supplementary angles are two angles, the sum of whose degree measures is $180°$. To find the supplement of an angle, subtract the measure of the angle from $180°$.

    $180° - 120° = 60°$ so $\angle LMO = 60°$.

14. Complementary angles are two angles, the sum of whose degree measure is $90°$. To find the complement of an angle, subtract the measure of the angle from $90°$.

    $90° - 28° = 62°$ so $\angle PDC = 62°$.

15. Complementary angles are two angles, the sum of whose degree measure is $90°$. To find the complement of an angle, subtract the measure of the angle from $90°$.

    $90° - 17° = 73°$ so $\angle OKH = 73°$.

16. Supplementary angles are two angles, the sum of whose degree measures is $180°$. To find the supplement of an angle, subtract the measure of the angle from $180°$.

    $180° - 25° = 155°$ so $\angle AXZ = 155°$.

17. The first triangle shown is an isosceles triangle because two sides have equal length. The triangle is also an acute triangle because all angles are acute.

    The second triangle shown is a scalene triangle because all sides have different lengths. The triangle is also an obtuse triangle because the triangle has an obtuse angle.

    The third triangle shown is a scalene triangle because all sides have different lengths. The triangle is also an obtuse triangle because the triangle has an obtuse angle.

    The fourth triangle shown is an equilateral or isosceles triangle because all sides have equal length. The triangle is also an acute triangle because all angles are acute.

18. The first triangle shown is a scalene triangle because all sides have different lengths. The triangle is also an obtuse triangle because the triangle has an obtuse angle.

    The second triangle shown is an isosceles triangle because two sides have equal length. The triangle is also an acute triangle because all angles are acute.

    The third triangle shown is an equilateral or isosceles triangle because all sides have equal length. The triangle is also an acute triangle because all angles are acute.

    The fourth triangle shown is an isosceles triangle because two sides have equal length. The triangle is also an acute triangle because all angles are acute.

19. The first triangle shown is a scalene triangle because all sides have different lengths. The triangle is also a right triangle because the triangle has a right angle.

    The second triangle shown is a scalene triangle because all sides have different lengths. The triangle is also an obtuse triangle because the triangle has an obtuse angle.

    The third triangle shown is an equilateral or isosceles triangle because all sides have equal length. The triangle is also an acute triangle because all angles are acute.

    The fourth triangle shown is an equilateral or isosceles triangle because all sides have equal length. The triangle is also an acute triangle because all angles are acute.

20. The first triangle shown is an isosceles triangle because two sides have equal length. The triangle is also an acute triangle because all angles are acute.

 The second triangle shown is a scalene triangle because all sides have different lengths. The triangle is also a right triangle because the triangle has a right angle.

 The third triangle shown is an isosceles triangle because two sides have equal length. The triangle is also an obtuse triangle because the triangle has an obtuse angle.

 The fourth triangle shown is a scalene triangle because all sides have different lengths. The triangle is also a right triangle because the triangle has a right angle.

For problems 21 through 24, find the measure of the unknown angle of each triangle by first finding the sum of the two given angles and subtracting the sum from 180°.

21. $20° + 128° = 148°$, so $180° - 148° = 32°$.   22. $62° + 60° = 122°$, so $180° - 122° = 58°$.

23. $118° + 15° = 133°$, so $180° - 133° = 47°$.   24. $28° + 90° = 118°$, so $180° - 118° = 62°$.

25. The first figure is a square, rectangle, or rhombus because all sides have equal length and there are four right angles.
 The second figure is a trapezoid because there is one pair of parallel sides.
 The third figure is a rectangle because there are four right angles.
 The fourth figure is a rhombus because all sides have equal length.

26. The first figure is a trapezoid because there is one pair of parallel sides.
 The second figure is a rectangle because there are four right angles.
 The third figure is a rhombus because all sides have equal length.
 The fourth figure is a square, rectangle, or rhombus because all sides have equal length and there are four right angles.

27. The first figure is a hexagon because it has 6 sides.
 The second figure is an octagon because it has 8 sides.
 The third figure is a quadrilateral because it has 4 sides.
 The fourth figure is a pentagon because it has 5 sides.

28. The first figure is an octagon because it has 8 sides.
 The second figure is a hexagon because it has 6 sides.
 The third figure is a quadrilateral because it has 4 sides.
 The fourth figure is a pentagon because it has 5 sides.

For problems 29 through 34, find the radius or diameter using the given information. If the diameter is given divide by 2 to find the radius. If the radius is given, multiply by 2 to find the diameter.

29. $\dfrac{56 \text{ m}}{2} = 28 \text{ m}$ 30. $\dfrac{15 \text{ in.}}{2} = 7.5 \text{ in.}$ 31. $25 \text{ ft} \cdot 2 = 50 \text{ ft}$

32. $49 \text{ yd} \cdot 2 = 98 \text{ yd}$ 33. $\dfrac{9 \text{ mi}}{2} = 4.5 \text{ mi}$ 34. $30 \text{ cm} \cdot 2 = 60 \text{ cm}$

35. The first solid is a cube because there are six square faces.
 The second solid is a rectangular solid because there are six rectangular faces.
 The third solid is a pyramid because there are four triangular-shaped faces with a common vertex.

36. The first solid is a cone because the solid has a circular base and a common vertex.
    The second solid is a sphere because the solid consists of all points that lie the same distance from some fixed point.
    The third solid is a cylinder because the solid has two identical circular bases joined by line segments perpendicular to these bases.

37. $P = 16$ cm $+ 12$ cm $+ 9.5$ cm $= 37.5$ cm

38. $P = 22$ in $+ 7.5$ in. $+ 23$ in. $+ 8$ in. $= 60.5$ in.

39. $P = 3$ m $+ 4.5$ m $+ 3$ m $+ 4.5$ m $= 15$ m

40. $P = 3$ mi $+ 3.5$ mi $+ 1.5$ mi $+ 2$ mi $+ 2$ mi $= 12$ mi

For problems 24 through 32, find the circumference of each circle. Use 3.14 for π. Use the formula $C = \pi d$ if the diameter is given or the formula $C = 2\pi r$ if the radius is given.

41. The radius is 50 ft.
    $C = 2\pi r$
    $\approx (2)(3.14)(50 \text{ ft})$
    $= 314$ ft

42. The radius is 15 m.
    $C = 2\pi r$
    $\approx (2)(3.14)(15 \text{ m})$
    $= 94.2$ m

43. The diameter is 18 mm.
    $C = \pi d$
    $\approx (3.14)(18 \text{ mm})$
    $= 56.52$ mm

44. The radius is 8 ft.
    $C = 2\pi r$
    $\approx (2)(3.14)(8 \text{ ft})$
    $= 50.24$ ft

45. The radius is 1080 mi.
    $C = 2\pi r$
    $\approx (2)(3.14)(1080 \text{ mi})$
    $= 6782.4$ mi

46. The diameter is 26 in.
    $C = \pi d$
    $\approx (3.14)(26 \text{ in.})$
    $= 81.64$ in.
    The circumference is 81.64 inches, and after 100 revolutions the bicycle has traveled
    $81.64 \text{ in.} \cdot 100 \text{ revolutions} = 8164 \text{ in.} = 8164 \text{ in.} \cdot \dfrac{1 \text{ ft}}{12 \text{ in.}} \approx 680 \text{ ft.}$

47. The figure is a square with $s = 2$ ft.
    $A = s^2$
    $A = (2 \text{ ft})^2$
    $A = 4 \text{ ft}^2$

48. The figure is a triangle with $b = 30$ mm and $h = 23$ mm.
    $A = \dfrac{1}{2} bh$
    $A = \dfrac{1}{2}(30 \text{ mm})(23 \text{ mm})$
    $A = 345 \text{ mm}^2$

49. The figure is a parallelogram with $b = 13$ yd and $h = 5.5$ yd.
    $A = bh$
    $A = (13 \text{ yd})(5.5 \text{ yd})$
    $A = 71.5 \text{ yd}^2$

50. The figure is a rectangle with $l = 41$ mi and $w = 18$ mi.

$$A = lw$$
$$A = (41 \text{ mi})(18 \text{ mi})$$
$$A = 738 \text{ mi}^2$$

51. The figure is a circle with $d = 20$ m, so $r = 10$ m.

$$A = \pi r^2$$
$$A \approx (3.14)(10 \text{ m})^2$$
$$A = 314 \text{ m}^2$$

52. The figure is a circle with $r = 44$ cm.

$$A = \pi r^2$$
$$A \approx (3.14)(44 \text{ cm})^2$$
$$A = 6079.04 \text{ cm}^2$$

53. The top is a rectangle with $l = 58$ cm and $w = 32$ cm.

$$A = lw$$
$$A = (58 \text{ cm})(32 \text{ cm})$$
$$A = 1856 \text{ cm}^2$$

54. The runway is a rectangle with $l = 8$ yd and $w = 3.5$ yd.

$$A = lw$$
$$A = (8 \text{ yd})(3.5 \text{ yd})$$
$$A = 28 \text{ yd}^2$$

55. The garden is a circle with $d = 6$ ft, so $r = 3$ ft.

$$A = \pi r^2$$
$$A \approx (3.14)(3 \text{ ft})^2$$
$$A = 28.26 \text{ ft}^2$$

56. The floor space is a circle with $r = 20$ m.

$$A = \pi r^2$$
$$A \approx (3.14)(20 \text{ m})^2$$
$$A = 1256 \text{ m}^2$$

57. $6^2 = 36$ so $\sqrt{36} = 6$.

58. $8^2 = 64$ so $\sqrt{64} = 8$.

59. $\sqrt{17} \approx 4.12$

60. $\sqrt{58} = 7.62$

For problems 61 through 64, find the unknown length in each triangle using the Pythagorean Theorem in an appropriate form. Round to the nearest hundredth, if necessary.

61. $c = \sqrt{a^2 + b^2}$

$$c = \sqrt{(3 \text{ m})^2 + (4 \text{ m})^2}$$
$$c = \sqrt{9 \text{ m}^2 + 16 \text{ m}^2}$$
$$c = \sqrt{25 \text{ m}^2}$$
$$c = 5 \text{ m}$$

62. $c = \sqrt{a^2 + b^2}$

$$c = \sqrt{(12 \text{ ft})^2 + (6.5 \text{ ft})^2}$$
$$c = \sqrt{144 \text{ ft}^2 + 42.25 \text{ ft}^2}$$
$$c = \sqrt{186.25 \text{ ft}^2}$$
$$c = 13.65 \text{ ft}$$

63. $b = \sqrt{c^2 - a^2}$

$$b = \sqrt{(20 \text{ in.})^2 - (12 \text{ in.})^2}$$
$$b = \sqrt{400 \text{ in.}^2 - 144 \text{ in.}^2}$$
$$b = \sqrt{256 \text{ in.}^2}$$
$$b = 16 \text{ in.}$$

64. $b = \sqrt{c^2 - a^2}$

$$b = \sqrt{(4 \text{ cm})^2 - (2.5 \text{ cm})^2}$$
$$b = \sqrt{16 \text{ cm}^2 - 6.25 \text{ cm}^2}$$
$$b = \sqrt{9.75 \text{ cm}^2}$$
$$b \approx 3.12 \text{ cm}$$

65. Find the hypotenuse of the triangle formed by leaning the ladder against the wall.

$$c = \sqrt{a^2 + b^2}$$

$$c = \sqrt{(3 \text{ m})^2 + (2 \text{ m})^2}$$

$$c = \sqrt{9 \text{ m}^2 + 4 \text{ m}^2}$$

$$c = \sqrt{13 \text{ m}^2}$$

$$c \approx 3.6 \text{ m}$$

Yes, Pete can use his ladder because the hypotenuse of the right triangle, which corresponds to the length of the ladder, is about 3.6 m.

66. Find the hypotenuse of the triangle formed by the diagonal.

$$c = \sqrt{a^2 + b^2}$$

$$c = \sqrt{(12 \text{ ft})^2 + (27.5 \text{ ft})^2}$$

$$c = \sqrt{144 \text{ ft}^2 + 756.25 \text{ ft}^2}$$

$$c = \sqrt{900.25 \text{ ft}^2}$$

$$c \approx 30 \text{ ft}$$

The diagonal is approximately 30 ft.

67. The figure is a rectangular solid with $l = 13$ in., $w = 6$ in., and $h = 18$ in.

$$V = lwh$$

$$V = (13 \text{ in.})(6 \text{ in.})(18 \text{ in.})$$

$$V = 1404 \text{ in.}^3$$

68. The figure is a rectangular solid with $l = 50$ cm, $w = 22$ cm, and $h = 27$ cm.

$$V = lwh$$

$$V = (50 \text{ cm})(22 \text{ cm})(27 \text{ cm})$$

$$V = 29,700 \text{ cm}^3$$

69. The figure is a cylinder with $r = 23$ cm and $h = 50$ cm.

$$V = \pi r^2 h$$

$$V \approx (3.14)(23 \text{ cm})^2 (50 \text{ cm})$$

$$= (3.14)(529 \text{ cm}^2)(50 \text{ cm})$$

$$= 83,053 \text{ cm}^3$$

70. The figure is a cylinder with $r = 3$ ft and $h = 10$ ft.

$$V = \pi r^2 h$$

$$V \approx (3.14)(3 \text{ ft})^2 (10 \text{ ft})$$

$$= (3.14)(9 \text{ ft}^2)(10 \text{ ft})$$

$$= 282.6 \text{ ft}^3$$

71. The figure is a cone with $r = 7$ m and $h = 22$ m.

$$V = \frac{1}{3}\pi r^2 h$$

$$V \approx \frac{1}{3}(3.14)(7 \text{ m})^2 (22 \text{ m})$$

$$= \frac{1}{3}(3.14)(49 \text{ m}^2)(22 \text{ m})$$

$$\approx 1128.31 \text{ m}^3$$

72. The figure is a cone with $r = 4$ mi and $h = 10$ mi.

$$V = \frac{1}{3}\pi r^2 h$$

$$V \approx \frac{1}{3}(3.14)(4 \text{ mi})^2 (10 \text{ mi})$$

$$= \frac{1}{3}(3.14)(16 \text{ mi}^2)(10 \text{ mi})$$

$$\approx 167.47 \text{ mi}^3$$

73. The figure is a sphere with $r = 8$ ft.

$$V = \frac{4}{3}\pi r^3$$

$$V \approx \frac{4}{3}(3.14)(8 \text{ ft})^3$$

$$= \frac{4}{3}(3.14)(512 \text{ ft}^3)$$

$$\approx 2143.57 \text{ ft}^3$$

74. The figure is a sphere with $r = 7$ in.

$$V = \frac{4}{3}\pi r^3$$

$$V \approx \frac{4}{3}(3.14)(7 \text{ in.})^3$$

$$= \frac{4}{3}(3.14)(343 \text{ in.}^3)$$

$$\approx 1436.03 \text{ in.}^3$$

75. The box is a rectangular solid with $l = 5.5$ in., $w = 4$ in., and $h = 5$ in.

$$V = lwh$$

$$V = (5.5 \text{ in.})(4 \text{ in.})(5 \text{ in.})$$

$$V = 110 \text{ in.}^3$$

76. The ball is a sphere with $r = 3$ in.

$$V = \frac{4}{3}\pi r^3$$

$$V \approx \frac{4}{3}(3.14)(3 \text{ in.})^3$$

$$= \frac{4}{3}(3.14)(27 \text{ in.}^3)$$

$$\approx 113.04 \text{ in.}^3$$

77. The pyramid has dimensions $B = (95 \text{ m})(80 \text{ m}) = 7600 \text{ m}^2$ and $h = 146$ m.

$$V = \frac{1}{3}Bh$$

$$V = \frac{1}{3}(7600 \text{ m}^2)(146 \text{ m})$$

$$\approx 369{,}867 \text{ m}^3$$

Chapter 7 Assessment Test

1. The figure shown is a line because it extends forever in either direction. It is named $\overleftrightarrow{LR}$ or $\overleftrightarrow{RL}$.

2. The figure shown is a line segment because it has two endpoints. It is named $\overline{PD}$ or $\overline{DP}$.

3. $\angle Y$, $\angle PYH$, $\angle HYP$; this angle is right because its measure is $90°$.

4. $\angle X$; this angle is straight because its measure is $180°$.

5. $\angle R$, $\angle ARJ$, $\angle JRA$; this angle is acute because its measure is greater than $0°$ and less than $90°$.

6. $\angle X$, $\angle VXF$, $\angle FXV$; this angle is obtuse because its measure is greater than $90°$ and less than $180°$.

7. Complementary angles are two angles, the sum of whose degree measure is $90°$. To find the complement of an angle, subtract the measure of the angle from $90°$.
   $90° - 38° = 52°$

8. Supplementary angles are two angles, the sum of whose degree measures is $180°$. To find the supplement of an angle, subtract the measure of the angle from $180°$.
   $180° - 52° = 128°$

9. Supplementary angles are two angles, the sum of whose degree measures is $180°$. To find the supplement of an angle, subtract the measure of the angle from $180°$.
   $180° - 130° = 50°$ so $\angle RPO = 50°$.

10. Complementary angles are two angles, the sum of whose degree measure is $90°$. To find the complement of an angle, subtract the measure of the angle from $90°$.
    $90° - 30° = 60°$ so $\angle TMK = 60°$.

11. The triangle shown is an isosceles triangle because two sides have equal length.

12. The triangle shown is an acute triangle because all angles are acute.

13. $72° + 90° = 162°$, so $180° - 162° = 18°$.

14. $79° + 20° = 99°$, so $180° - 99° = 81°$.

15. The first figure is a trapezoid because there is one pair of parallel sides.
    The second figure is a square, rectangle, or rhombus because all sides have equal length and there are four right angles.
    The third figure is a rhombus because all sides have equal length.
    The fourth figure is a rectangle because there are four right angles.

16. The first figure is a hexagon because it has 6 sides.
    The second figure is a pentagon because it has 5 sides.
    The third figure is a quadrilateral because it has 4 sides.
    The fourth figure is an octagon because it has 8 sides.

17. $\dfrac{20 \text{ in.}}{2} = 10 \text{ in.}$ 18. $8 \text{ m} \cdot 2 = 16 \text{ m}$

19. The first solid is a cube because there are six square faces.
    The second solid is a rectangular solid because there are six rectangular faces.
    The third solid is a pyramid because there are four triangular-shaped faces with a common vertex.

20. The first solid is a cone because the solid has a circular base and a common vertex.
    The second solid is a sphere because the solid consists of all points that lie the same distance from some fixed point.
    The third solid is a cylinder because the solid has two identical circular bases joined by line segments perpendicular to these bases.

21. $P = 10 \text{ yd} + 14 \text{ yd} + 10 \text{ yd} = 34 \text{ yd}$

$A = \dfrac{1}{2}bh$

$A = \dfrac{1}{2}(14 \text{ yd})(9 \text{ yd})$

$A = 63 \text{ yd}^2$

22. $P = (2 \cdot 3.5 \text{ in.}) + (2 \cdot 6.5 \text{ in.}) = 7 \text{ in.} + 13 \text{ in.} = 20 \text{ in.}$

$A = lw$

$A = (6.5 \text{ in.})(3.5 \text{ in.})$

$A = 22.75 \text{ in.}^2$

23. $P = 15 \text{ ft} + 11.7 \text{ ft} + 15 \text{ ft} + 11.7 \text{ ft} = 53.4 \text{ ft}$

$A = bh$

$A = (15 \text{ ft})(11.5 \text{ ft})$

$A = 172.5 \text{ ft}^2$

24. $P = 9 \text{ cm} + 7.6 \text{ cm} + 13 \text{ cm} + 7.1 \text{ cm} = 36.7 \text{ cm}$

$A = \dfrac{1}{2}(a+b)h$

$A = \dfrac{1}{2}(13 \text{ cm} + 9 \text{ cm})7 \text{ cm}$

$A = 77 \text{ cm}^2$

25. If $d = 50$ ft, then $r = 25$ ft.

$C = \pi d$

$\approx (3.14)(50 \text{ ft})$

$= 157 \text{ ft}$

$A = \pi r^2$

$A \approx (3.14)(25 \text{ ft})^2$

$A = 1962.5 \text{ ft}^2$

26. $C = 2\pi r$

$C \approx (2)(3.14)(9 \text{ m})$

$= 56.52 \text{ m}$

$A = \pi r^2$

$A \approx (3.14)(9 \text{ m})^2$

$A = 254.34 \text{ m}^2$

27. If $d = 70$ mi, then $r = 35$ mi.

$A = \pi r^2$

$A \approx (3.14)(35 \text{ mi})^2$

$A = 3846.5 \text{ mi}^2$

28. The tile is a rectangle with $l = 115$ cm and $w = 23$ cm.

$A = lw$

$A = (115 \text{ cm})(23 \text{ cm})$

$A = 2645 \text{ cm}^2$

29. $12^2 = 144$ so $\sqrt{144} = 12$.

30. $\sqrt{55} \approx 7.42$

31. $c = \sqrt{a^2 + b^2}$

$c = \sqrt{(5 \text{ yd})^2 + (9 \text{ yd})^2}$

$c = \sqrt{25 \text{ yd}^2 + 81 \text{ yd}^2}$

$c = \sqrt{106 \text{ yd}^2}$

$c \approx 10.30 \text{ yd}$

32. $b = \sqrt{c^2 - a^2}$

$b = \sqrt{(62 \text{ m})^2 - (45 \text{ m})^2}$

$b = \sqrt{3844 \text{ m}^2 - 2025 \text{ m}^2}$

$b = \sqrt{1819 \text{ m}^2}$

$b \approx 42.65 \text{ m}$

33. The figure is a rectangular solid with $l = 6$ mi, $w = 4$ mi, and $h = 12$ mi.

$V = lwh$

$V = (6 \text{ mi})(4 \text{ mi})(12 \text{ mi})$

$V = 288 \text{ mi}^3$

34. The figure is a cylinder with $r = 20$ cm and $h = 60$ cm.

$V = \pi r^2 h$

$V \approx (3.14)(20 \text{ cm})^2 (60 \text{ cm})$

$\quad = (3.14)(400 \text{ cm}^2)(60 \text{ cm})$

$\quad = 75{,}360 \text{ cm}^3$

35. The figure is a pyramid with $B = (9 \text{ m})(8 \text{ m}) = 72 \text{ m}^2$ and $h = 11$ m.

$V = \dfrac{1}{3} Bh$

$V = \dfrac{1}{3}(72 \text{ m}^2)(11 \text{ m})$

$\quad = 264 \text{ m}^3$

36. The figure is a cone with $r = 3$ ft and $h = 12$ ft.

$V = \dfrac{1}{3}\pi r^2 h$

$V \approx \dfrac{1}{3}(3.14)(3 \text{ ft})^2 (12 \text{ ft})$

$\quad = \dfrac{1}{3}(3.14)(9 \text{ ft}^2)(12 \text{ ft})$

$\quad = 113.04 \text{ ft}^3$

37. The figure is a sphere with $r = 21$ mi.

$V = \dfrac{4}{3}\pi r^3$

$V \approx \dfrac{4}{3}(3.14)(21 \text{ mi})^3$

$\quad = \dfrac{4}{3}(3.14)(9261 \text{ mi}^3)$

$\quad = 38{,}772.72 \text{ mi}^3$

38. The figure is a sphere with $r = 9.5$ in.

$V = \dfrac{4}{3}\pi r^3$

$V \approx \dfrac{4}{3}(3.14)(9.5 \text{ in.})^3$

$\quad = \dfrac{4}{3}(3.14)(857.375 \text{ in.}^3)$

$\quad \approx 3589.54 \text{ in.}^3$

39. Each leg resembles a pyramid with $B = (5 \text{ in.})(8 \text{ in.}) = 40 \text{ in.}^2$ and $h = 17$ in.

$V = \dfrac{1}{3} Bh$

$V = \dfrac{1}{3}(40 \text{ in.}^2)(17 \text{ in.})$

$\quad \approx 226.67 \text{ in.}^3$

40. The volcano resembles a cone with $r = 6.5$ km and $h = 4.17$ km.

$$V = \frac{1}{3}\pi r^2 h$$

$$V \approx \frac{1}{3}(3.14)(6.5 \text{ km})^2 (4.17 \text{ km})$$

$$= \frac{1}{3}(3.14)(42.25 \text{ km}^2)(4.17 \text{ km})$$

$$\approx 184.4 \text{ km}^3$$

Chapter 8   Statistics and Data Presentation

Section 8.1   Data Presentation – Tables and Graphs

Concept Check

2.   A table is a collection of related data arranged in labeled _ columns _ and _ rows _ for ease of reference and comparison.

4.   In graphs, the horizontal axis is commonly labeled the _ x _-axis and the vertical axis is commonly labeled the _ y _-axis.

6.   A _ bar _ graph is a graphical presentation of quantities or percentages using horizontal or vertical bars.

8.   A circle graph is created by converting the data to percents and then multiplying each percentage by _ 360 _ degrees. We then use a _ protractor _ to mark the number of degrees for each segment.

Guide Problems

10. a. Which occupation has the lowest median salary?
        Look at the dollar amounts in the column titled Median Salary. The smallest amount is $51,800. Read across the row containing $51,800 and find the entry in that row under the Occupation column. The occupation with the lowest Median Salary is network and computer systems administrator.

     b. What is the median salary for a database administrator?
        Read down the Occupation column and find the row containing database administrator. Read across this row to the Median Salary column to find the corresponding salary of $60,650.

     c. Which occupation had a 36.7 percent increase in jobs from 2006?
        Read down the column titled Percentage Increase in Jobs from 2006 to find the value 36.7. Look to the left of this value to find the corresponding occupation is physical therapist.

12. First, find the Diamond Princess in the Ship column. It is in the last row. Read across the last row to the Passengers column and note the value in the Passengers column. The Diamond princess can accommodate 2600 passengers.

14. For each ship, find the ship name under the Ship title and read across the row to find the number of passengers in the Passenger column. The *Queen Mary 2* can accommodate 2620 passengers while the *Adventure of the Seas* accommodates 3114 passengers. The *Queen Mary 2* accomodates $3114 - 2620 = 494$ passengers.

16. The largest value in the Passengers column is 3600 which corresponds to the *Ultra Voyager*. Thus, the *Ultra Voyager* carries the most passengers.

18. The values in the Horsepower column are 155, 155, 340, 187, 110, 268, 140, and 71. The value 71 is the smallest of these and corresponds to the row for the Honda Insight. Thus the Honda Insight has the least horsepower at 71 hp.

20. Locate Mercury Mariner under the Make and Model column. Read across the Mercury mariner row to the Base Price column to find the cost of the Mercury mariner is $28,535.

22. The two largest values in the City Mileage column are 56 (in the row for the Honda Insight) and 51 (in the row for the Toyota Prius.) Thus the Toyota Prius, at 51 mpg, and the Honda Insight, at 56 mpg, get the best mileage in city driving.

24. a. The line graph shows cell phone ownership within several teen age groups.

   b. The y-axis represents percentages of age groups that own cell phones.

   c. The x-axis represents time, in years, from 2000 to 2004.

   d. The three lines represent different age groups among teenagers: 12-15, 16-17, and 18-19.

   e. The line graph for Ages 18-19 is higher than both the Ages 16-17 and Ages 12-15 line graphs and so represents higher percentages. So Ages 18-19 have higher percentages of cell phone ownership.

   f. Locate the year 2000 ('00) on the x-axis. This happens to be the point at the bottom of the y-axis. Move up the y-axis until you reach the line graph for Ages 16-17. The graph hits the y-axis a little below the halfway point between 20% and 40% so the percentage of 16-17 year olds that owned cell phones in 2000 was approximately 28%.

26. a. The time data is in units of years so label the x-axis "Year". There are two columns of numerical value data. Both columns represent cost per credit in dollars, so label the y-axis "Cost per Credit (in dollars)".

   b. and c. Mark each data point and connect the dots. The graph for the out-of-state cost is drawn using a dashed line.

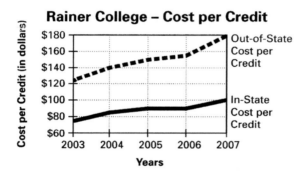

28. Locate sales of 4 million units on the y-axis. Move horizontally to the line graph and then vertically to the x-axis. Four million units were sold in 2006.

30. Examine the line segments that connect one year to the next. The greatest growth corresponds to the steepest line segment. The greatest growth occurred between the years 2000 and 2001.

32. Starting at the '04 mark on the x-axis, move vertically to the graph that represents Home Equity Line of Credit, the upper graph in this case. Moving horizontally to the y-axis, we find the percentage of home equity lines of credit applied for was 60%.

34. Note the percentages for the year 2007 are labeled on each graph, 68% for a line of credit and 16% for a loan. The difference is $68\% - 16\% = 52\%$.

36. From the home equity lines of credit graph, the percentage in 2006 was roughly 50% and increased to 68% in 2007. This represents an increase of $68\% - 50\% = 18\%$.

38. The time variable is in months so label the *x*-axis "Month". The numerical value variables both represent the cost of gasoline so label the *y*-axis "Gasoline Price". Then plot the data and connect the dots using a dashed line for the premium gas data. The multiple line graph is shown below.

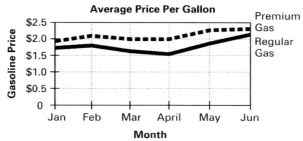

Guide Problems

40. a. What does this comparative bar graph illustrate?
    From the title and the labels on the axes, this comparative bar graph shows the salaries of U.S. sales of Lexus SUVs vs. cars, 1996-2004.

   b. What does the *x*-axis measure?
    The *x*-axis measures Time, in years, 1996-2004.

   c. What does the *y*-axis measure?
    Vehicles sold, in thousands.

   d. What do the yellow and orange bars represent?
    From the key, the yellow bars represent cars while the orange bars represent SUVs.

   e. In what year were car sales the highest.?
    Since the yellow bars represent cars, look for the tallest yellow bar. The tallest bar, and greatest sales, were in 2002.

   f. In what year did SUV sales first surpass car sales?
    SUV sales are greater than car sales in years where the orange bar is taller than the yellow bar. This first occurs in the year 2000.

   g. In what year did car sales first surpass 100,000 vehicles?
    Moving from left to right, look for the first yellow bar to cross the 100 mark on the *y*-axis. This occurs in the year 2001.

   h. In what year did SUV sales reach 150,000 units?
    Moving from left to right, look for the first yellow bar to reach the 150 mark on the *y*-axis. This occurs in the year 2004.

42. a. through c. The *x*-axis is labeled with the time unit Year and the *y*-axis with "Number of Transactions (in billions)." Two bars are drawn over each year one representing electronic payments for that year and the other representing paper checks for the same year. To uniformly distinguish between the two, the bars for electronic payments are light and those for paper checks are dark. The comparative bar graph is shown below.

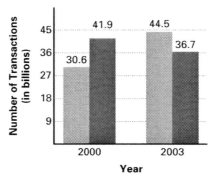

44. The years indicated on the *x*-axis range from 1974 to 2005.

46. The bars over 2005 and 1984 are at heights of 25.4 and 19.9 respectively so there were $25.4 - 19.9 = 5.5$ million more passengers in 2005 than in 1984.

48. The orange bar represents calories. For 2 percent milk, this bar is at a height of 200 so a serving of 2 percent milk contains 200 calories.

50. The orange or calorie bar for Powerade is at a height of 150 so a serving contains 150 calories. Similarly, a serving of orange juice contains 300 calories. A serving of Powerade contains of $300 - 150 = 150$ fewer calories.

52. From the bar graph, a serving of orange juice contains 70 grams of sugar and a serving of Powerade contains 38 grams of sugar. Two servings of orange juice and four servings of Powerade per week would contain $2 \cdot 70 + 4 \cdot 38 = 292$ grams of sugar. Over four weeks you would consume $4 \cdot 292 = 1168$ grams of sugar.

54. Label the *x*-axis with the merchandise categories: Apparel, Lingerie, and Personal Care. Over each category draw two bar to the indicated heights for 1997 and 2007. Use a light bar for 1997 and a dark bar for 2007. The resulting comparative bar graph is shown below.

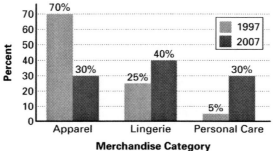

Guide Problems

56. a. Convert each component to a percent.
    First note the total number of viewers is $6.5 + 10.4 + 9.1 = 26$ million.
    Convert each component to a percent of this total.

NETWORK	MILLIONS OF VIEWERS	PERCENT
ABC	6.5	$\dfrac{6.5}{26} = 0.25 = 25\%$
NBC	10.4	$\dfrac{10.4}{26} = 0.4 = 40\%$
CBS	9.1	$\dfrac{9.1}{26} = 0.35 = 35\%$

    b.   Multiply each percent by $360°$ to find the degrees for each segment.

NETWORK	MILLIONS OF VIEWERS	PERCENT	DEGREES
ABC	6.5	25%	$25\% \cdot 360 = 0.25 \cdot 360 = 90$
NBC	10.4	40%	$40\% \cdot 360 = 0.4 \cdot 360 = 144$
CBS	9.1	35%	$35\% \cdot 360 = 0.35 \cdot 360 = 126$

c. Use a protractor to mark the number of degrees for each segment
d. Label each segment by name and percent.

The completed circle graph is shown below.

Evening News — Viewers by Network

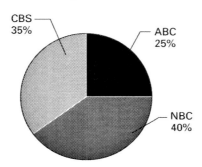

58. The segments labeled "One" and "Two" represent 66% and 24% of dog owners respectively. Together they represent $66\% + 24\% = 90\%$.

60. The segments representing four or more dogs are labeled "Four" (3%) and "Five or more" (2%) for a total of 5%.

62. The segment representing 12% corresponds to complaints regarding Internet Auctions.

64. The Internet Services segment represents 5% of those surveyed.

66. The total sales of all departments were
$$\$212,500 + \$85,000 + \$170,000 + \$85,000 + \$42,500 + \$255,000 = \$850,000.$$
Next convert the sales data to percentages and then multiply by $360°$ to determine the degrees of each segment.

DEPARTMENT	MILLIONS OF VIEWERS	PERCENT	DEGREES
Clothing	$212,500	$\dfrac{212,500}{850,000} = 0.25 = 25\%$	$25\% \cdot 360 = 0.25 \cdot 360 = 90$
Tools	85,000	$\dfrac{85,000}{850,000} = 0.10 = 10\%$	$10\% \cdot 360 = 0.1 \cdot 360 = 36$
Appliances	170,000	$\dfrac{170,000}{850,000} = 0.20 = 20\%$	$20\% \cdot 360 = 0.2 \cdot 360 = 72$

Household goods	85,000	$\frac{85,000}{850,000} = 0.10 = 10\%$	$10\% \cdot 360 = 0.1 \cdot 360 = 36$
Linens	42,500	$\frac{42,500}{850,000} = 0.05 = 5\%$	$5\% \cdot 360 = 0.05 \cdot 360 = 18$
Other	255,000	$\frac{255,000}{850,000} = 0.30 = 30\%$	$30\% \cdot 360 = 0.3 \cdot 360 = 108$

After using a protractor to create the segments having the degrees computed above and adding the labels, the completed circle graph is shown below.

**Morley's Department Store
Merchandise Mix**

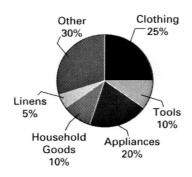

Cumulative Skills Review

2. The amount is unknown, use the variable n. The word "of" indicates multiplication. The corresponding equation is
    $$n = 0.15 \cdot 1250$$
    where the percent has been written as a decimal.

4. Use the formula
    $$F = \frac{9}{5}C + 32 = \frac{9}{5} \cdot 5 + 32 = 9 + 32 = 41$$
    5° Celsius is equivalent to 41° Fahrenheit.

6. Use the percent proportion with p being the unknown percent.
    $$\frac{54}{200} = \frac{p}{100}$$
    Set the cross products equal
    $$200p = 54 \cdot 100$$
    and solve
    $$p = \frac{54 \cdot 100}{200} = 27.$$
    So 54 is 27% of 200.

8. Mary spent
    $$\$122.00 + \$315.38 + \$938.16 = \$1375.54.$$
    Her new balance is
    $$\$12,233.10 - \$1375.54 = \$10,857.56.$$

10. The length of the diameter is twice that of the radius or $2 \cdot 7 = 14$ meters.

Section 8.2   Mean, Median, Mode, and Range

Concept Check

2.   An _average_ is a numerical value that represents an entire set.

4.   The sum of the values of a set divided by the number of values in that set is known as the _mean_.

6.   Describe the steps for calculating the mean.
      Find the sum of the values of a set. Divide the sum by the number of values in the set

8.   The median of a set is the _"middle"_ _value_ when the numbers are listed in numerical order.

10.   When we list the values of a set in numerical order, and there is an *odd* number of values, the median is the _middle_ value. When we list the values of a set in numerical order, and there is an *even* number of values, the median is the _mean_ of the two middle values.

12.   In statistics, the mean, median, and mode are all measures of _central_ tendency.

14.   The range is a measure of the _spread or dispersion_ of a set.

Guide Problems

16. a. Complete the table.
        The credits are given in the problem statement as are Sandra's grades in each course. The grade values are $A = 4$ and $B = 3$. Lastly, the quality points are computed by multiplying the course credits by the grade value.

COURSE	CREDITS	GRADE VALUE	QUALITY POINTS
Science	3	B = 3	$3 \cdot 3 = 9$
French	3	A = 4	$3 \cdot 4 = 12$
Chemistry	4	B = 3	$3 \cdot 4 = 12$
Chemistry Lab	1	A = 4	$1 \cdot 4 = 4$

b. How many total credits did Sandra earn?
   $3 + 3 + 4 + 1 = 11$

c. How many total quality points did Sandra earn?
   $9 + 12 + 12 + 4 = 37$

d. Divide the sum of Sandra's quality points by the total number of credits earned to find her GPA. Round to the nearest hundredth.
   $$\frac{37}{11} = 3.363636...$$
   Sandra has a 3.36 GPA.

In Problems 18 through 24, a mean is computed by first determining the number of values in the set, then computing the sum of the values in the set, and lastly dividing the sum by the number of values. If units are present, simply add and divide as usual. If necessary, round the mean computation to the nearest tenth.

18. Number of values: 6
     Sum of values: $64 + 87 + 22 + 53 + 85 + 87 = 398$
     Mean: $\dfrac{398}{6} = 66.333...$ or 66.3 rounded.

20. Number of values: 8
     Sum of values: 149 kg + 952 kg + 775 kg
            + 143 kg + 965 kg + 964 kg
            + 998 kg + 112 kg = 5058 kg
     Mean: $\dfrac{5058 \text{ kg}}{8} = 632.25$ kg or 632.3 kg rounded.

22. Number of values: 9
    Sum of values:

    $$\$3160 + \$4569 + \$3971 + \$2730$$
    $$+ \$4366 + \$3378 + \$3713$$
    $$+ \$2954 + \$4000 = \$32{,}841$$

    Mean: $\dfrac{\$32{,}841}{9} = \$3649$

24. Number of values: 7
    Sum of values: $62° + 63° + 70° + 54°$

    $$+ 53° + 32° + 92° = 426°$$

    Mean: $\dfrac{426°}{7} = 60.857°...$ or $60.9°$ rounded.

In Problems 26 and 28, a GPA is computed. The grade values are the usual values: A = 4, B = 3, C = 2, D = 1, *and* F = 0. *The quality points for a given course are computed by multiplying the credits by the grade value. The quality points are then added and divided by the total number of credits to find the GPA. The GPA is expressed as a decimal rounded to the hundredths place.*

26.

COURSE	CREDITS	GRADE VALUE	QUALITY POINTS
Economics	3	A = 4	$3 \cdot 4 = 12$
Physics	5	B = 3	$5 \cdot 3 = 15$
Calculus	4	A = 4	$4 \cdot 4 = 16$
English	3	C = 2	$3 \cdot 2 = 6$
History	3	B = 3	$3 \cdot 3 = 9$
Total	18		58

$\text{GPA} = \dfrac{58}{18} = 3.222... \approx 3.22$

28.

COURSE	CREDITS	GRADE VALUE	QUALITY POINTS
Music	2	C = 2	$2 \cdot 2 = 4$
French	3	B = 3	$3 \cdot 3 = 9$
Business Math	3	C = 2	$3 \cdot 2 = 6$
Accounting	3	A = 4	$3 \cdot 4 = 12$
Total	11		31

$\text{GPA} = \dfrac{31}{11} = 2.818... \approx 2.82$

Guide Problems

30. Consider this set: 15, 61, 47, 20, 35, 49
    a. List the values in numerical order.
       15, 20, 35, 47, 49, 61

    c. Calculate the mean of the two numbers in part b.
       $\dfrac{35 + 47}{2} = \dfrac{82}{2} = 41$

    b. Because there is an *even* number of values, identify the two middle values. 35 and 47

    d. The result is called the _median_ .

In problems 32 through 38, the median of a set is computed. First, the values in the set are listed in increasing order. If the number of values is odd, the middle value is identified as the median. If the number of values is even, the two middle values are identified and their mean is the median of the set.

32. Values in order: 18, 31, 40, 49, 65, 75, 83
    Number of values: odd
    Median: 49

34. Values in order: 11 mm, 17 mm, 28 mm,
                      39 mm, 41 mm, 76 mm
    Number of values: even
    Median: $\dfrac{28\text{ mm} + 39\text{ mm}}{2} = \dfrac{67\text{ mm}}{2} = 33.5\text{ mm}$

36. Values in order:
    22%, 25%, 49%, 66%, 78%, 91%
    Number of values: even
    Median: $\dfrac{49\% + 66\%}{2} = \dfrac{115\%}{2} = 57.5\%$

38. Values in order:
    148 cars, 185 cars, 381 cars, 486 cars,
    620 cars, 733 cars, 931 cars
    Number of values: odd
    Median: 486 cars

Guide Problems

40. Consider this set: 32, 12, 41, 24, 60, 52, 16, 57.
    a. Which value or values appear most often?
       none. Each value in the set appears only once
       in the set.

    b. Which value or values is the mode of this set?
       This set has no mode. If no value occurs more
       often than any other value in a set, then the set
       has no mode.

In Problems 42 through 48, a mode is determined. Analyze the data set to find the value or values that occur most often in the set. All such values are modes.

42. Set: 52 75 14 52 83 42 14 52
    52 occurs most often
    Mode: 52

44. Set: 597° 597° 733° 331° 269°
         776° 597° 331° 331° 733°
    Both 331° and 597° occur most often, three times
    each.
    Mode: 331° , 597°

46. Set: 48 mm 51 mm 76 mm 50 mm
         90 mm 67 mm 29 mm
    No value appears more than once.
    Mode: no mode

48. Set: 22 pages 45 pages 45 pages 37 pages
         22 pages 60 pages 26 pages 37 pages
    The values 22, 45, and 37 pages all appear twice,
    while the remaining values appear only once
    Mode: 22 pages, 37 pages, and 45 pages

Guide Problems

50. Consider this set: 9, 45, 21, 1, 37, 22, 11.

    a. Which value is the smallest?   1

    b. Which value is the largest?   45

    c. Calculate the difference between the largest and
       smallest values. $45 - 1 = 44$

    d. This number is called the range .

In Problems 52 through 58, the range of a set is computed. First, determine the smallest value in the set, then the largest value. Subtract the smallest value from the largest to find the range.

52. Smallest value: 1196
    Largest value: 2303
    Range: $2303 - 1196 = 1107$

54. Smallest value: $132
    Largest value: $957
    Range: $\$957 - \$132 = \$825$

56. Smallest value: 148 ft
    Largest value: 788 ft
    Range: $788 \text{ ft} - 148 \text{ ft} = 640 \text{ ft}$

58. Smallest value: 48 flights
    Largest value: 96 flights
    Range: $96 \text{ flights} - 48 \text{ flights} = 48 \text{ flights}$

60. The data in ascending order is 3.2, 4.2, 5.3, 5.8.

    Mean: $\dfrac{3.2 + 4.2 + 5.8 + 5.3}{4} = \dfrac{18.5}{4} = 4.625$ or 4.6 miles rounded.

    Median: $\dfrac{4.2 + 5.3}{2} = 4.75$ or 4.8 miles rounded.   Range: $5.8 - 3.2 = 2.6$ miles.

62. Total credits: $3+5+5+3=16$ Total quality points: $3\cdot4+5\cdot3+5\cdot3+3\cdot4=54$

    GPA: $\dfrac{54}{16}=3.375\approx3.38$

64. The data in ascending order is $33,000 $60,000 $60,000 $75,500 $120,000.

    Mean: $\dfrac{\$33,000+\$60,000+\$60,000+\$75,500+\$120,000}{5}=\dfrac{\$348,500}{5}=\$69,700$

    Median: $60,000
    Mode: $60,000
    Range: $120,000-\$33,000=\$87,000$

66. The data in ascending order is
    $39,000 $46,000 $55,000 $55,000 $63,000 $64,000 $78,000 $82,000 $84,000
    The sum of the values is $566,000.

    Mean: $\dfrac{\$566,000}{9}\approx\$62,889$

    Median: $63,000
    Mode: $55,000
    Range: $84,000-\$39,000=\$45,000$

68. The data in ascending order is
    10 14 33 45 47 57 62 63 65 70 84 88 89 96 96
    The sum of the values is 919

    Mean: $\dfrac{919}{15}\approx61$

    Median: 63
    Mode: 96
    Range: $96-10=86$

Cumulative Skills Review

2. Fraction notation: $\dfrac{85}{15}$

    Simplify: $\dfrac{85}{15}=\dfrac{5\cdot17}{5\cdot3}=\dfrac{\cancel{5}\cdot17}{\cancel{5}\cdot3}=\dfrac{17}{3}$

4. $15\text{ grams}=15\text{ grams}\cdot\dfrac{10\text{ decigrams}}{1\text{ grams}}$

    $=15\cdot10\text{ decigrams}$

    $=150\text{ decigrams}$

6. The size of each plot is

    $\dfrac{1}{3}\cdot16\dfrac{7}{8}=\dfrac{1}{3}\cdot\dfrac{135}{8}=\dfrac{135}{24}=\dfrac{\overset{45}{\cancel{135}}}{\underset{8}{\cancel{24}}}=\dfrac{45}{8}=5\dfrac{5}{8}$ acres.

8. $\dfrac{18\text{ pizza slices}}{12\text{ students}}=\dfrac{\overset{3}{\cancel{18}}\text{ pizza slices}}{\underset{2}{\cancel{12}}\text{ students}}$

    $=\dfrac{3\text{ pizza slices}}{2\text{ students}}$

    Word form: 3 pizza slices for every 2 students.

10. Note $1\text{ square foot}=(1\text{ foot})^2=(12\text{ inches})^2$

    $=144\text{ square inches}$

    so the unit ratio is $\dfrac{144\text{ square inches}}{1\text{ square foot}}$.

    Then

80 square foot

$$= 80 \text{ square foot} \cdot \frac{144 \text{ square inches}}{1 \text{ square foot}}$$

$$= 80 \cdot 144 \text{ square inches}$$

$$= 11,520 \text{ square inches.}$$

Chapter 8 Numerical Facts Of Life

2. The table indicates that from 1986 to 2006, the cost of eggs increased by 58.1%. A dozen eggs that cost $1.70 in 1986 would cost

$$\$1.70 + \$1.70(58.1\%) = \$1.70 + \$1.70 \cdot 0.581 = \$1.70 + \$0.9877 = \$2.6877$$

or about $2.69 in 2006.

4. Gasoline falls under the Fuels category of the table and so gasoline increased in cost by 81.9% from 1986 to 2006. Note that to convert from 1986 prices to 2006 prices we would add 81.9% of the 1986 cost to 100% of the 1986 cost, or equivalently *multiply* by 181.9%. Thus, to convert from 2006 to 1986 costs, *divide* the 2006 cost by 181.9%. If a gallon of gas costs $2.50 in 2006, then in 1986 it cost

$$\frac{\$2.50}{181.9\%} = \frac{\$2.50}{1.819} = \$1.3743...$$

or around $1.37.

Chapter 8 Review Exercises

1. Locate sodium under the Amount Per Serving heading. The indicated amount is 190 mg.

2. The information at the top of the table indicates the values are for a 3/4 cup serving. The top of the right most column accounts for 1/2 cup milk. Under skim milk, we see the calories total 130,

3. Below the calories information, the table gives daily values as a percentage. Find the row for potassium and look under the heading for skim milk, to find that a serving of cereal with skim milk will provide 8% of the daily potassium value.

4. Locate Vitamin C in the Daily Value portion of the table. The percentage on the left corresponds to cereal without milk. One serving without milk will provide 10% of the daily value.

5. Under Amount Per Serving, the total Cholesterol is given as 0 mg.

6. From the table, a single serving contains 5 g of sugars. Three servings per week would amount to $3 \cdot 5 = 15$ g per week. Over six weeks, the amount of sugar would be $6 \cdot 15 = 90$ grams.

7. Locate Indonesia under the Country column. Move right to the Estimated Population column to find the value 336. Note under the table title that the values are in units of millions. The estimated population of Indonesia in 2050 is 336 million.

8. Locate Brazil under the Country column. Move right to the Population 2005 column to find the value 186. Note under the table title that the values are in units of millions. The population of Brazil in 2005 was 186 million.

9. Looking down the Estimated Population 2050 column, the largest value is 9084. However, this value does not correspond to a country but represents the world population. The largest value for a country is 1601 million corresponding to India.

10. For each country, compute the increase in population from 2005 to 2050.

China	$1418 - 1302 = 116$
India	$1601 - 1080 = 521$
United States	$420 - 296 = 124$
Indonesia	$336 - 242 = 94$
Brazil	$228 - 186 = 42$

The smallest growth belongs to Brazil.

11. From the computations in Exercise 10, the U.S. population will grow by 124 million.

12. The difference in the world total population from 2005 to 2050 is $9084 - 6449 = 2635$ million.

13. Looking at the Viewership graph on the right, the lowest point is along the horizontal line through '03 on the time axis. The lowest viewership was in 2003.

14. Using the Ad Prices graph on the left, the costs of 30-second ads in 1994 and 2005 were $643,500 and $1.6 million respectively. This is an increase of $\$1,600,000 - \$643,500 = \$956,500$.

15. Start at the 40 mark on the y-axis of the Viewership graph. Scan horizontally until you find a point where the graph is just above the 40 mark and note the year on the time axis. In 2002, the viewership was just over 40 million.

16. Other than the period from 2001 to 2002, ad prices have steadily increased. Viewership, on the other hand, has steadily decreased.

17. Of the three line graphs, Social Security is represented by the uppermost line graph. This graph crosses over the 700 billion mark in the year 2010.

18. Locate the '15 label on the time axis. Scan vertically to the Medicaid line graph (the lowest graph) to find the graph labeled $392. Since the indicated values are in billions, Medicaid is projected to be $392 billion in 2016.

19. Moving vertically from the '15 mark to the social security line graph, we see the graph crosses at roughly the $900 value. Social security is projected to be at $900 billion in 2015.

20. Scan vertically from the '13 mark on the time axis. The Medicaid curve is around the $300 mark but the Medicare curve is at about $700. So Medicare is predicted to reach $700 billion in 2013.

21. Label the time axis with "Academic Year": 2000-2001, 2001-2002, etc. Label the y-axis "Loan Rate" with percentage values. Then plot the values from the table with a dot and connect the dots. The completed line graph is shown below.

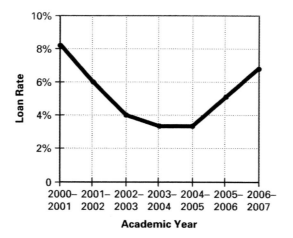

Stafford Student Loan Rates

22. Label the time axis with "Year": 2000, 2001, etc. Label the *y*-axis with numbers of prints 0, 10, 20, 30, and 40. Plot the points corresponding to the Traditional column of values and connect these dots with solid lines. Label this curve Traditional. Similarly, plot the points corresponding to the Digital column of values. Connect these points with dashed lines and label the graph Digital. The completed multiple line graph is shown below.

Photo Prints Made at Labs
(in billions)

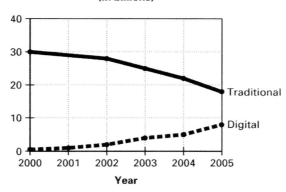

23. The bars represent the increase in home price so the shortest bar would represent the lowest increase. This occurred in 1996.

24. Start at the 8 percent mark on the *y*-axis. Scan horizontally until a bar just touches the 8 percent mark. This bar corresponds to 2003. There was an 8 percent increase in home prices in 2003.

25. Scan the tops of the bars to locate two bars that are at the same height. Home prices rose at the same rate in 2001 and 2002.

26. The top of the bar over '06 lies halfway between the 4 and 6 marks on the *y*-axis. So in 2006, home prices increased by 5%.

27. Of the two bars next to Italy, the orange bar represents 2003 according to the key. This bar indicates 714 million gallons of wine were consumed in Italy in 2003.

28. Looking only at the ends of the orange bars, for 2003, the greatest value is seen to be 774 million in France.

29. From the bar graph, Italy will consume 730 million gallons of wine in 2008 compared to 714 million consumed in 2003, an increase of $730 - 714 = 16$ million gallons.

30. Looking only at the green bars, for 2008, the largest value, 740, is associated with the United States. The United States is projected to consume the most wine in 2008.

31. Label the time axis with "Year" and use the values from the Year column: 2004, 2005, …,2009. Label the *y*-axis "Subscribers" and mark values 20, 40, 60, 80. Indicate in the graph title or on the *y*-axis that the values are in millions. Over each year construct a bar to the height indicated by the numerical value of subscribers for that year. The resulting bar graph is shown below.

Estimated U.S. Residential
Broadband Subscribers
(millions)

32. Label the time axis with "Position" and use the names from the Position column such as Quarterback and Defensive End. Label the *y*-axis "Salary" and mark values 1, 2, 3, and so on, representing millions of dollars. Indicate in the graph title or on the *y*-axis that the values are in millions. Over each position construct two bar, one to the height indicated by the salary for starters and one to the height indicated by the salary for all players at that position. Use a dark color for the starters and a light color for all players. Create a key to indicate which color represents which category. The resulting bar graph is shown below.

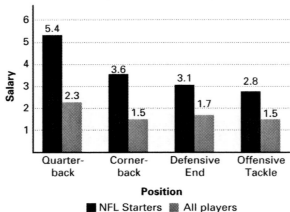

33. The largest segment belongs to SBC/AT&T so SBC/AT&T has the greatest market share.

34. The segment on the graph labeled Verizon shows a share of 15%.

35. Note that the segment for MCI is larger than that for Sprint so MCI has the greater market share. Note also that Sprint's segment is labeled 6% while MCI's segment is labeled 8%.

36. It is clear visually that if the segments for Verizon, MCI and Sprint were joined as one segment, that segment would still be smaller than that of SBC/AT&T. This can be confirmed by adding their respective shares
$$15\% + 8\% + 6\% = 29\%$$
which is less than the 37% held by SBC/AT&T.

37. From the circle graph on the left interest payments were at 7% in 1969. From the graph on the right, interest payments will be at 10% in 2009, an increase of 3%.

38. It is clear visually that the segment for Benefits grows the most in the circle graph for 2009 when compared to that for 1969.

39. National defense spending will change from 43% to 16%, a decrease of $43\% - 16\% = 27\%$.

40. Benefits and interest payments both increase while national defense and all else decrease. The decrease in all else is predicted to be 2%.

41. Since the data is already in percent form, the only calculation is to determine the number of degrees in each segment. These calculation are shown in the table below.

REGION	PERCENT	DEGREES
Latin America	53%	$53\% \cdot 360 = 0.53 \cdot 360 \approx 191$
Europe	14%	$14\% \cdot 360 = 0.14 \cdot 360 \approx 50$
Asia	25%	$25\% \cdot 360 = 0.25 \cdot 360 = 90$
Other	8%	$0.08\% \cdot 360 = 0.08 \cdot 360 \approx 29$

Use a protractor to measure segments having the calculated angles and then label with the region and corresponding percentages to generate the circle graph shown below.

U.S. Foreign-Born Population

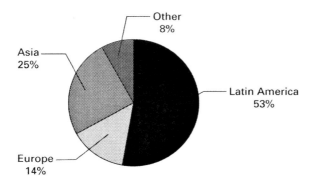

42. a. and b. The total spending is $\$3.9 + \$3.4 + \$7.6 + \$2.9 = \$17.8$ billion dollars. Convert each dollar value in the spending column to a percent of this total. Then multiply by 360 to find the number of degrees in the corresponding segment of the circle graph. These calculation are shown in the table below.

CATEGORY	MILLIONS OF VIEWERS	PERCENT	DEGREES
Electronics and computers	$3.9	$\dfrac{\$3.9}{\$17.8} \approx 22\%$	$22\% \cdot 360 = 0.22 \cdot 360 \approx 79$
Shoes	$3.4	$\dfrac{\$3.4}{\$17.8} \approx 19\%$	$19\% \cdot 360 = 0.19 \cdot 360 \approx 68$
Clothing and accessories	$7.6	$\dfrac{\$7.6}{\$17.8} \approx 43\%$	$43\% \cdot 360 = 0.43 \cdot 360 \approx 155$
School supplies	$2.9	$\dfrac{\$2.9}{\$17.8} \approx 16\%$	$16\% \cdot 360 = 0.16 \cdot 360 \approx 58$

Use a protractor to measure segments having the calculated angles and then label with the category and corresponding percentages to generate the circle graph shown below.

Back-to-School Spending

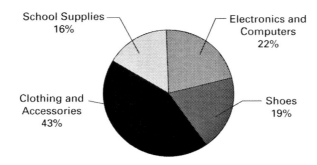

43. Values in order: 14, 21, 35, 58, 60
    Number of values: odd
    Median: 35
    Mean: $\dfrac{35+21+58+14+60}{5} = \dfrac{188}{5} = 37.6$

44. Values in order: 44, 53, 71, 85, 98, 99
    Number of values: even
    Median: $\dfrac{71+85}{2} = 78$
    Mean: $\dfrac{85+71+98+44+53+99}{6} = \dfrac{450}{6} = 75$

45. Values in order: 27, 64, 77, 90
    Number of values: even
    Median: $\dfrac{64+77}{2} = 70.5$
    Mean: $\dfrac{27+90+64+77}{4} = \dfrac{258}{4} = 64.5$

46. Values in order: 34, 52, 64
    Number of values: odd
    Median: 52
    Mean: $\dfrac{64+34+52}{3} = \dfrac{150}{3} = 50$

47. Values in order: 11, 17, 20, 28, 62
    Number of values: odd
    Median: 20
    Mean: $\dfrac{62+11+28+17+20}{5} = \dfrac{138}{5} = 27.6$

48. Values in order: 10, 12, 30, 84
    Number of values: even
    Median: $\dfrac{12+30}{2} = 21$
    Mean: $\dfrac{84+12+10+30}{5} = \dfrac{136}{4} = 34$

49. Set: 56, 63, 48, 85, 48, 54, 77, 79
    48 occurs most often
    Mode: 48
    Smallest value: 48
    Largest value: 85
    Range: $85 - 48 = 37$

50. Set: 18, 49, 19, 50, 68, 68
    68 occurs most often
    Mode: 68
    Smallest value: 18
    Largest value: 68
    Range: $68 - 18 = 50$

51. Set: 66, 36, 13, 28
    No value occurs more than once
    Mode: none
    Smallest value: 13
    Largest value: 66
    Range: $66 - 13 = 53$

52. Set: 51, 35, 35, 79, 72, 51, 60
    35 and 51 occur most often, twice each
    Modes: 35 and 51
    Smallest value: 35
    Largest value: 79
    Range: $79 - 35 = 44$

53. Set: 70, 43, 37, 80, 43
    43 occurs most often
    Mode: 43
    Smallest value: 37
    Largest value: 80
    Range: $80 - 37 = 43$

54. Set: 14, 14, 15, 14, 73, 15
    14 occurs most often
    Mode: 14
    Smallest value: 14
    Largest value: 73
    Range: $73 - 14 = 59$

55. Set: 22, 43, 24, 16, 24, 8, 16, 9, 12
    16 and 24 occur most often, twice each
    Modes: 16 and 24
    Smallest value: 8
    Largest value: 43
    Range: $43 - 8 = 35$

56. Set: 135, 180, 240, 160, 210, 201
    No value occurs more than once
    Mode: none
    Smallest value: 135
    Largest value: 240
    Range: $240 - 135 = 105$

Chapter 8 Assessment Test

1. Look in the row corresponding to the academic year 2000-2001 and find the value under the column heading of Private Colleges. The value $22,240 is the average cost for a private college in 2000-2001.

2. Look in the row corresponding to the academic year 1995-1996 and find the value under the column heading of Public Colleges. The value $6743 is the average cost for a public college in 1995-1996.

3. From the table, the average costs in 2005-2006 for private and public colleges were $29,026 and $12,127 respectively. The costs for a private college were $29,026 - $12,127 = $16,899$ more than that for a public college.

4. Locate Sept. on the time axis. Move vertically until you reach the blue line graph, corresponding to cell phones with cameras. The point on the graph lies about halfway between the 40 and 60 marks on the Sales axis so about 50 phones were sold with cameras in September.

5. Locate Nov. on the time axis. Move vertically until you reach the red line graph, corresponding to cell phones without cameras. The point on the graph lies about halfway between the 60 and 80 marks on the Sales axis so about 70 phones were sold without cameras in November.

6. The lowest point on the red line graph (without cameras) is above July on the time axis. The fewest phones without cameras were sold in July.

7. Under the heading of the business travel, the year 2006 shows a yellow bar (representing major carriers) labeled 81%. Thus 81% of business travelers choose major carriers in 2006.

8. Under the heading of personal travelers, the year 2004 shows a green bar (representing low-cost carriers) labeled 41%. Thus 41% of personal travelers chose low-cost carriers in 2004.

9. Under business travel, the low cost carrier (green bar) labeled 23% corresponds to the year 2004.

10. Looking at the personal travel portion of the bar graph and the major carrier bars (yellow bar), 53% chose major carriers in 2004 and 65% chose major carriers in 2006. Thus 2006 was the year 65% of personal travelers chose major carriers.

11. The largest and smallest segments of the circle graph correspond to Phillips and Samsung respectively. Thus, Phillips had the highest sales while Samsung had the lowest sales.

12. Toshiba had 18% of DVD player sales while Panasonic had 30% of the sales for combined sales of $18\% + 30\% = 48\%$.

13. Panasonic's 30% share of sales was higher than Samsung's 12% by $30\% - 12\% = 18\%$.

14. Since 40% of sales were attributed to Phillips, if 2000 DVD players were sold then $40\% \cdot 2000 = 0.40 \cdot 2000 = 800$ units were sold by Phillips.

15. The x-axis is labeled with the different types of food in the table. The y-axis is labeled with values for steps. Bars are drawn over each food to the height specified by the numerical value of steps in the table. The resulting bar graph is shown here.

Approximate Number of Steps to Burn Off Various Foods

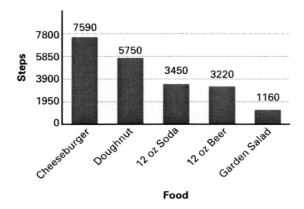

16. The total revenue from all division is
    $6 + $12 + $9 + $3 = $30 billion.

    Next convert each division's revenue to percentages of this total and then multiply by 360° to determine the degrees of each segment in the circle graph.

DEGREE	DEGREES GRANTED	PERCENT	DEGREES
Electronics	$6	$\frac{\$6}{\$30} = 0.2 = 20\%$	$20\% \cdot 360 = 0.2 \cdot 360 = 72$
Games	$12	$\frac{\$12}{\$30} = 0.4 = 40\%$	$40\% \cdot 360 = 0.4 \cdot 360 = 144$
Pictures and Music	$9	$\frac{\$9}{\$30} = 0.3 = 30\%$	$30\% \cdot 360 = 0.3 \cdot 360 = 108$
Other	$3	$\frac{\$3}{\$30} = 0.1 = 10\%$	$10\% \cdot 360 = 0.1 \cdot 360 = 36$

After using a protractor to create the segments having the degrees computed above and adding the labels, the completed circle graph is shown below.

Apex Entertainment, Inc. 2007 Revenue
(by Division)

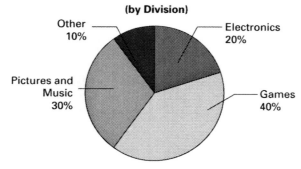

17. The mean is $\dfrac{24+49+39+46+31+51}{6} = \dfrac{240}{6} = 40$.

18. The data in ascending order is: 28 32 36 40 46 54. The number of values is even so the median is given by $\dfrac{36+40}{2} = 38$.

19. Both values 60 and 69 occur three times in the set, the most any value occurs. The modes are 60 and 69.

20. The largest value is 293 and the smallest value is 75. The range is $293 - 75 = 218$.

Chapter 9   Signed Numbers

Section 9.1   Introduction to Signed Numbers

Concept Check

2.   A _negative_ number is a number that is less than 0.

4.   A number that is either positive or negative is called a _signed number_ .

6.   The numbers … −3, −2, −1, 0, 1, 2, 3, … are known as the _integers_ .

8.   The _absolute value_ of a number is the distance between the number and zero on the number line.

Guide Problems

10. The opposite of a negative number is positive, so the opposite of −3 is 3.

In Problems 12 through 18, find the opposite of the number by changing the sign of the number.

12. −69   14. 67.25   16. $-\dfrac{3}{4}$ 18. $7\dfrac{4}{13}$

Guide Problems

20. Graph the signed numbers $-8.5, 2.25, -3\dfrac{1}{2},$ and $\dfrac{3}{4}.$

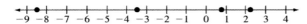

In Problems 22 and 24, graph the given numbers on a number line.

22. $1.5, -2.25, -1\dfrac{1}{3}, 4\dfrac{1}{2}$

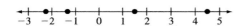

24. $2.3, -0.75, -3\dfrac{3}{4}, 5\dfrac{2}{5}$

Guide Problems

26. $\left|-12.3\right| = 12.3$

In Exercises 28 through 34, the absolute value of a positive number is the number itself, the absolute value of a negative number is the opposite of the number, and the absolute value of 0 is 0.

28. $\left|59\right| = 59$ 30. $\left|-70\right| = 70$ 32. $\left|-58.3\right| = 58.3$

34. $\left|-13\frac{5}{11}\right| = 13\frac{5}{11}$

Guide Problems

36. Compare $-\frac{2}{9}$ and $-\frac{4}{15}$.

The LCD of $-\frac{2}{9}$ and $-\frac{4}{15}$ is 45.

$-\frac{2}{9} = -\frac{2\cdot 5}{9\cdot 5} = -\frac{10}{45}$; $-\frac{4}{15} = -\frac{4\cdot 3}{15\cdot 3} = -\frac{12}{45}$

$-\frac{2}{9} > -\frac{4}{15}$ or $-\frac{4}{15} < -\frac{2}{9}$

For problems 38−48, when comparing two signed numbers, the number farthest to the left on a number line is the smaller number.

38. $3 < 16, 16 > 3$

40. $-32.75 < -32.0,$
$-32.0 > -32.75$

42. $83 > -11, -11 < 83$

44. $-40.0 > -40.3, -40.3 < -40.0$

46. $\frac{1}{3} < \frac{3}{8}, \frac{3}{8} > \frac{1}{3}$

48. $-\frac{3}{7} > -\frac{7}{16}, -\frac{7}{16} < -\frac{3}{7}$

50. $-273°C$

52. $37°C, 98.6°F$

54. -160 feet

Cumulative Skills Review

2. $5\frac{1}{3} - 3\frac{3}{4}$ The LCD of $\frac{1}{3}$ and $\frac{3}{4}$ is 12.

Rewrite the fractional parts.

$\frac{1}{3} = \frac{1\cdot 4}{3\cdot 4} = \frac{4}{12}$ $\frac{3}{4} = \frac{3\cdot 3}{4\cdot 3} = \frac{9}{12}$

$\begin{array}{r} 5\frac{4}{12} = 4\frac{16}{12} \\ -3\frac{9}{12} = -3\frac{9}{12} \\ \hline 1\frac{7}{12} \end{array}$

4. $0.38 = 38\%$

6. $C = 2\pi r \approx 2\cdot 3.14\cdot 2 \text{ mi} \approx 12.56 \text{ mi}$

8. $\frac{59 + 88 + 21 + 63 + 33}{5} = \frac{264}{5} = 52.8$

10. $x^2 + 40^2 = 90^2$

$x^2 + 1600 = 8100$

$x^2 = 6500$

$x = \sqrt{6500} \approx 80.62 \text{ ft}$

Section 9.2   Adding Signed Numbers

Concept Check

2.   When adding two negative numbers, the sum will be   <u>negative</u> .

4.   When adding two numbers with different signs, the sum will have the same sign as the addend that is <u>larger</u> in absolute value.

Guide Problems

6.   Add $-\dfrac{5}{6} + \left(-\dfrac{3}{8}\right)$.

a.   Determine the absolute value of each addend.

$$\left|-\frac{5}{6}\right| = \frac{5}{6}; \qquad \left|-\frac{3}{8}\right| = \frac{3}{8}$$

b.   Write each fraction as an equivalent fraction with the LCD. LCD(6, 8) = 24.

$$\frac{5}{6} = \frac{5 \cdot 4}{6 \cdot 4} = \frac{20}{24}; \qquad \frac{3}{8} = \frac{3 \cdot 3}{8 \cdot 3} = \frac{9}{24}$$

c.   Add the absolute values of the addends.

$$\frac{20}{24} + \frac{9}{24} = \frac{29}{24} = 1\frac{5}{24}$$

d.   Attach the common sign of the addends to the sum of part b.

$$-\frac{5}{6} + \left(-\frac{3}{8}\right) = -1\frac{5}{24}$$

In Problems 8 through 46, add the signed numbers using the procedure outlined above. Simplify fractions, if possible. All of the steps are shown for problems 10 through 14.

8. $8 + 7 = 15$

10. $-6 + (-11)$
     $|-6| = 6; \ |-11| = 11$
     $6 + 11 = 17$
     $-6 + (-11) = -17$

12. $-17 + (-9)$
     $|-17| = 17; \ |-9| = 9$
     $17 + 9 = 26$
     $-17 + (-9) = -26$

14. $-18 + (-28)$
     $|-18| = 18; \ |-28| = 28$
     $18 + 28 = 46$
     $-18 + (-28) = -46$

16. $-30 + (-90) = -120$

18. $-162 + (-247) = -409$

20. $-1042 + (-139) = -1181$

22. $-182 + (-80) = -262$

24. $6.81 + 18.02 = 24.83$

26. $-1.09 + (-9.21) = -10.3$

28. $-42.1 + (-9.07) = -51.17$

30. $-17.43 + (-15.012) = -32.442$

In Problems 32 through 46, find the least common denominator and then write each fraction as an equivalent fraction with the LCD before adding the signed numbers.

32. $-\dfrac{2}{9}+\left(-\dfrac{4}{9}\right)$

    Determine the absolute value of each addend.

    $\left|-\dfrac{2}{9}\right|=\dfrac{2}{9};\qquad\left|-\dfrac{4}{9}\right|=\dfrac{4}{9}$

    Add the absolute values of the addends.
    LCD = 9

    $\dfrac{2}{9}+\dfrac{4}{9}=\dfrac{6}{9}=\dfrac{2}{3}$

    Attach the common sign of the addends
    to the sum.

    $-\dfrac{2}{9}+\left(-\dfrac{4}{9}\right)=-\dfrac{2}{3}$

34. $-\dfrac{1}{2}+\left(-\dfrac{5}{9}\right)$

    Determine the absolute value of each addend.

    $\left|-\dfrac{1}{2}\right|=\dfrac{1}{2};\qquad\left|-\dfrac{5}{9}\right|=\dfrac{5}{9}$

    Add the absolute values of the addends.
    LCD = 18

    $\dfrac{1}{2}+\dfrac{5}{9}=\dfrac{1\cdot 9}{2\cdot 9}+\dfrac{5\cdot 2}{9\cdot 2}$

    $=\dfrac{9}{18}+\dfrac{10}{18}=\dfrac{19}{18}=1\dfrac{1}{18}$

    Attach the common sign of the addends
    to the sum.

    $-\dfrac{1}{2}+\left(-\dfrac{5}{9}\right)=-1\dfrac{1}{18}$

36. $-\dfrac{3}{8}+\left(-\dfrac{3}{12}\right)$

    Determine the absolute value of each addend.

    $\left|-\dfrac{3}{8}\right|=\dfrac{3}{8};\qquad\left|-\dfrac{3}{12}\right|=\dfrac{3}{12}$

    Add the absolute values of the addends.
    LCD = 24

    $\dfrac{3}{8}+\dfrac{3}{12}=\dfrac{3\cdot 3}{8\cdot 3}+\dfrac{3\cdot 2}{12\cdot 2}$

    $=\dfrac{9}{24}+\dfrac{6}{24}=\dfrac{15}{24}=\dfrac{5}{8}$

    Attach the common sign of the addends
    to the sum.

    $-\dfrac{3}{8}+\left(-\dfrac{3}{12}\right)=-\dfrac{5}{8}$

38. $-\dfrac{1}{6}+\left(-\dfrac{7}{12}\right)$

    Determine the absolute value of each addend.

    $\left|-\dfrac{1}{6}\right|=\dfrac{1}{6};\qquad\left|-\dfrac{7}{12}\right|=\dfrac{7}{12}$

    Add the absolute values of the addends.
    LCD = 12

    $\dfrac{1}{6}+\dfrac{7}{12}=\dfrac{1\cdot 2}{6\cdot 2}+\dfrac{7}{12}$

    $=\dfrac{2}{12}+\dfrac{7}{12}=\dfrac{9}{12}=\dfrac{3}{4}$

    Attach the common sign of the addends
    to the sum.

    $-\dfrac{1}{6}+\left(-\dfrac{7}{12}\right)=-\dfrac{3}{4}$

40. $-2\dfrac{3}{5}+\left(-4\dfrac{2}{15}\right)$

Determine the absolute value of each addend.

$\left|-2\dfrac{3}{5}\right|=2\dfrac{3}{5};\qquad\left|-4\dfrac{2}{15}\right|=4\dfrac{2}{15}$

Add the absolute values of the addends.
LCD = 15

$2\dfrac{3}{5}+4\dfrac{2}{15}=\dfrac{13}{5}+\dfrac{62}{15}=\dfrac{13\cdot3}{5\cdot3}+\dfrac{62}{15}$

$\qquad=\dfrac{39}{15}+\dfrac{62}{15}=\dfrac{101}{15}=6\dfrac{11}{15}$

Attach the common sign of the addends to the sum.

$-2\dfrac{3}{5}+\left(-4\dfrac{2}{15}\right)=-6\dfrac{11}{15}$

42. $-18\dfrac{7}{12}+\left(-29\dfrac{5}{18}\right)$

Determine the absolute value of each addend.

$\left|-18\dfrac{7}{12}\right|=18\dfrac{7}{12};\qquad\left|-29\dfrac{5}{18}\right|=29\dfrac{5}{18}$

Add the absolute values of the addends.
LCD = 36

$18\dfrac{7}{12}+29\dfrac{5}{18}=18\dfrac{7\cdot3}{12\cdot3}+29\dfrac{5\cdot2}{18\cdot2}$

$\qquad=18\dfrac{21}{36}+29\dfrac{10}{36}=47\dfrac{31}{36}$

Attach the common sign of the addends to the sum.

$-18\dfrac{7}{12}+\left(-29\dfrac{5}{18}\right)=-47\dfrac{31}{36}$

44. $-21\dfrac{1}{3}+\left(-49\dfrac{11}{12}\right)$

Determine the absolute value of each addend.

$\left|-21\dfrac{1}{3}\right|=21\dfrac{1}{3};\qquad\left|-49\dfrac{11}{12}\right|=49\dfrac{11}{12}$

Add the absolute values of the addends.
LCD = 12

$21\dfrac{1}{3}+49\dfrac{11}{12}=21\dfrac{1\cdot4}{3\cdot4}+49\dfrac{11}{12}$

$\qquad=21\dfrac{4}{12}+49\dfrac{11}{12}=70\dfrac{15}{12}=70+1\dfrac{3}{12}$

$\qquad=71\dfrac{3}{12}=71\dfrac{1}{4}$

Attach the common sign of the addends to the sum.

$-21\dfrac{1}{3}+\left(-49\dfrac{11}{12}\right)=-71\dfrac{1}{4}$

46. $-58\dfrac{5}{8}+\left(-29\dfrac{7}{12}\right)$

Determine the absolute value of each addend.

$\left|-58\dfrac{5}{8}\right|=58\dfrac{5}{8};\qquad\left|-29\dfrac{7}{12}\right|=29\dfrac{7}{12}$

Add the absolute values of the addends.
LCD = 24

$58\dfrac{5}{8}+29\dfrac{7}{12}=58\dfrac{5\cdot3}{8\cdot3}+29\dfrac{7\cdot2}{12\cdot2}$

$\qquad=58\dfrac{15}{24}+29\dfrac{14}{24}=87\dfrac{29}{24}$

$\qquad=87+1\dfrac{5}{24}=88\dfrac{5}{24}$

Attach the common sign of the addends to the sum.

$-58\dfrac{5}{8}+\left(-29\dfrac{7}{12}\right)=-88\dfrac{5}{24}$

Guide Problems

48. Add $\dfrac{3}{8}+\left(-\dfrac{1}{12}\right)$

a. Determine the absolute value of each addend.

$\left|\dfrac{3}{8}\right|=\dfrac{3}{8};\qquad\left|-\dfrac{1}{12}\right|=\dfrac{1}{12}$

b. Write each fraction as an equivalent fractions with the LCD.
LCD = 24

$\dfrac{3}{8}=\dfrac{3\cdot3}{8\cdot3}=\dfrac{9}{24};\qquad\dfrac{1}{12}=\dfrac{1\cdot2}{12\cdot2}=\dfrac{2}{24}$

c. Subtract the smaller absolute value from the larger.

$$\frac{9}{24} - \frac{2}{24} = \frac{7}{24}$$

c. Attach the sign of the addend having the larger absolute value to the difference of part c.

$$\frac{3}{8} + \left(-\frac{1}{12}\right) = \frac{7}{24}$$

In Problems 50 through 96, add the signed numbers using the procedure outlined above. Simplify fractions, if possible. All of the steps are shown for problems 58 through 68.

50. $5 + (-4) = 1$

52. $21 + (-12) = 9$

54. $-6 + 13 = 7$

56. $-7 + 22 = 15$

58. $15 + (-29)$
Determine the absolute value of each addend.
$|15| = 15; \quad |-29| = 29$
Subtract the smaller absolute value from the larger.
$29 - 15 = 14$
Attach the sign of the addend having the larger absolute value to the difference.
$15 + (-29) = -14$

60. $103 + (-62)$
Determine the absolute value of each addend.
$|103| = 103; \quad |-62| = 62$
Subtract the smaller absolute value from the larger.
$103 - 62 = 41$
Attach the sign of the addend having the larger absolute value to the difference.
$103 + (-62) = 41$

62. $-162 + (200)$
Determine the absolute value of each addend.
$|-162| = 162; \quad |200| = 200$
Subtract the smaller absolute value from the larger.
$200 - 162 = 38$
Attach the sign of the addend having the larger absolute value to the difference.
$-162 + (200) = 38$

64. $284 + (-181)$
Determine the absolute value of each addend.
$|284| = 284; \quad |-181| = 181$
Subtract the smaller absolute value from the larger.
$284 - 181 = 103$
Attach the sign of the addend having the larger absolute value to the difference.
$284 + (-181) = 103$

66. $2794 + (-4215)$
$|2794| = 2794; \quad |-4215| = 4215$
Subtract the smaller absolute value from the larger.
$4215 - 2794 = 1421$
Attach the sign of the addend having the larger absolute value to the difference.
$2794 + (-4215) = -1421$

68. $28{,}093 + (-16{,}520)$
$|28{,}093| = 28{,}093; \quad |-16{,}520| = 16{,}520$
Subtract the smaller absolute value from the larger.
$28{,}093 - 16{,}520 = 11{,}573$
Attach the sign of the addend having the larger absolute value to the difference.
$28{,}093 + (-16{,}520) = 11{,}573$

70. $10.25 + (-9.41) = 0.84$

72. $-5.03 + (2.37) = -2.66$

74. $14.21 + (-19.02) = -4.81$

76. $-19.01 + 8.73 = -10.28$

78. $315.34 + (-149.38) = 165.96$

80. $-529.76 + 672.83 = 143.07$

In problems 82 through 96, find the least common denominator and then write each fraction as an equivalent fraction with the LCD before adding. All steps are shown for these problems.

82. $-\dfrac{5}{7}+\dfrac{4}{7}$

$\left|-\dfrac{5}{7}\right|=\dfrac{5}{7};\quad \left|\dfrac{4}{7}\right|=\dfrac{4}{7}$

Subtract the smaller absolute value from the larger.

LCD = 7

$\dfrac{5}{7}-\dfrac{4}{7}=\dfrac{1}{7}$

Attach the sign of the addend having the larger absolute value to the difference.

$-\dfrac{5}{7}+\dfrac{4}{7}=-\dfrac{1}{7}$

84. $-\dfrac{3}{8}+\dfrac{1}{2}$

$\left|-\dfrac{3}{8}\right|=\dfrac{3}{8};\quad \left|\dfrac{1}{2}\right|=\dfrac{1}{2}$

LCD = 8

Subtract the smaller absolute value from the larger.

$\dfrac{1}{2}-\dfrac{3}{8}=\dfrac{1\cdot 4}{2\cdot 4}-\dfrac{3}{8}=\dfrac{4}{8}-\dfrac{3}{8}=\dfrac{1}{8}$

Attach the sign of the addend having the larger absolute value to the difference.

$-\dfrac{3}{8}+\dfrac{1}{2}=\dfrac{1}{8}$

86. $\dfrac{1}{12}+\left(-\dfrac{7}{18}\right)$

$\left|\dfrac{1}{12}\right|=\dfrac{1}{12};\quad \left|-\dfrac{7}{18}\right|=\dfrac{7}{18}$

LCD = 36

Subtract the smaller absolute value from the larger.

$\dfrac{7}{18}-\dfrac{1}{12}=\dfrac{7\cdot 2}{18\cdot 2}-\dfrac{1\cdot 3}{12\cdot 3}=\dfrac{14}{36}-\dfrac{3}{36}=\dfrac{11}{36}$

Attach the sign of the addend having the larger absolute value to the difference.

$\dfrac{1}{12}+\left(-\dfrac{7}{18}\right)=-\dfrac{11}{36}$

88. $\dfrac{3}{7}+\left(-\dfrac{4}{21}\right)$

$\left|\dfrac{3}{7}\right|=\dfrac{3}{7};\quad \left|-\dfrac{4}{21}\right|=\dfrac{4}{21}$

LCD = 21

Subtract the smaller absolute value from the larger.

$\dfrac{3}{7}-\dfrac{4}{21}=\dfrac{3\cdot 3}{7\cdot 3}-\dfrac{4}{21}=\dfrac{9}{21}-\dfrac{4}{21}=\dfrac{5}{21}$

Attach the sign of the addend having the larger absolute value to the difference.

$\dfrac{3}{7}+\left(-\dfrac{4}{21}\right)=\dfrac{5}{21}$

90. $-6\dfrac{2}{9}+8\dfrac{1}{3}$

$\left|-6\dfrac{2}{9}\right|=6\dfrac{2}{9};\quad \left|8\dfrac{1}{3}\right|=8\dfrac{1}{3}$

LCD = 9

Subtract the smaller absolute value from the larger.

$8\dfrac{1}{3}-6\dfrac{2}{9}=8\dfrac{1\cdot 3}{3\cdot 3}-6\dfrac{2}{9}$

$=8\dfrac{4}{9}-6\dfrac{2}{9}=2\dfrac{2}{9}$

Attach the sign of the addend having the larger absolute value to the difference.

$-6\dfrac{2}{9}+8\dfrac{1}{3}=2\dfrac{1}{9}$

92. $17\dfrac{1}{6}+\left(-21\dfrac{2}{3}\right)$

$\left|17\dfrac{1}{6}\right|=17\dfrac{1}{6};\quad \left|-21\dfrac{2}{3}\right|=21\dfrac{2}{3}$

LCD = 6

Subtract the smaller absolute value from the larger.

$21\dfrac{2}{3}-17\dfrac{1}{6}=21\dfrac{2\cdot 2}{3\cdot 2}-17\dfrac{1}{6}$

$=21\dfrac{4}{6}-17\dfrac{1}{6}=4\dfrac{3}{6}=4\dfrac{1}{2}$

Attach the sign of the addend having the larger absolute value to the difference.

$17\dfrac{1}{6}+\left(-21\dfrac{2}{3}\right)=-4\dfrac{1}{2}$

94. $-19 + 10\frac{2}{3}$

$|-19| = 19; \quad \left|10\frac{2}{3}\right| = 10\frac{2}{3}$

LCD = 3
Subtract the smaller absolute value from the larger.

$19 - 10\frac{2}{3} = 18\frac{3}{3} - 10\frac{2}{3} = 8\frac{1}{3}$

Attach the sign of the addend having the larger absolute value to the difference.

$-19 + 10\frac{2}{3} = -8\frac{1}{3}$

96. $86\frac{7}{8} + \left(-101\frac{1}{3}\right)$

$\left|86\frac{7}{8}\right| = 86\frac{7}{8}; \quad \left|-101\frac{1}{3}\right| = 101\frac{1}{3}$

LCD = 24
Subtract the smaller absolute value from the larger.

$101\frac{1}{3} - 86\frac{7}{8} = 101\frac{1 \cdot 8}{3 \cdot 8} - 86\frac{7 \cdot 3}{8 \cdot 3}$

$= 101\frac{8}{24} - 86\frac{21}{24}$

$= 100\frac{32}{24} - 86\frac{21}{24} = 14\frac{11}{24}$

Attach the sign of the addend having the larger absolute value to the difference.

$86\frac{7}{8} + \left(-101\frac{1}{3}\right) = -14\frac{11}{24}$

98. The morning temperature is −6°F, then the temperature rose by 15°. This translates into
−6°F + 15°F = 9°F
The noontime temperature was 9°F.

100. The level of the Caspian Sea can be represented by −92 feet. Since Mt. Kilimanjaro is 19,432 feet higher, this translates to −92 + 19,432 = 19,340. Mount Kilimanjaro is 19,340 feet tall.

Cumulative Skills Review

2. $53 - 14\frac{2}{5} = 52\frac{5}{5} - 14\frac{2}{5} = 38\frac{3}{5}$

4. $\frac{16}{48} = \frac{1}{3}$

6. 13,396 m = 13.396 km

8. Arrange the set of numbers in ascending order:
2, 13, 28, 46, 96
Since there are five numbers in the data set, the median is the middle item, 28.

10. $|55| = 55$

Section 9.3   Subtracting Signed Numbers

Concept Check

2. To solve the subtraction problem 3 − 7, it is helpful to write it as 3 + (−7) .

Guide Problems

4. Subtract −1.2 − 1.7

a. Write the subtraction problem as an addition problem.
−1.2 − 1.7 = −1.2 + (−1.7)

b. Determine the absolute value of each addend in the addition problem of part a.
$|-1.2| = 1.2; \quad |-1.7| = 1.7$

c. Since the addends in part a have the same sign, add the absolute values of the addends.
$1.2 + 1.7 = \underline{2.9}$

d. Attach the common sign of the addends to the sum of part c.
$-1.2 - 1.7 = -1.2 + \underline{(-1.7)} = -2.9$

In Problems 6 through 60, subtract the signed numbers using the procedure outlined above. Simplify fractions, if possible.

6. $18 - 7 = 11$

8. $35 - 23 = 12$

10. $6 - 14$
Write the subtraction problem as an addition problem.
$6 - 14 = 6 + (-14)$
Determine the absolute value of each addend in the addition problem of part a.
$|6| = 6; \quad |-14| = 14$
Since the addends in the addition have different signs, subtract the smaller absolute value from the larger.
$14 - 6 = 8$
Attach the sign of the addend having the larger absolute value to the difference.
$6 - 14 = 6 + (-14) = -8$

12. $28 - 55$
Write the subtraction problem as an addition problem.
$28 - 55 = 28 + (-55)$
Determine the absolute value of each addend in the addition problem.
$|28| = 28; \quad |-55| = 55$
Since the addends in the addition have different signs, subtract the smaller absolute value from the larger.
$55 - 28 = 27$
Attach the sign of the addend having the larger absolute value to the difference
$28 - 55 = 28 + (-55) = -27$

14. $18 - (-12)$
Write the subtraction problem as an addition problem.
$18 - (-12) = 18 + 12$
Both addends are positive, so the sum is positive.
$18 - (-12) = 18 + 12 = 30$

16. $45 - (-21)$
Write the subtraction problem as an addition problem.
$45 - (-21) = 45 + 21$
Both addends are positive, so the sum is positive.
$45 - (-21) = 45 + 21 = 66$

18. $215 - 163 = 52$
Subtract as usual.

20. $-10 - (-11)$
Write the subtraction problem as an addition problem.
$-10 - (-11) = -10 + 11$
Determine the absolute value of each addend in the addition problem.
$|-10| = 10; \quad |11| = 11$
Since the addends in the addition have different signs, subtract the smaller absolute value from the larger.
$11 - 10 = 1$
Attach the sign of the addend having the larger absolute value to the difference
$-10 - (-11) = -10 + 11 = 1$

22. $-182 - 807$

 Write the subtraction problem as an addition problem.

 $-182 - 807 = -182 + (-807)$

 Determine the absolute value of each addend in the addition problem.

 $|-182| = 182; \quad |-807| = 807$

 Since the addends in the addition have the same sign, add the absolute values.

 $182 + 807 = 989$

 Since both addends are negative, the sum is negative.

 $-182 - 807 = -182 + (-807) = -989$

24. $-656 - 450$

 Write the subtraction problem as an addition problem.

 $-656 - 450 = -656 + (-450)$

 Determine the absolute value of each addend in the addition problem.

 $|-656| = 656; \quad |-450| = 450$

 Since the addends in the addition have the same sign, add the absolute values.

 $656 + 450 = 1106$

 Since both addends are negative, the sum is negative.

 $-656 - 450 = -656 + (-450) = -1106$

26. $478 - 1249$

 Write the subtraction problem as an addition problem.

 $478 - 1249 = 478 + (-1249)$

 Determine the absolute value of each addend in the addition problem.

 $|478| = 478; \quad |-1249| = 1249$

 Since the addends in the addition have different signs, subtract the smaller absolute value from the larger.

 $1249 - 478 = 771$

 Attach the sign of the addend having the larger absolute value to the difference.

 $478 - 1249 = 478 + (-1249) = -771$

28. $-874 - (-2197)$

 Write the subtraction problem as an addition problem.

 $-874 - (-2197) = -874 + 2197$

 Determine the absolute value of each addend in the addition problem.

 $|-874| = 874; \quad |2197| = 2197$

 Since the addends in the addition have different signs, subtract the smaller absolute value from the larger.

 $2197 - 874 = 1323$

 Attach the sign of the addend having the larger absolute value to the difference.

 $-874 - (-2197) = -874 + 2197 = 1323$

In problems 30 through 44, find the least common denominator and then write each fraction as an equivalent fraction with the LCD before subtracting.

30. $\dfrac{2}{9} - \dfrac{5}{9}$

 Write the subtraction problem as an addition problem.

 $\dfrac{2}{9} - \dfrac{5}{9} = \dfrac{2}{9} + \left(-\dfrac{5}{9}\right)$

 $\left|\dfrac{2}{9}\right| = \dfrac{2}{9}; \quad \left|-\dfrac{5}{9}\right| = \dfrac{5}{9}$

 Since the addends in the addition have different signs, subtract the smaller absolute value from the larger.

 $LCD = 9$

 $\dfrac{5}{9} - \dfrac{2}{9} = \dfrac{3}{9} = \dfrac{1}{3}$

 Attach the sign of the addend having the larger absolute value to the difference.

 $\dfrac{2}{9} - \dfrac{5}{9} = -\dfrac{1}{3}$

32. $-\dfrac{1}{12} - \dfrac{5}{8}$

 Write the subtraction problem as an addition problem.

 $-\dfrac{1}{12} - \dfrac{5}{8} = -\dfrac{1}{12} + \left(-\dfrac{5}{8}\right)$

 $\left|-\dfrac{1}{12}\right| = \dfrac{1}{12}; \quad \left|-\dfrac{5}{8}\right| = \dfrac{5}{8}$

 Since the addends in the addition have the same sign, add the absolute values.

 $LCD = 24$

 $\dfrac{1}{12} + \dfrac{5}{8} = \dfrac{1 \cdot 2}{12 \cdot 2} + \dfrac{5 \cdot 3}{8 \cdot 3} = \dfrac{2}{24} + \dfrac{15}{24} = \dfrac{17}{24}$

 Attach the common sign to the sum.

 $-\dfrac{1}{12} - \dfrac{5}{8} = -\dfrac{1}{12} + \left(-\dfrac{5}{8}\right) = -\dfrac{17}{24}$

34. $-\dfrac{1}{5} - \left(-\dfrac{1}{8}\right)$

Write the subtraction problem as an addition problem.

$$-\dfrac{1}{5} - \left(-\dfrac{1}{8}\right) = -\dfrac{1}{5} + \dfrac{1}{8}$$

$$\left|-\dfrac{1}{5}\right| = \dfrac{1}{5}; \quad \left|\dfrac{1}{8}\right| = \dfrac{1}{8}$$

Since the addends in the addition have different signs, subtract the smaller absolute value from the larger.

LCD = 40

$$\dfrac{1}{5} - \dfrac{1}{8} = \dfrac{1 \cdot 8}{5 \cdot 8} - \dfrac{1 \cdot 5}{8 \cdot 5} = \dfrac{8}{40} - \dfrac{5}{40} = \dfrac{3}{40}$$

Attach the sign of the addend having the larger absolute value to the difference.

$$-\dfrac{1}{5} - \left(-\dfrac{1}{8}\right) = -\dfrac{1}{5} + \dfrac{1}{8} = -\dfrac{3}{40}$$

36. $\dfrac{3}{15} - \left(-\dfrac{7}{20}\right)$

Write the subtraction problem as an addition problem.

$$\dfrac{3}{15} - \left(-\dfrac{7}{20}\right) = \dfrac{3}{15} + \dfrac{7}{20} = \dfrac{1}{5} + \dfrac{7}{20}$$

Both addends are positive, so add. The sum is positive.

LCD = 20

$$\dfrac{1}{5} + \dfrac{7}{20} = \dfrac{1 \cdot 4}{5 \cdot 4} + \dfrac{7}{20} = \dfrac{4}{20} + \dfrac{7}{20} = \dfrac{11}{20}$$

$$\dfrac{3}{15} - \left(-\dfrac{7}{20}\right) = \dfrac{3}{15} + \dfrac{7}{20} = \dfrac{1}{5} + \dfrac{7}{20} = \dfrac{11}{20}$$

38. $3\dfrac{1}{3} - 8\dfrac{5}{7}$

Write the subtraction problem as an addition problem.

$$3\dfrac{1}{3} - 8\dfrac{5}{7} = 3\dfrac{1}{3} + \left(-8\dfrac{5}{7}\right)$$

$$\left|3\dfrac{1}{3}\right| = 3\dfrac{1}{3}; \quad \left|-8\dfrac{5}{7}\right| = 8\dfrac{5}{7}$$

Since the addends in the addition have different signs, subtract the smaller absolute value from the larger.

LCD = 21

$$8\dfrac{5}{7} - 3\dfrac{1}{3} = 8\dfrac{5 \cdot 3}{7 \cdot 3} - 3\dfrac{1 \cdot 7}{3 \cdot 7} = 8\dfrac{15}{21} - 3\dfrac{7}{21}$$

$$= 5\dfrac{8}{21}$$

Attach the sign of the addend having the larger absolute value to the difference.

$$3\dfrac{1}{3} - 8\dfrac{5}{7} = 3\dfrac{1}{3} + \left(-8\dfrac{5}{7}\right) = -5\dfrac{8}{21}$$

40. $6\dfrac{2}{21} - \left(-4\dfrac{3}{14}\right)$

Write the subtraction problem as an addition problem.

$$6\dfrac{2}{21} - \left(-4\dfrac{3}{14}\right) = 6\dfrac{2}{21} + 4\dfrac{3}{14}$$

Since the addends in the addition are both positive, just add. The sign of the sum is positive.

LCD = 42

$$6\dfrac{2}{21} + 4\dfrac{3}{14} = 6\dfrac{2 \cdot 2}{21 \cdot 2} + 4\dfrac{3 \cdot 3}{14 \cdot 3} = 6\dfrac{4}{42} + 4\dfrac{9}{42}$$

$$= 10\dfrac{13}{42}$$

$$6\dfrac{2}{21} - \left(-4\dfrac{3}{14}\right) = 6\dfrac{2}{21} + 4\dfrac{3}{14} = 10\dfrac{13}{42}$$

42. $-8\dfrac{2}{9} - 6\dfrac{3}{15}$

    Write the subtraction problem as an addition problem.

    $$-8\dfrac{2}{9} - 6\dfrac{3}{15} = -8\dfrac{2}{9} + \left(-6\dfrac{3}{15}\right) = -8\dfrac{2}{9} + \left(-6\dfrac{1}{5}\right)$$

    $$\left|-8\dfrac{2}{9}\right| = 8\dfrac{2}{9}; \quad \left|-6\dfrac{1}{5}\right| = 6\dfrac{1}{5}$$

    Since the addends in the addition have the same sign, add the absolute values.
    LCD = 45

    $$8\dfrac{2}{9} + 6\dfrac{1}{5} = 8\dfrac{2\cdot 5}{9\cdot 5} + 6\dfrac{1\cdot 9}{5\cdot 9} = 8\dfrac{10}{45} + 6\dfrac{9}{45}$$
    $$= 14\dfrac{19}{45}$$

    Attach the common sign to the sum.

    $$-8\dfrac{2}{9} - 6\dfrac{3}{15} = -8\dfrac{2}{9} + \left(-6\dfrac{3}{15}\right) = -14\dfrac{19}{45}$$

44. $9\dfrac{1}{2} - 17\dfrac{7}{23}$

    Write the subtraction problem as an addition problem.

    $$9\dfrac{1}{2} - 17\dfrac{7}{23} = 9\dfrac{1}{2} + \left(-17\dfrac{7}{23}\right)$$

    $$\left|9\dfrac{1}{2}\right| = 9\dfrac{1}{2}; \quad \left|-17\dfrac{7}{23}\right| = 17\dfrac{7}{23}$$

    Since the addends in the addition have different signs, subtract the smaller absolute value from the larger.
    LCD = 46

    $$17\dfrac{7}{23} - 9\dfrac{1}{2} = 17\dfrac{7\cdot 2}{23\cdot 2} - 9\dfrac{1\cdot 23}{2\cdot 23} = 17\dfrac{14}{46} - 9\dfrac{23}{46}$$
    $$= 16\dfrac{60}{46} - 9\dfrac{23}{46} = 7\dfrac{37}{46}$$

    Attach the sign of the addend having the larger absolute value to the difference.

    $$9\dfrac{1}{2} - 17\dfrac{7}{23} = 9\dfrac{1}{2} + \left(-17\dfrac{7}{23}\right) = -7\dfrac{37}{46}$$

46. $7.02 - 5.03 = 1.99$

48. $5.21 - 7.31 = 5.21 + (-7.31) = -2.1$

50. $-1.15 - 9.12 = -1.15 + (-9.12) = -10.27$

52. $-7.98 - (-10.86) = -7.98 + 10.86 = 2.88$

54. $24.32 - 57.3 = 24.32 + (-57.3) = -32.98$

56. $-47.21 - (-61.6) = -47.21 + 61.6 = 14.39$

58. $187.2 - 95.1 = 92.1$

60. $-78.2 - 86.3 = -78.2 + (-86.3) = -164.5$

62. The year 2000 BC can be represented as -2000. Find the difference in the years:
    $1295 - (-2000) = 1295 + 2000 = 3295$ years.
    The Chinese were eating pasta 3295 years before the Italians.

63. $32°F - (-97°F) = 32°F + 97°F = 129°F$.
    The difference between the two temperatures is $129°F$.

Cumulative Skills Review

2. The problem translates to
   $\$12,388.14 - (\$1420.12 + \$522.18 + \$125.50) = \$12,388.14 - \$2067.80 = \$10,320.34$

4. $V = \pi r^2 h \approx 3.14 \cdot 27^2 \cdot 29 \approx 66,382.74 \text{ mm}^2$

6. $42 + (-16) + (-18) = 26 + (-18) = 8$

8. $45\% = \dfrac{45}{100} = \dfrac{9}{20}$

10. $\dfrac{42}{3} = \dfrac{14}{1}$

Section 9.4   Multiplying and Dividing Signed Numbers

Concept Check

2.   The product or quotient of two numbers with the same sign is always __positive__.

Guide Problems

4.   Multiply $-8 \cdot (-1.1)$

   a.   Determine the absolute value of each factor.
$$|-8| = 8; \quad |1.1| = 1.1$$

   b.   Multiply the absolute values
$$8 \cdot \underline{1.1} = \underline{8.8}$$

   c.   Since the factors have the same sign, the product is positive.
$$-8 \cdot (-1.1) = 8.8$$

6.   Multiply $-6\frac{2}{3} \cdot \left(-1\frac{1}{5}\right)$. Simplify, if possible.

   a.   Determine the absolute value of each factor.
$$\left|-6\frac{2}{3}\right| = 6\frac{2}{3}; \quad \left|-1\frac{1}{5}\right| = 1\frac{1}{5}$$

   b.   Multiply the absolute values
$$6\frac{2}{3} \cdot 1\frac{1}{5} = \frac{\overset{4}{\cancel{20}}}{\cancel{3}} \cdot \frac{\overset{2}{\cancel{6}}}{\cancel{5}} = \frac{8}{1} = 8$$

   c.   Since the factors have the same sign, the product is positive.
$$-6\frac{2}{3} \cdot \left(-1\frac{1}{5}\right) = 8$$

In Problems 8 through 66, multiply the signed numbers using the procedure outlined in the Guide problems. Simplify fractions, if possible.

8. $4 \cdot 12 = 48$

10. $-6 \cdot 10 = -60$

12. $6 \cdot (-13) = -78$

14. $-15 \cdot (-12) = 180$

16. $201 \cdot (-5) = -1005$

18. $-141 \cdot (-8) = 1128$

20. $15 \cdot (-407) = -6105$

22. $-28 \cdot (-182) = 5096$

24. $-\frac{4}{9} \cdot \frac{6}{13} = -\frac{4}{\cancel{9}_{3}} \cdot \frac{\overset{2}{\cancel{6}}}{13} = -\frac{8}{39}$

26. $-\frac{3}{8} \cdot \left(-\frac{4}{5}\right) = -\frac{3}{\cancel{8}_{2}} \cdot \left(-\frac{\overset{1}{\cancel{4}}}{5}\right) = \frac{3}{10}$

28. $\frac{7}{12} \cdot \left(-\frac{3}{5}\right) = \frac{7}{\cancel{12}_{4}} \cdot \left(-\frac{\overset{1}{\cancel{3}}}{5}\right) = -\frac{7}{20}$

30. $\frac{4}{3} \cdot \frac{3}{8} = \frac{\overset{1}{\cancel{4}}}{\cancel{3}_{1}} \cdot \frac{\overset{1}{\cancel{3}}}{\cancel{8}_{2}} = \frac{1}{2}$

32. $-\frac{4}{9} \cdot \left(-\frac{3}{16}\right) = -\frac{\overset{1}{\cancel{4}}}{\cancel{9}_{3}} \cdot \left(-\frac{\overset{1}{\cancel{3}}}{\cancel{16}_{4}}\right) = \frac{1}{12}$

34. $\dfrac{5}{24}\left(-\dfrac{18}{25}\right) = \dfrac{\cancel{5}^{1}}{\cancel{24}_{4}}\left(-\dfrac{\cancel{18}^{3}}{\cancel{25}_{5}}\right) = -\dfrac{3}{20}$

36. $3\dfrac{1}{3}\cdot\left(-5\dfrac{1}{4}\right) = \dfrac{10}{3}\cdot\left(-\dfrac{21}{4}\right) = \dfrac{\cancel{10}^{5}}{\cancel{3}_{1}}\cdot\left(-\dfrac{\cancel{21}^{7}}{\cancel{4}_{2}}\right)$

$\qquad = -\dfrac{35}{2} = -17\dfrac{1}{2}$

38. $-3\dfrac{3}{11}\cdot\left(-2\dfrac{1}{5}\right) = -\dfrac{36}{11}\cdot\left(-\dfrac{11}{5}\right) = -\dfrac{36}{\cancel{11}_{1}}\cdot\left(-\dfrac{\cancel{11}^{1}}{5}\right)$

$\qquad = \dfrac{36}{5} = 7\dfrac{1}{5}$

40. $-\dfrac{2}{11}\cdot(-5) = \dfrac{10}{11}$

42. $2\dfrac{3}{13}\cdot(-3) = \dfrac{29}{13}\cdot(-3) = -\dfrac{87}{13} = -6\dfrac{9}{13}$

44. $7.9\cdot0.61 = 4.819$

46. $410\cdot(-0.25) = -102.50$

48. $-0.15\cdot0.23 = -0.0345$

50. $3.1\cdot(-0.72) = -2.232$

52. $-51\cdot14 = -714$

54. $46\cdot(-349) = -16,054$

56. $12\cdot(-3)\cdot(10) = -360$

58. $18\cdot(-6)\cdot(-9) = 972$

60. $-5\cdot14\cdot20 = -1400$

62. $\dfrac{21}{5}\left(-\dfrac{5}{4}\right)\left(-\dfrac{4}{21}\right) = \dfrac{\cancel{21}^{1}}{\cancel{5}_{1}}\left(-\dfrac{\cancel{5}^{1}}{\cancel{4}_{1}}\right)\left(-\dfrac{\cancel{4}^{1}}{\cancel{21}_{1}}\right) = 1$

64. $\left(-4\dfrac{1}{3}\right)(-2)\left(-3\dfrac{1}{2}\right) = -\dfrac{13}{3}(-2)\left(-\dfrac{7}{2}\right) = -\dfrac{13}{3}\left(-\cancel{2}^{1}\right)\left(-\dfrac{7}{\cancel{2}_{1}}\right) = -\dfrac{91}{3} = -30\dfrac{1}{3}$

66. $5.1(-0.3)(2.2) = -3.366$

Guide Problems

68. Divide $-1.08 \div (-0.9)$

    a.   Determine the absolute values of the dividend and divisor.

$\qquad |-1.08| = 1.08; \qquad |-0.9| = 0.9$

    b.   Divide the absolute values

$\qquad 0.9\overline{)1.08} \qquad\qquad 9\overline{)10.8}^{\,1.2}$

    c.   Since the dividend and divisor have the same sign, the quotient is positive.

$\qquad -1.08 \div (-0.9) = 1.2$

70. Divide $-1\dfrac{3}{7} \div 2\dfrac{4}{5}$. Simplify, if possible.

    a. Determine the absolute values of the dividend and divisor.

$$\left|-1\dfrac{3}{7}\right| = 1\dfrac{3}{7}; \qquad \left|2\dfrac{4}{5}\right| = 2\dfrac{4}{5}$$

    b. Divide the absolute values

$$1\dfrac{3}{7} \div 2\dfrac{4}{5} = \dfrac{10}{7} \div \dfrac{14}{5} = \dfrac{10}{7} \cdot \dfrac{5}{14} = \dfrac{25}{49}$$

    c. Since the dividend and divisor have different signs, the quotient is negative. Attach a negative sign to the result of part b.

$$-1\dfrac{3}{7} \div 2\dfrac{4}{5} = -\dfrac{25}{49}$$

In Problems 72 through 114, divide the signed numbers using the procedure outlined in the Guide problems. Simplify fractions, if possible.

72. $-15 \div 5 = -3$

74. $-32 \div 4 = -8$

76. $56 \div (-8) = -7$

78. $-63 \div (-9) = 7$

80. $213 \div (-3) = -71$

82. $-126 \div 7 = -18$

84. $-630 \div (-18) = 35$

86. $-495 \div (-45) = 11$

88. $-\dfrac{1}{3} \div \left(-\dfrac{2}{3}\right) = -\dfrac{1}{3} \cdot \left(-\dfrac{3}{2}\right) = \dfrac{1}{2}$

90. $-\dfrac{4}{7} \div \left(-\dfrac{8}{11}\right) = -\dfrac{4}{7} \cdot \left(-\dfrac{11}{8}\right) = \dfrac{11}{14}$

92. $-\dfrac{8}{9} \div \left(-\dfrac{4}{5}\right) = -\dfrac{8}{9} \cdot \left(-\dfrac{5}{4}\right) = \dfrac{10}{9} = 1\dfrac{1}{9}$

94. $\dfrac{1}{4} \div \left(-\dfrac{5}{9}\right) = \dfrac{1}{4} \cdot \left(-\dfrac{9}{5}\right) = -\dfrac{9}{20}$

96. $2 \div \left(-3\dfrac{1}{6}\right) = 2 \div \left(-\dfrac{19}{6}\right) = 2 \cdot \left(-\dfrac{6}{19}\right) = -\dfrac{12}{19}$

98. $-5\dfrac{3}{8} \div \left(-2\dfrac{3}{4}\right) = -\dfrac{43}{8} \div \left(-\dfrac{11}{4}\right) = -\dfrac{43}{8} \cdot \left(-\dfrac{4}{11}\right) = \dfrac{43}{22} = 1\dfrac{21}{22}$

100. $-36\dfrac{2}{3} \div \left(3\dfrac{2}{3}\right) = -\dfrac{110}{3} \div \left(\dfrac{11}{3}\right) = -\dfrac{110}{3} \cdot \dfrac{3}{11} = -10$

102. $49 \div \left(-1\dfrac{3}{4}\right) = 49 \div \left(-\dfrac{7}{4}\right) = 49 \cdot \left(-\dfrac{4}{7}\right) = -28$

104. $\dfrac{-6.586}{7.4} = -0.89$

106. $\dfrac{15.18}{-0.69} = -22$

108. $89.27 \div (-11.3) = -7.9$

110. $-6.885 \div 76.5 = -0.09$

112. $-195.25 \div (-2.5) = 78.1$

114. $1067.781 \div (-51.09) = -20.9$

116. $(-18) \div 3 = -6$, so the average daily change was a loss of 6 points.

118. The temperature dropped from 80ºF to 59ºF (a drop of 21ºF) between 5:00 PM and 8:00 PM, a three-hour time span. The average change in temperature per hour was $-21 \div 3 = -7$, a drop of 7ºF per hour.

Cumulative Skills Review

2. 7% of $\$375 = 0.07 \times \$375 = \$26.25$

4. $\dfrac{12 + 23 + 57 + 8 + 42}{5} = \dfrac{142}{5} = 28.4$

6. $P = 20 \text{ ft} + 19 \text{ ft} + 17 \text{ ft} = 56 \text{ ft}$

8. $-8.3 + 7.4 = -0.9$

10. $23 - 49 = 23 + (-49) = -26$

Section 9.5   Signed Numbers and Order of Operations

Concept Check

2. Next, we evaluate expression with <u>exponents</u> .

4. Finally, we perform all <u>additions</u> and <u>subtractions</u> as they occur from left to right.

Guide Problems

6. Simplify $5^3 - (4 + 3 \cdot 2)^2 \div 4$ using order of operations.

$$5^3 - (4 + 3 \cdot 2)^2 \div 4 = 5^3 - (4 + \underline{6})^2 \div 4$$
$$= 5^3 - (\underline{10})^2 \div 4$$
$$= \underline{125} - 100 \div 4$$
$$= 125 - \underline{25}$$
$$= 100$$

In Problems 8 through 52, use the order of operations to simplify each expression. First perform all operations within grouping symbols (parentheses, brackets, curly braces, fraction bars.) Next evaluate all exponential expressions. Then perform all multiplications and divisions as they appear in reading from left to right, followed by all additions and subtractions as they appear in reading from left to right.

8. $12 + (-8) + 4 = 4 + 4$
$$= 8$$

10. $9 - 4 \times (-2) + 5 = 9 - (-8) + 5$
$$= 9 + 8 + 5$$
$$= 17 + 5 = 22$$

12. $42 \div 7 - 2(-4) = 6 - (-8)$
$$= 6 + 8$$
$$= 14$$

14. $-15 \div 5 + (-9) \cdot 3 + (-12) = -3 + (-27) + (-12)$
$$= -30 + (-12)$$
$$= -42$$

16. $2^2 \cdot (-2) \cdot 4^2 = 4 \cdot (-2) \cdot 16$
$$= -8 \cdot 16$$
$$= -128$$

18. $(-7)^2 + 21 - 8 = 49 + 21 - 8$
$$= 70 - 8$$
$$= 62$$

20. $\begin{aligned} 8+(-6)^2-30 &= 8+36-30 \\ &= 44-30 \\ &= 14 \end{aligned}$

22. $\begin{aligned} \left(2^5-12\right)\div(-4) &= (32-12)\div(-4) \\ &= 20\div(-4) \\ &= -5 \end{aligned}$

24. $\begin{aligned} -12-(4)^2+(-3)^2 &= -12-16+9 \\ &= -28+9 \\ &= -19 \end{aligned}$

26. $\begin{aligned} (41+7)\div(16\div 2) &= 48\div 8 \\ &= 6 \end{aligned}$

28. $\begin{aligned} \left[9^2-5\cdot 12+9\right]\div(-3) &= [81-5\cdot 12+9]\div(-3) \\ &= [81-60+9]\div(-3) \\ &= (21+9)\div(-3) \\ &= 30\div(-3) \\ &= -10 \end{aligned}$

30. $\begin{aligned} 10^2-\left(4^2+8\cdot 9\right)\div 2^2 &= 10^2-(16+8\cdot 9)\div 2^2 \\ &= 10^2-(16+72)\div 2^2 \\ &= 10^2-88\div 2^2 \\ &= 100-88\div 4 \\ &= 100-22=78 \end{aligned}$

32. $\begin{aligned} (8+4)^2\div\left[(-3)^2-7\right] &= 12^2\div[9-7] \\ &= 144\div 2 \\ &= 72 \end{aligned}$

34. $\begin{aligned} 12+(4-5)^2\cdot\left(12-3^2\right) &= 12+(-1)^2\cdot(12-9) \\ &= 12+1\cdot 3 \\ &= 12+3 \\ &= 15 \end{aligned}$

36. $\begin{aligned} -\frac{2}{5}\div\frac{6}{25}+\frac{2}{3}\left(\frac{1}{10}\right) &= -\frac{2}{5}\cdot\frac{25}{6}+\frac{2}{3}\left(\frac{1}{10}\right) \\ &= -\frac{5}{3}+\frac{1}{15}=-\frac{5\cdot 5}{3\cdot 5}+\frac{1}{15} \\ &= -\frac{25}{15}+\frac{1}{15}=-\frac{24}{15}=-\frac{8}{5} \end{aligned}$

38. $\begin{aligned} \left(-\frac{1}{3}\right)^2+\left(-\frac{1}{2}\right)\div\frac{3}{16} &= \frac{1}{9}+\left(-\frac{1}{2}\right)\div\frac{3}{16} \\ &= \frac{1}{9}+\left(-\frac{1}{2}\right)\cdot\frac{16}{3}=\frac{1}{9}+\left(-\frac{8}{3}\right) \\ &= \frac{1}{9}+\left(-\frac{8\cdot 3}{3\cdot 3}\right)=\frac{1}{9}+\left(-\frac{24}{9}\right) \\ &= -\frac{23}{9} \end{aligned}$

40. $\begin{aligned} (-2)^3-\left[\frac{1}{3}+\frac{5}{6}\left(\frac{2}{15}\right)\right]\div\frac{1}{9} &= (-2)^3-\left[\frac{1}{3}+\frac{1}{9}\right]\div\frac{1}{9} \\ &= (-2)^3-\left[\frac{3}{9}+\frac{1}{9}\right]\div\frac{1}{9} \\ &= (-2)^3-\frac{4}{9}\div\frac{1}{9} \\ &= -8-\frac{4}{9}\div\frac{1}{9} \\ &= -8-\frac{4}{9}\cdot\frac{9}{1} \\ &= -8-4=-12 \end{aligned}$

42. $\begin{aligned} 0.31(6.4-2.5)\div(-0.4) &= 0.31(3.9)\div(-0.4) \\ &= 1.209\div(-0.4) \\ &= -3.0225 \end{aligned}$

44. $0.8 + (0.6)^2(-4) = 0.8 + 0.36(-4)$
$= 0.8 + (-1.44)$
$= -0.64$

46. $(-8.6 + 7.5)^3 - 3(0.4)^3 = (-1.1)^3 - 3(0.4)^3$
$= -1.331 - 3(0.064)$
$= -1.331 - 0.192$
$= -1.523$

48. $180 \div 3\left[(5-3)^3 - (-4)\right] - 4^3 = 180 \div 3\left[2^3 - (-4)\right] - 4^3 = 180 \div 3\left[8 - (-4)\right] - 4^3 = 180 \div 3(8+4) - 4^3$
$= 180 \div 3[12] - 4^3 = 180 \div 3[12] - 64 = 60 \cdot 12 - 64 = 720 - 64 = 656$

50. $12 + \dfrac{32 - 4^2}{4^2 - 2^3} - 5 = 12 + \dfrac{32 - 16}{16 - 8} - 5$
$= 12 + \dfrac{16}{8} - 5$
$= 12 + 2 - 5$
$= 14 - 5 = 9$

52. $7^2 + \left(\dfrac{6^2 - 2^4}{4^2 - 6}\right)^2 - 21 = 7^2 + \left(\dfrac{36 - 16}{16 - 6}\right)^2 - 21$
$= 7^2 + \left(\dfrac{20}{10}\right)^2 - 21$
$= 7^2 + 2^2 - 21$
$= 49 + 4 - 21 = 53 - 21 = 32$

54. A birdie is one stroke under par (−1), an eagle is two strokes under par (−2), and a birdie is one stroke over par (1). Represent par by 0.

   a. $2(-2) + 6(0) + 6(1) + 2 \cdot 2(-1)$

   b. $2(-2) + 6(0) + 6(1) + 2\left[2(-1)\right] = 2(-2) + 6(0) + 6(1) + 2[-2]$
   $= -4 + 0 + 6 + (-4)$
   $= -2$

56. $59 - \dfrac{10{,}000}{1000}(3) = 59 - (10)3 = 59 - 30 = 29$; $59 - \dfrac{20{,}000}{1000}(3) = 59 - (20)3 = 59 - 60 = -1$
   At 10,000 feet, the average air temperature will be 29°F.
   At 20,000 feet, the average air temperature will be −1°F.

Cumulative Skills Review

2. $22.5 \text{ mi} \times \dfrac{5280 \text{ ft}}{\text{mi}} = 118{,}800$ feet

4. $(6 + 3 \cdot 8) - 2^2 = (6 + 24) - 2^2$
$= 30 - 4 = 26$

6. $20\% = 0.20$

8. $1417.\underline{7}877$ rounded to the nearest tenth is 1417.8.

10. Since the lengths of all the sides of the triangle are equal, the triangle is equilateral. Since all the angles are acute angles, the triangle is also an acute triangle.

Chapter 9 Numerical Facts of Life

2. $-5°F - (-33°F) = -5°F + 33°F = 28°F$

4. $48°F - (-33°F) = 48°F + 33°F = -15°F$

Chapter 9 Review Exercises

1. The opposite of 15 is −15.

2. The opposite of 2.34 is −2.34.

3. The opposite of −47 is 47.

4. The opposite of −8.094 is 8.094.

5.
$$-6 \quad -5 \quad -4 \quad -3 \quad -2 \quad -1 \quad 0 \quad 1 \quad 2 \quad 3 \quad 4 \quad 5 \quad 6$$

6.
$$-4 \quad -3 \quad -2 \quad -1 \quad 0 \quad 1 \quad 2 \quad 3 \quad 4$$

7. $|12| = 12$

8. $|-52| = 52$

9. $|-2.314| = 2.314$

10. $|7436| = 7436$

11. $2 < 7, 7 > 2$

12. $-3 > -8, -8 < -3$

13. $-2.05 < -2, -2 > -2.05$

14. $7 < 7.4, 7.4 > 7$

15. −210°F

16. 1,000,000°K

17. −$45.00

18. 3500 ft

19. $21 + 89 = 110$

20. $-117 + (-37) = -154$

21. $\dfrac{4}{5} + \left(-\dfrac{1}{6}\right)$

Determine the absolute value of each addend.
$$\left|\dfrac{4}{5}\right| = \dfrac{4}{5}; \quad \left|-\dfrac{1}{6}\right| = \dfrac{1}{6}$$
Subtract the smaller absolute value from the larger.
LCD = 30
$$\dfrac{4}{5} - \dfrac{1}{6} = \dfrac{4 \cdot 6}{5 \cdot 6} - \dfrac{1 \cdot 5}{6 \cdot 5}$$
$$= \dfrac{24}{30} - \dfrac{5}{30} = \dfrac{19}{30}$$
Attach the sign of the addend having the larger absolute value to the difference.
$$\dfrac{4}{5} + \left(-\dfrac{1}{6}\right) = \dfrac{19}{30}$$

22. $-\dfrac{8}{9} + \dfrac{5}{12}$

Determine the absolute value of each addend.
$$\left|-\dfrac{8}{9}\right| = \dfrac{8}{9}; \quad \left|\dfrac{5}{12}\right| = \dfrac{5}{12}$$
Subtract the smaller absolute value from the larger.
LCD = 36
$$\dfrac{8}{9} - \dfrac{5}{12} = \dfrac{8 \cdot 4}{9 \cdot 4} - \dfrac{5 \cdot 3}{12 \cdot 3}$$
$$= \dfrac{32}{36} - \dfrac{15}{36} = \dfrac{17}{36}$$
Attach the sign of the addend having the larger absolute value to the difference.
$$-\dfrac{8}{9} + \dfrac{5}{12} = -\dfrac{17}{36}$$

23. $-2\dfrac{1}{2} + 1\dfrac{3}{7}$

Determine the absolute value of each addend: $\left|-2\dfrac{1}{2}\right| = \left|-\dfrac{5}{2}\right| = \dfrac{5}{2}; \quad \left|1\dfrac{3}{7}\right| = \left|\dfrac{10}{7}\right| = \dfrac{10}{7}$

Subtract the smaller absolute value from the larger.
LCD = 14
$$\dfrac{5}{2} - \dfrac{10}{7} = \dfrac{5 \cdot 7}{2 \cdot 7} - \dfrac{10 \cdot 2}{7 \cdot 2} = \dfrac{35}{14} - \dfrac{20}{14} = \dfrac{15}{14} = 1\dfrac{1}{14}$$

Attach the sign of the addend having the larger absolute value to the difference: $-2\dfrac{1}{2} + 1\dfrac{3}{7} = -1\dfrac{1}{14}$

24. $4\dfrac{5}{6} + \left(-1\dfrac{1}{8}\right)$

Determine the absolute value of each addend: $\left|4\dfrac{5}{6}\right| = \left|\dfrac{29}{6}\right| = \dfrac{29}{6}$; $\left|-1\dfrac{1}{8}\right| = \left|\dfrac{9}{8}\right| = \dfrac{9}{8}$

Subtract the smaller absolute value from the larger.
LCD = 24

$\dfrac{29}{6} - \dfrac{9}{8} = \dfrac{29 \cdot 4}{6 \cdot 4} - \dfrac{9 \cdot 3}{8 \cdot 3} = \dfrac{116}{24} - \dfrac{27}{24} = \dfrac{89}{24} = 3\dfrac{17}{24}$

Attach the sign of the addend having the larger absolute value to the difference: $4\dfrac{5}{6} + \left(-1\dfrac{1}{8}\right) = 3\dfrac{17}{24}$

25. $-0.45 + 2.01$
Determine the absolute value of each addend.
$\left|-0.45\right| = 0.45$; $\left|2.01\right| = 2.01$
Subtract the smaller absolute value from the larger.
$2.01 - 0.45 = 1.56$
Attach the sign of the addend having the larger absolute value to the difference.
$-0.45 + 2.01 = 1.56$

26. $-12.1 + (-4.8)$
The signs are the same, so add the absolute values and attach the common negative sign to the sum.
$-12.1 + (-4.8) = -16.9$

27. $54 - 82$
Write the subtraction problem as an addition problem.
$54 - 82 = 54 + (-82)$
Since the addends in the addition have different signs, subtract the smaller absolute value from the larger.
$82 - 54 = 28$
Attach the sign of the addend having the larger absolute value to the difference.
$54 - 82 = -28$

28. $2.3 - (-5.41)$
Write the subtraction problem as an addition problem.
$2.3 - (-5.41) = 2.3 + 5.41$
Since the addends in the addition have the same sign, add the absolute values and attach the common positive sign to the sum.
$2.3 - (-5.41) = 2.3 + 5.41 = 7.71$

29. $\dfrac{1}{4} - \dfrac{5}{8}$

Write the subtraction problem as an addition problem.
$\dfrac{1}{4} - \dfrac{5}{8} = \dfrac{1}{4} + \left(-\dfrac{5}{8}\right)$

$\left|\dfrac{1}{4}\right| = \dfrac{1}{4}$; $\left|-\dfrac{5}{8}\right| = \dfrac{5}{8}$

Since the addends in the addition have different signs, subtract the smaller absolute value from the larger.
LCD = 8

$\dfrac{5}{8} - \dfrac{1}{4} = \dfrac{5}{8} - \dfrac{2}{8} = \dfrac{3}{8}$

Attach the sign of the addend having the larger absolute value to the difference.

$\dfrac{1}{4} - \dfrac{5}{8} = -\dfrac{3}{8}$

30. $5\dfrac{2}{9} - 7\dfrac{1}{3}$

Write the subtraction problem as an addition problem.
$5\dfrac{2}{9} - 7\dfrac{1}{3} = 5\dfrac{2}{9} + \left(-7\dfrac{1}{3}\right)$

$\left|5\dfrac{2}{9}\right| = \left|\dfrac{47}{9}\right| = \dfrac{47}{9}$; $\left|-7\dfrac{1}{3}\right| = \left|-\dfrac{22}{3}\right| = \dfrac{22}{3}$

Since the addends in the addition have different signs, subtract the smaller absolute value from the larger.
LCD = 9

$\dfrac{22}{3} - \dfrac{47}{9} = \dfrac{66}{9} - \dfrac{47}{9} = \dfrac{19}{9} = 2\dfrac{1}{9}$

Attach the sign of the addend having the larger absolute value to the difference.

$5\dfrac{2}{9} - 7\dfrac{1}{3} = -2\dfrac{1}{9}$

31. $-3 \cdot 5 = -15$

32. $-0.6 \cdot (-1.5) = 0.9$

33. $\dfrac{2}{3}\left(-\dfrac{7}{8}\right) = \dfrac{\overset{1}{\cancel{2}}}{3}\left(-\dfrac{7}{\underset{4}{\cancel{8}}}\right) = -\dfrac{7}{12}$

34. $\left(-1\dfrac{2}{5}\right)\left(-2\dfrac{6}{7}\right) = \left(-\dfrac{7}{5}\right)\left(-\dfrac{20}{7}\right)$

$= \left(-\dfrac{\overset{1}{\cancel{7}}}{\underset{1}{\cancel{5}}}\right)\left(-\dfrac{\overset{4}{\cancel{20}}}{\underset{1}{\cancel{7}}}\right) = 4$

35. $81 \div (-9) = -9$

36. $-1.21 \div (-0.11) = 11$

37. $-\dfrac{2}{9} \div \dfrac{1}{3} = -\dfrac{2}{9} \cdot \dfrac{3}{1} = -\dfrac{2}{\underset{3}{\cancel{9}}} \cdot \dfrac{\overset{1}{\cancel{3}}}{1} = -\dfrac{2}{3}$

38. $-2\dfrac{7}{8} \div 3\dfrac{3}{4} = -\dfrac{23}{8} \div \dfrac{15}{4} = -\dfrac{23}{8} \cdot \dfrac{4}{15}$

$= -\dfrac{23}{\underset{2}{\cancel{8}}} \cdot \dfrac{\overset{1}{\cancel{4}}}{15} = -\dfrac{23}{30}$

39. $\left[9^2 - (3-8)^2\right] \div 8 = \left[9^2 - (-5)^2\right] \div 8 = [81 - 25] \div 8 = 56 \div 8 = 7$

40. $-2 + \left[-2^2 - (21+7)\right]^2 + 10 = -2 + \left[-2^2 - 28\right]^2 + 10 = -2 + [-4 - 28]^2 + 10$

$= -2 + [-32]^2 + 10 = -2 + 1024 + 10 = 1022 + 10 = 1032$

41. $(-4)^2 + \dfrac{3^2 - 1}{2^2} - 3 = (-4)^2 + \dfrac{9-1}{4} - 3 = (-4)^2 + \dfrac{8}{4} - 3 = (-4)^2 + 2 - 3 = 16 + 2 - 3 = 16 + 2 - 3 = 18 - 3 = 15$

42. $5 - \left(\dfrac{8^2 - 1}{2^4 + 5}\right)^2 = 5 - \left(\dfrac{64-1}{16+5}\right)^2 = 5 - \left(\dfrac{63}{21}\right)^2 = 5 - 3^2 = 5 - 9 = -4$

43. a. Represent the deposits as positive numbers, and represent the withdrawals as negative numbers.
    $250 + $105 + $215 + (−$55)

   b. $250 + $105 + $215 + (−$55) = $570 + (−$55) = $515
   Mr. Cortez has $515 in his account at the end of the month.

44. a. Represent 323 BC as −323, and represent 46 AD as 46. 46 AD is the later year, so the subtraction is
    46 − (−323).

   b. 46 − (−323) = 46 + 323 = 369.
   369 years separate Alexander the Great from his primary historian.

45. 188 − 226 = 188 + (−226) = −38.
   The base of the construction site is 38 feet below ground level.

46. a. Represent the price decrease as −$2.40.
    500(−$2.40)

   b. 500(−$2.40) = −$1200. You lost $1200.

47. Represent the salary increase as \$175, the tax increase as −\$62, and the social security deduction as −\$27.
    \$175 + (−\$62) + (−\$27) = \$113 + (−\$27) = \$86.
    Your net raise is \$86.

Chapter 9 Assessment Test

1. The opposite of 457 is −457.

2. The opposite of −5713 is 5713.

3.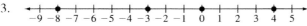

4.

5. $|350| = 350$

6. $|-453| = 453$

7. $7 > 4, 4 < 7$

8. $-19.5 < -19.0, -19.0 > -19.5$

9. −39°C

10. −\$3.24

11. $-25 + (-78)$
    Since the addends in the addition have the same sign, add the absolute values and attach the common positive sign to the sum.
    $-25 + (-78) = -103$

12. $-91 + 118$
    Since the addends in the addition have different signs, subtract the smaller absolute value from the larger. Then, attach the sign of the addend having the larger absolute value to the difference.
    $-91 + 118 = 27$

13. $-14.7 + 2.64$
    Since the addends in the addition have different signs, subtract the smaller absolute value from the larger. Then, attach the sign of the addend having the larger absolute value to the difference.
    $-14.7 + 2.64 = -12.06$

14. $13.05 + (-7.2)$
    Since the addends in the addition have different signs, subtract the smaller absolute value from the larger. Then, attach the sign of the addend having the larger absolute value to the difference.
    $13.05 + (-7.2) = 5.85$

15. $-\dfrac{1}{12} + \left(-\dfrac{5}{16}\right)$

    Since the addends in the addition have the same signs, add the absolute values. Then, attach the common negative sign of the addends to the sum.
    LCD = 48
    $$-\frac{1}{12} + \left(-\frac{5}{16}\right) = -\frac{4}{48} + \left(-\frac{15}{48}\right) = -\frac{19}{48}$$

16. $2\dfrac{4}{5} + \left(-5\dfrac{1}{2}\right)$

    Since the addends in the addition have different signs, subtract the smaller absolute value from the larger. Then, attach the sign of the addend having the larger absolute value to the difference.
    LCD = 10
    $$2\frac{4}{5} + \left(-5\frac{1}{2}\right) = \frac{14}{5} + \left(-\frac{11}{2}\right)$$
    $$= \frac{28}{10} + \left(-\frac{55}{10}\right) = -\frac{27}{10} = -2\frac{7}{10}$$

17. $75 - 48 = 27$

18. $-0.47 - 8.9$
    Write the subtraction problem as an addition problem.
    $-0.47 + (-8.9) = -9.37$

19. $\dfrac{5}{6} - \dfrac{4}{9} = \dfrac{15}{18} - \dfrac{8}{18} = \dfrac{7}{18}$

20. $-3\dfrac{7}{8} - 1\dfrac{1}{6} = -3\dfrac{21}{24} - 1\dfrac{4}{24} = -3\dfrac{21}{24} + \left(-1\dfrac{4}{24}\right)$

$= -4\dfrac{25}{24} = -5\dfrac{1}{24}$

21. $1.2 \cdot (-0.5) = -0.6$

22. $\left(-\dfrac{8}{15}\right)\left(-\dfrac{1}{6}\right) = \left(-\dfrac{\overset{4}{\cancel{8}}}{15}\right)\left(-\dfrac{1}{\underset{3}{\cancel{6}}}\right) = \dfrac{4}{45}$

23. $-72 \div (-0.9) = 80$

24. $1\dfrac{4}{5} \div \left(-4\dfrac{1}{2}\right) = \dfrac{9}{5} \div \left(-\dfrac{9}{2}\right) = \dfrac{9}{5} \cdot \left(-\dfrac{2}{9}\right) = -\dfrac{2}{5}$

25. $4^3 + \left(3^3 - 30\right)^2 + (-65) = 4^3 + (27 - 30)^2 + (-65) = 4^3 + (-3)^2 + (-65) = 64 + 9 + (-65) = 73 + (-65) = 8$

26. $100 - \dfrac{(-12)^2 + 6}{(-4)^2 - 1} + (-50) = 100 - \dfrac{144 + 6}{16 - 1} + (-50) = 100 - \dfrac{150}{15} + (-50) = 100 - 10 + (-50) = 90 + (-50) = 40$

27. Represent 1300 feet below sea level as -1300 feet.
$29{,}000 - (-1300) = 29{,}000 + 1300 = 30{,}300$ feet
The difference in altitude between the Dead Sea and Mount Everest is 30,300 feet.

28. $-\$37.21 + 150.00 - \$60.00 = \$112.79 - \$60.00 = \$52.72$
Steven's balance is \$52.72.

29. The average change is $-3420 \div 12 = -285$ students per year.

30. There are 2 large orders at \$10 each, 2 medium orders at \$8 each, 2 side dishes for each of the 4 orders at \$2.50 each, a \$4 delivery charge, a \$6 tip, and a \$3 discount.
$2(\$10.00) + 2(\$8.00) + 2(4)(\$2.50) + \$4.00 + \$6.00 - \$3.00$

$= \$20.00 + \$16.00 + \$20.00 + \$4.00 + \$6.00 - \$3.00 = \$63.00$
The total cost of the order is \$63.00

Chapter 10 Introduction to Algebra

Section 10.1   Algebraic Expressions

Concept Check

2.   A mathematical statement that consists of numbers, variables, operation symbols, and possibly grouping symbols is called an _algebraic_ expression.

4.   A _term_ is an addend in an algebraic expression.

6.   A _coefficient_ is a number factor in a variable term.

8.   The process of adding like terms in an algebraic expression is called _combining_ like terms.

Guide Problems

10.   Evaluate each algebraic expression when $a = 1$ and $b = -3$.

    a. $a - b$

        $\underline{1} - (\underline{-3}) = \underline{1} + \underline{3} = \underline{4}$

    b. $5a + b$

        $5(\underline{1}) + (\underline{-3}) = \underline{5} - \underline{3} = \underline{2}$

    c. ab

        $\underline{1}(\underline{-3}) = \underline{-3}$

In Problems 12 through 14, evaluate each algebraic expression when $x = 7$.

12. $9 \div (x - 4)$

     $9 \div (7 - 4) = 9 \div 3 = 3$

14. $(x + 5) \div 3$

     $(7 + 5) \div 3 = 12 \div 3 = 4$

In Problems 16 through 20, evaluate each algebraic expression when $y = 5$.

16. $-3y$

     $-3(5) = -15$

18. $3(y + 5)$

     $3(5 + 5) = 3(10) = 30$

20. $4y^2 + 3y$

     $4(5^2) + 3(5) = 4(25) + 3(5)$

                 $= 100 + 15 = 115$

In Problems 22 through 24, evaluate each algebraic expression when $x = -3$ and $y = 2$.

22. $13y - 5x$

     $13(2) - 5(-3) = 26 - (-15)$

                  $= 26 + 15 = 41$

24. $\dfrac{2x + 1}{3y + 4}$

     $\dfrac{2(-3) + 1}{3(2) + 4} = \dfrac{-6 + 1}{6 + 4} = \dfrac{-5}{10} = -\dfrac{1}{2}$

In Problems 26 through 30, evaluate each algebraic expression when $x = 10$ and $y = 15$.

26. $2x + 3y$

     $2(10) + 3(15) = 20 + 45 = 65$

28. $(-3x)(4y)$

     $[-3(10)][4(15)] = (-30)(60) = -1800$

30. $\dfrac{8x + 6}{3y - 2}$; $\dfrac{8(10) + 6}{3(15) - 2} = \dfrac{80 + 6}{45 - 2} = \dfrac{86}{43} = 2$

Guide Problems

32. Combine like terms to simplify $3x^2 + 7x + 8y - 5x^2 - 5x + 9y$

  a.   Collect like terms.

  $\left(3x^2 + \left(\underline{-5x^2}\right)\right) + \left(\underline{7x} + (-5x)\right) + \left(8y + \underline{9y}\right)$

  b.   Combine like terms.

  $\underline{-2}x^2 + \underline{2}x + \underline{17}y$

In Problems 34 and 36, identify the variable and constant terms in each expression, along with the coefficient of each variable term.

34. $-7x^5 + 8x^4 - 3x^3 + 6x^2 - 10$

  Variable terms: $-7x^5, 8x^4, -3x^3, 6x^2$

  Constant term: -10

  Coefficient in $-7x^5$: $\underline{-7}$.

  Coefficient in $8x^4$: $\underline{8}$.

  Coefficient in $-3x^3$: $\underline{-3}$.

  Coefficient in $6x^2$: $\underline{6}$.

36. $-3m^3 + 2m^2 - 3m - 7$

  Variable terms: $-3m^3, 2m^2, -3m$

  Constant term: -7

  Coefficient in $-3m^3$: $\underline{-3}$.

  Coefficient in $2m^2$: $\underline{2}$.

  Coefficient in $-3m$: $\underline{-3}$.

In Exercises 38 through 50, remember that like terms have the same variables and same exponents.

38. $5a + 3b - a + 6b = (5a - a) + (3b + 6b) = 4a + 9b$

40. $5m + 7n + \dfrac{1}{2}m - \dfrac{2}{3}n = \left(5m + \dfrac{1}{2}m\right) + \left(7n - \dfrac{2}{3}n\right) = \left(5\dfrac{1}{2}\right)m + \left(6\dfrac{1}{3}\right)n = \dfrac{11}{2}m + \dfrac{19}{3}n$

42. $a^3 - a^2b + 4a^2b + b^3 = a^3 + \left(-a^2b + 4a^2b\right) + b^3 = a^3 + 3a^2b + b^3$

44. $2p^2q - 8pq^2 - 4p^2q + 10pq^2 = \left(2p^2q - 4p^2q\right) + \left(-8pq^2 + 10pq^2\right) = -2p^2q + 2pq^2$

46. $3x^2yz^3 - 2xy^2 + x^2yz^3 + x^2y^2 + 2xy^2 = \left(3x^2yz^3 + x^2yz^3\right) + x^2y^2 + \left(-2xy^2 + 2xy^2\right) = 4x^2yz^3 + x^2y^2$

48. $3p^2 + 4pq + q^2 - 2p^2 - pq + 7q^2 = \left(3p^2 - 2p^2\right) + (4pq - pq) + \left(q^2 + 7q^2\right) = p^2 + 3pq + 8q^2$

50. $\dfrac{1}{3}d^2 + \dfrac{1}{4} - d + \dfrac{1}{2} + \dfrac{2}{3}d^2 + 3d = \left(\dfrac{1}{3}d^2 + \dfrac{2}{3}d^2\right) + (-d + 3d) + \left(\dfrac{1}{4} + \dfrac{1}{2}\right) = d^2 + 2d + \dfrac{3}{4}$

Guide Problems

52. Simplify each expression by applying the distributive property.

  a. $5(4x + 3) = 5(4x) + 5(3)$

  $\qquad\qquad\quad = 20x + 15$

  b. $0.7(2a - 9) = (0.7)2a - 0.7(9)$

  $\qquad\qquad\qquad\;\; = 1.4a - 6.3$

c.　$-\dfrac{1}{2}(2r+4) = -\dfrac{1}{2}(2r) + \left(-\dfrac{1}{2}\right)4 = -r - 2$

For problems 54–64, apply the associative property of multiplication and the commutative property of multiplication as necessary to multiply the expression.

54.　$8(3m) = (8 \cdot 3)m$
　　　$= 24m$

56.　$(-8y)4 = (-8 \cdot 4)y$
　　　$= -32y$

58.　$-(15x) = -15x$

60.　$0.9(0.1a) = (0.9 \cdot 0.1)a$
　　　$= 0.09a$

62.　$(-1.1b)5 = (-1.1 \cdot 5)b$
　　　$= -5.5b$

64.　$\dfrac{9}{20}\left(-\dfrac{5}{12}y\right) = \dfrac{9}{20}\left(-\dfrac{5}{12}\right)y$
　　　$= -\dfrac{3}{16}y$

For problems 66–88, use the distributive property $a(b+c) = ab + ac$ or $(a+b)c = ac + bc$.

66.　$7(r+5) = 7r + 35$

68.　$3(y-4) = 3y - 12$

70.　$-5(a+7) = -5a - 35$

72.　$7(5d-3) = 35d - 21$

74.　$(4s+3)5 = 20s + 15$

76.　$(13-3x)6 = 78 - 18x$

78.　$-\dfrac{1}{4}(12d-72) = -3d + 18$

80.　$\dfrac{3}{8}\left(\dfrac{1}{5}z - 7\right) = \dfrac{3}{8}\left(\dfrac{1}{5}z\right) + \dfrac{3}{8}(-7) = \dfrac{3}{40}z - \dfrac{21}{8}$

82.　$0.3(0.5v+8) = 0.15v + 2.4$

84.　$0.1(3.5b-7) = 0.35b - 0.7$

86.　$4(a^2 - 3a - 5) = 4a^2 - 12a - 20$

88.　$-3(x^2 + 3x + 5) = -3x^2 - 9x - 15$

90.　Five less than 3 times x can be represented by $3x - 5$.

92.　a.　Since the Sears Tower is 324 taller than the John Hancock building, represent the height of the Sears Tower by $x + 324$..

　　　b.　If $x = 1127$ feet, then $x + 324 = 1127 + 324 = 1451$ feet. The Sears Tower is 1451 feet tall.

Cumulative Skills Review

2.　$14\dfrac{3}{8}\% = 14.375\% = 0.14375$

4.　$C = 2\pi r \approx 2 \cdot 3.14 \cdot 8 \approx 50.24$ cm

6.　$C = \dfrac{5}{9}(F-32) = \dfrac{5}{9}(190-32) = \dfrac{5}{9}(158) \approx 88$
　　　$190°F \approx 88°C$

8.　$\dfrac{4.25}{18} = \dfrac{x}{108}$
　　　$4.25 \cdot 108 = 18x$
　　　$\dfrac{459}{18} = \dfrac{18x}{18}$
　　　$25.5 = x$

10.　Arrange the set of numbers in ascending order: 10, 25, 32, 67, 70
　　　There are 5 numbers in the set, so the median is the third number, 32.

Section 10.2   Solving an Equation Using the Addition Property of Equality

Concept Check

2. A value of the variable that makes the equation a true statement is called a <u>solution</u> of an equation.

4. Adding a negative number to each side of an equation is the same as <u>subtracting</u> the opposite of the negative number.

6. The process of verifying that we get a true statement when we substitute the answer into the original equation is called <u>checking</u> the solution.

Guide Problems

8. Determine whether 7 is a solution of the equation $-2x + 5 = -10$.

$$-2x + 5 = -10$$
$$-2(\underline{7}) + 5 \overset{?}{=} -10$$
$$\underline{-14} + 5 \overset{?}{=} -10$$
$$\underline{-9} \overset{?}{=} -10 \qquad \text{7 is not a solution to the equation } -2x + 5 = -10.$$

In Problems 10 through 36, determine whether the given value is a solution to the given equation by substituting the value for the unknown in the equation.

10. $y = 8; y + 7 = 15$
$$y + 7 = 15$$
$$8 + 7 \overset{?}{=} 15$$
$$15 = 15$$
8 is a solution.

12. $v = 15; v + 6 = 19$
$$v + 6 = 19$$
$$15 + 6 \overset{?}{=} 19$$
$$21 \neq 19$$
15 is not a solution.

14. $a = 21; a + 13 = 33$
$$a + 13 = 33$$
$$21 + 13 \overset{?}{=} 33$$
$$34 \neq 33$$
21 is not a solution.

16. $p = 24; p - 5 = 19$
$$p - 5 = 19$$
$$24 - 5 \overset{?}{=} 19$$
$$19 = 19$$
24 is a solution.

18. $h = 306; h + 19 = 325$
$$h + 19 = 325$$
$$306 + 19 \overset{?}{=} 325$$
$$325 = 325$$
306 is a solution.

20. $m = 219; m - 19 = 210$
$$m - 19 = 210$$
$$219 - 19 \overset{?}{=} 210$$
$$200 \neq 210$$
219 is not a solution.

22. $b = -\dfrac{9}{8}; b + \dfrac{5}{8} = -\dfrac{1}{2}$
$$b + \frac{5}{8} = -\frac{1}{2}$$
$$-\frac{9}{8} + \frac{5}{8} \overset{?}{=} -\frac{1}{2}$$
$$-\frac{4}{8} \overset{?}{=} -\frac{1}{2} \Rightarrow -\frac{1}{2} = -\frac{1}{2}$$
$-\dfrac{9}{8}$ is a solution.

24. $y = 54; 35 - y = -19$
$$35 - y = -19$$
$$35 - 54 \overset{?}{=} -19$$
$$-19 = -19$$
54 is a solution.

26. $p = -40; 18 - p = 58$
$$18 - p = 58$$
$$18 - (-40) \overset{?}{=} 58$$
$$18 + 40 \overset{?}{=} 58$$
$$58 = 58$$
−40 is a solution.

28. $r = -12$; $30 - r = 18$

$$30 - r = 18$$
$$30 - (-12) \overset{?}{=} 18$$
$$30 + 12 \overset{?}{=} 18$$
$$42 \neq 18$$

-12 is not a solution.

30. $y = 6.90$; $y - 2.07 = 4.73$

$$y - 2.07 = 4.73$$
$$6.90 - 2.07 \overset{?}{=} 4.73$$
$$4.83 \neq 4.73$$

6.90 is not a solution.

32. $s = 6.25$; $s + 7.50 = 13.75$

$$s + 7.50 = 13.75$$
$$6.25 + 7.50 \overset{?}{=} 13.75$$
$$13.75 = 13.75$$

6.25 is a solution.

34. $x = -8$; $x + 8 = 0$

$$x + 8 = 0$$
$$-8 + 8 \overset{?}{=} 0$$
$$0 = 0$$

-8 is a solution.

36. $y = 12$; $6 - y = 6$

$$6 - y = 6$$
$$6 - 12 \overset{?}{=} 6$$
$$-6 \neq 6$$

12 is not a solution.

Guide Problems

38. Solve $11 + x = -5$.

$$11 + x = -5$$
$$\underline{-11 \qquad -11}$$
$$0 + x = -16$$
$$x = -16$$

Check:
$$11 + (-16) \overset{?}{=} -5$$
$$-5 = -5 \text{ }^a$$

Use the method shown in the Guide Problem to solve problems 40 through 78. Be sure to check each solution.

40. $b + 5 = 44$

$$\underline{-5 \quad -5}$$
$$b + 0 = 39$$
$$b = 39$$

Check:
$$39 + 5 \overset{?}{=} 54$$
$$54 = 54 \text{ }^a$$

42. $d + 13 = 35$

$$\underline{-13 \quad -13}$$
$$d + 0 = 22$$
$$d = 22$$

Check:
$$22 + 13 \overset{?}{=} 35$$
$$35 = 35 \text{ }^a$$

44. $m + 13 = 8$

$$\underline{-13 \quad -13}$$
$$m + 0 = -5$$
$$m = -5$$

Check:
$$-5 + 13 \overset{?}{=} 8$$
$$8 = 8 \text{ }^a$$

46. $12 = p + 5$

$$\underline{-5 \qquad -5}$$
$$7 = p$$

Check:
$$12 \overset{?}{=} 7 + 5$$
$$12 = 12 \text{ }^a$$

48. $7 = y + 11$

$$\underline{-11 \quad -11}$$
$$-4 = y + 0$$
$$-4 = y$$

Check:
$$7 \overset{?}{=} -4 + 11$$
$$7 = 7 \text{ }^a$$

50. $q + 15 = 0$

$$\underline{-15 \quad -15}$$
$$q + 0 = -15$$
$$q = -15$$

Check:
$$-15 + 15 \overset{?}{=} 0$$
$$0 = 0 \text{ }^a$$

52. $m - 11 = 27$

$$\underline{+11 \quad +11}$$
$$m + 0 = 38$$
$$m = 38$$

Check:
$$38 - 11 \overset{?}{=} 27$$
$$27 = 27 \text{ }^a$$

54. $x - 19 = 50$

$$\underline{+19 \quad +19}$$
$$x + 0 = 69$$
$$x = 69$$

Check:
$$69 - 19 \overset{?}{=} 50$$
$$50 = 50 \text{ }^a$$

56. $37 = p - 35$ Check:

$$\begin{array}{c} +35 \quad +35 \\ \hline 72 = p \end{array} \quad \begin{array}{c} 37 \overset{?}{=} 72 - 35 \\ 37 = 37^{\text{a}} \end{array}$$

58. $76 = t - 13$ Check:

$$\begin{array}{c} +13 \quad +13 \\ \hline 89 = t \end{array} \quad \begin{array}{c} 76 \overset{?}{=} 89 - 13 \\ 76 = 76^{\text{a}} \end{array}$$

60. $c - 32 = 32$ Check:

$$\begin{array}{c} +32 \quad +32 \\ \hline c + 0 = 64 \\ c = 64 \end{array} \quad \begin{array}{c} 64 - 32 \overset{?}{=} 32 \\ 32 = 32^{\text{a}} \end{array}$$

62. $b - 29 = 0$ Check:

$$\begin{array}{c} +29 \quad +29 \\ \hline b + 0 = 29 \\ b = 29 \end{array} \quad \begin{array}{c} 29 - 29 \overset{?}{=} 0 \\ 0 = 0^{\text{a}} \end{array}$$

64. $s - 12 = -12$ Check:

$$\begin{array}{c} +12 \quad +12 \\ \hline s + 0 = 0 \\ s = 0 \end{array} \quad \begin{array}{c} 0 - 12 \overset{?}{=} -12 \\ -12 = -12^{\text{a}} \end{array}$$

66. $b + 4 = 19$ Check:

$$\begin{array}{c} -4 \quad -4 \\ \hline b + 0 = 15 \\ b = 15 \end{array} \quad \begin{array}{c} 15 + 4 \overset{?}{=} 19 \\ 19 = 19^{\text{a}} \end{array}$$

68. $2.1 = y - 1.3$ Check:

$$\begin{array}{c} +1.3 \quad +1.3 \\ \hline 3.4 = y + 0 \\ 3.4 = y \end{array} \quad \begin{array}{c} 2.1 \overset{?}{=} 3.4 - 1.3 \\ 2.1 = 2.1^{\text{a}} \end{array}$$

70. $0 = m - 1.6$ Check:

$$\begin{array}{c} +1.6 \quad +1.6 \\ \hline 1.6 = m + 0 \\ 1.6 = m \end{array} \quad \begin{array}{c} 0 \overset{?}{=} 1.6 - 1.6 \\ 0 = 0^{\text{a}} \end{array}$$

72. $t - 1.25 = 30$ Check:

$$\begin{array}{c} +1.25 \quad +1.25 \\ \hline t + 0 = 31.25 \\ t = 31.25 \end{array} \quad \begin{array}{c} 31.25 - 1.25 \overset{?}{=} 30 \\ 30 = 30^{\text{a}} \end{array}$$

74. $k + \dfrac{1}{2} = -\dfrac{2}{3}$ Check:

$$k + \frac{1}{2} - \frac{1}{2} = -\frac{2}{3} - \frac{1}{2}$$
$$k = -\frac{4}{6} - \frac{3}{6}$$
$$k = -\frac{7}{6} \text{ or } -1\frac{1}{6}$$

$$-\frac{7}{6} + \frac{1}{2} \overset{?}{=} -\frac{2}{3}$$
$$-\frac{7}{6} + \frac{3}{6} \overset{?}{=} -\frac{2}{3}$$
$$-\frac{4}{6} \overset{?}{=} -\frac{2}{3}$$
$$-\frac{2}{3} = -\frac{2}{3}^{\text{a}}$$

76. $\dfrac{3}{4} = v - \dfrac{1}{2}$ Check:

$$\frac{3}{4} + \frac{1}{2} = v - \frac{1}{2} + \frac{1}{2}$$
$$\frac{3}{4} + \frac{2}{4} = v$$
$$\frac{5}{4} \text{ or } 1\frac{1}{4} = v$$

$$\frac{3}{4} \overset{?}{=} \frac{5}{4} - \frac{1}{2}$$
$$\frac{3}{4} \overset{?}{=} \frac{5}{4} - \frac{2}{4}$$
$$\frac{3}{4} = \frac{3}{4}^{\text{a}}$$

78. $n + 2\dfrac{2}{3} = 7$ Check:

$$n + 2\frac{2}{3} - 2\frac{2}{3} = 7 - 2\frac{2}{3}$$
$$n = 6\frac{3}{3} - 2\frac{2}{3}$$
$$n = 4\frac{1}{3}$$

$$4\frac{1}{3} + 2\frac{2}{3} \overset{?}{=} 7$$
$$6\frac{4}{4} \overset{?}{=} 7$$
$$7 = 7^{\text{a}}$$

For problem 80, use the formula $R - C = P$, where R represents a company's revenue, C represents a company's cost, and P represents a company's profit.

80. $R - C = P$, $C = \$18{,}042{,}000{,}000$, $P = \$3{,}544{,}000{,}000$

$$R - 18{,}042{,}000{,}000 = \quad 3{,}544{,}000{,}000$$

$$\underline{+18{,}042{,}000{,}000 \quad +18{,}042{,}000{,}000}$$

$$R + 0 \qquad = \quad 21{,}586{,}000{,}000$$

$$R = 21{,}586{,}000{,}000$$

McDonald's revenue for 2006 was $21,586,000,000.

Cumulative Skills Review

2. $-75 + (-122) = -197$

4. $3.4284,\ 3.405,\ 3.108,\ 3.0865$

6. $a = 3$; $28 - 8a$
   $28 - 8 \cdot 3 = 28 - 24 = 4$

8. $\dfrac{16}{6} = \dfrac{8}{3}$

10. 25 occurs three times, while each of the other numbers in the set occur once, so 25 is the mode.

Section 10.3   Solving an Equation Using the Multiplication Property of Equality

Concept Check

1. To solve equations of the form $bx = c$, where b and c are numbers, $b \neq 0$, and x is a variable, either multiply each side of the equation by the __reciprocal__ of b or, equivalently, divide each side by b.

Guide Problems

4. Solve $2.5x = 100$.

$$\dfrac{2.5x}{2.5} = \dfrac{100}{2.5} \quad \text{Check:}$$
$$x = \underline{40} \qquad 2.5 \cdot 40 \overset{?}{=} 100$$
$$100 = 100 \text{ }^{a}$$

6. Solve $-x = 15$.

$$\dfrac{-x}{-1} = \dfrac{15}{-1} \quad \text{Check:}$$
$$x = -15 \qquad -(-15) \overset{?}{=} 15$$
$$15 = 15 \text{ }^{a}$$

Use the method shown in the Guide Problem to solve problems 8 through 42. Be sure to check each solution.

8. $2x = 18$ Check:
$$\dfrac{2x}{2} = \dfrac{18}{2} \qquad 2 \cdot 9 \overset{?}{=} 18$$
$$x = 9 \qquad 18 = 18 \text{ }^{a}$$

10. $6s = -48$ Check:
$$\dfrac{6s}{6} = \dfrac{-48}{6} \qquad 6 \cdot (-8) \overset{?}{=} -48$$
$$s = -8 \qquad -48 = -48^{a}$$

12. $-k = -13$ Check:
$$(-1)(-k) = (-13)(-1) \qquad -(13) \overset{?}{=} -13$$
$$k = 13 \qquad -13 = -13^{a}$$

14. $-n = 1$ Check:
$$(-1)(-n) = (1)(-1) \qquad -(-1) \overset{?}{=} 1$$
$$n = -1 \qquad 1 = 1^{a}$$

16. $36 = 4b$ Check:

$$\frac{36}{4} = \frac{4b}{4} \qquad 36 \overset{?}{=} 4 \cdot 9$$
$$9 = b \qquad\quad 36 = 36 \text{ }^a$$

18. $64 = -8q$ Check:

$$\frac{64}{-8} = \frac{-8q}{-8} \qquad 64 \overset{?}{=} -8 \cdot (-8)$$
$$-8 = q \qquad\quad 64 = 64 \text{ }^a$$

20. $\frac{1}{3}r = 6$ Check:

$$\frac{3}{1} \cdot \frac{1}{3}r = 6 \cdot 3 \qquad \frac{1}{3} \cdot 18 \overset{?}{=} 6$$
$$r = 18 \qquad\qquad 6 = 6^a$$

22. $-\frac{h}{3} = 7$ Check:

$$\left(-\frac{3}{1}\right) \cdot \left(-\frac{h}{3}\right) = 7 \cdot (-3) \qquad -\frac{-21}{3} \overset{?}{=} 7$$
$$h = -21 \qquad\qquad -(-7) \overset{?}{=} 7$$
$$7 = 7^a$$

24. $\frac{1}{5}y = 16$ Check:

$$\frac{5}{1} \cdot \frac{1}{5}y = 16 \cdot 5 \qquad \frac{1}{5} \cdot 80 \overset{?}{=} 16$$
$$x = 80 \qquad\qquad 16 = 16^a$$

26. $\frac{2}{3}k = \frac{2}{9}$ Check:

$$\frac{3}{2} \cdot \frac{2}{3}k = \frac{2}{9} \cdot \frac{3}{2} \qquad \frac{2}{3} \cdot \frac{1}{3} \overset{?}{=} \frac{2}{9}$$
$$k = \frac{1}{3} \qquad\qquad \frac{2}{9} = \frac{2}{9}^a$$

28. $-7a = \frac{1}{6}$ Check:

$$\left(-\frac{1}{7}\right)(-7a) = \frac{1}{6}\left(-\frac{1}{7}\right) \qquad -7\left(-\frac{1}{42}\right) \overset{?}{=} \frac{1}{6}$$
$$a = -\frac{1}{42} \qquad\qquad \frac{1}{6} = \frac{1}{6}^a$$

30. $-\frac{6}{11}p = -21$

$$\left(-\frac{11}{6}\right) \cdot \left(-\frac{6}{11}\right)p = -21 \cdot \left(-\frac{11}{6}\right)$$
$$p = \frac{231}{6} = \frac{77}{2} = 38\frac{1}{2}$$

Check:

$$-\frac{6}{11} \cdot \left(38\frac{1}{2}\right) \overset{?}{=} -21$$
$$-\frac{6}{11} \cdot \frac{231}{6} \overset{?}{=} -21$$
$$-21 = -21^a$$

32. $-\frac{3}{5}r = 12$ Check:

$$\left(-\frac{5}{3}\right) \cdot \left(-\frac{3}{5}\right)r = 12 \cdot \left(-\frac{5}{3}\right) \qquad -\frac{3}{5} \cdot (-20) \overset{?}{=} 12$$
$$r = -20 \qquad\qquad 12 = 12^a$$

34. $\frac{3}{11} = \frac{1}{2}l$ Check:

$$\frac{2}{1} \cdot \frac{3}{11} = \frac{1}{2}l \cdot \frac{2}{1} \qquad \frac{3}{11} \overset{?}{=} \frac{1}{2} \cdot \frac{6}{11}$$
$$\frac{6}{11} = l \qquad\qquad \frac{3}{11} = \frac{3}{11}^a$$

36. $-3.5w = 21$ Check:

$$\frac{-3.5}{-3.5} = \frac{21}{-3.5} \qquad -3.5 \cdot (-6) \overset{?}{=} 21$$
$$x = -6 \qquad\qquad 12 = 21^a$$

38. $3.4d = 7.004$ Check:

$$\frac{3.4d}{3.4} = \frac{7.004}{3.4} \qquad 3.4 \cdot (2.06) \overset{?}{=} 7.004$$
$$d = 2.06 \qquad\qquad 7.004 = 7.004 \text{ }^a$$

40. $0.8p = 6.4$ Check:

$$\frac{0.8p}{0.8} = \frac{6.4}{0.8} \qquad 0.8 \cdot 8 \overset{?}{=} 6.4$$
$$p = 8 \qquad\qquad 6.4 = 6.4^{a}$$

42. $0.9y = 0.63$ Check:

$$\frac{0.9y}{0.9} = \frac{0.63}{0.9} \qquad 0.9 \cdot 0.7 \overset{?}{=} 0.63$$
$$y = 0.7 \qquad\qquad 0.63 = 0.63^{a}$$

For problem 44, use the formula d = rt, where d represents distance, r represents rate, and t represents time.

44. $d = rt$, $d = 1463$ miles, $t = 3.5$ hours

$$1463 = 3.5r$$
$$\frac{1463}{3.5} = \frac{3.5r}{3.5}$$
$$418 = r$$

The plane's average speed was 418 miles per hour.

Cumulative Skills Review

2. $65\% = \dfrac{65}{100} = \dfrac{13}{20}$

4. $C = 2\pi r \approx 2 \cdot 3.14 \cdot 60 \approx 376.8$ ft

6. $7(6p - 5q + 2) = 42p - 35q + 14$

8. Identify the terms of $40x + 18y + 25z - 99$.
Variable terms: $40x$, $18y$, $25z$
Constant term: -99

10. $a + 16 = 29$ Check:

$$a + 16 - 16 = 29 - 16 \qquad 13 + 16 \overset{?}{=} 29$$
$$a = 13 \qquad\qquad 29 = 29^{a}$$

Section 10.4   Solving an Equation Using the Addition and Multiplication Properties

Concept Check

1. To solve the equation $\dfrac{2}{3}x - 3 = 4$, first __add__ 3 to each side of the equation. Then __multiply__ each side of the equation by $\dfrac{3}{2}$.

Guide Problems

4. Solve $5 - x = 11$.

   a. Apply the addition property to isolate the variable term on one side of the equation.

$$5 - x = 11$$
$$\underline{-5 \qquad -5}$$
$$0 - x = 6$$

   b. Apply the multiplication property to solve for the variable.

$$\frac{-x}{-1} = \frac{6}{-1}$$
$$x = -6$$

   c. Check the solution.

$$5 - (-6) \overset{?}{=} 11$$
$$11 = 11^{a}$$

6.   Solve $5x + 11 = 3x + 33$.

a.   Apply the addition property to isolate the variable term on one side of the equation.

$$5x + 11 = 3x + 33$$
$$\underline{-3x \qquad -3x}$$
$$2x + 11 = \ 0 + 33$$
$$2x + 11 = 33$$

b.   Apply the addition property to isolate the variable term on one side of the equation.

$$2x + 11 = \ 33$$
$$\underline{-11 \ -11}$$
$$2x + \ 0 = \ 22$$
$$2x = 22$$

c.   Apply the multiplication property to solve for the variable.

$$\frac{2x}{2} = \frac{22}{2}$$
$$x = 11$$

d.   Check the solution.

$$5(11) + 11 \overset{?}{=} 3(11) + 33$$
$$55 + 11 \overset{?}{=} 33 + 33$$
$$66 = 66^{\text{a}}$$

Use the method shown in the Guide Problem to solve problems 8 through 66. Be sure to check each solution. Note that we drop the zeros starting with problem 52. Starting with problem 54, we use the horizontal format in order to save space.

8. $4y + 3 = \ 19$ Check:

$$\underline{-3 \quad -3}$$
$$4y + 0 = \ 16$$
$$4y = 16$$
$$\frac{4y}{4} = \frac{16}{4}$$
$$y = 4$$

$$4 \cdot (4) + 3 \overset{?}{=} 19$$
$$16 + 3 \overset{?}{=} 19$$
$$19 = 19^{\,\text{a}}$$

10. $5t + 8 = \ 43$ Check:

$$\underline{-8 \quad -8}$$
$$5t + 0 = \ 35$$
$$5t = 35$$
$$\frac{5t}{5} = \frac{35}{5}$$
$$n = 7$$

$$5 \cdot (7) + 8 \overset{?}{=} 43$$
$$35 + 8 \overset{?}{=} 43$$
$$43 = 43^{\,\text{a}}$$

12. $4d - 3 = -3$ Check:

$$\underline{+3 \quad +3}$$
$$4d + 0 = \ 0$$
$$4d = 0$$
$$\frac{4d}{4} = \frac{0}{4}$$
$$d = 0$$

$$4 \cdot (0) - 3 \overset{?}{=} -3$$
$$0 - 3 \overset{?}{=} -3$$
$$-3 = -3^{\,\text{a}}$$

14. $7b - 8 = \ 48$ Check:

$$\underline{+8 \quad +8}$$
$$7b + 0 = \ 56$$
$$7b = 56$$
$$\frac{7b}{7} = \frac{56}{7}$$
$$b = 8$$

$$7 \cdot (8) - 8 \overset{?}{=} 48$$
$$56 - 8 \overset{?}{=} 48$$
$$48 = 48^{\,\text{a}}$$

16. $5d + 3 = -22$ Check:

$$\underline{-3 \quad -3}$$
$$5d + 0 = -25$$
$$5d = -25$$
$$\frac{5d}{5} = \frac{-25}{5}$$
$$d = -5$$

$$5 \cdot (-5) + 3 \overset{?}{=} -22$$
$$-25 + 3 \overset{?}{=} -22$$
$$-22 = -22^{\text{a}}$$

18. $-8t + 3 = \ 27$ Check:

$$\underline{-3 \quad -3}$$
$$-8t + 0 = \ 24$$
$$-8t = 24$$
$$\frac{-8t}{-8} = \frac{24}{-8}$$
$$t = -3$$

$$-8 \cdot (-3) + 3 \overset{?}{=} 27$$
$$24 + 3 \overset{?}{=} 27$$
$$27 = 27^{\,\text{a}}$$

20. $-6v - 7 = 53$ Check:

$$\frac{+7 \quad +7}{-6v + 0 = 60}$$

$-6 \cdot (-10) - 7 \stackrel{?}{=} 53$

$-6v = 60$

$60 - 7 \stackrel{?}{=} 53$

$$\frac{-6v}{-6} = \frac{60}{-6}$$

$53 = 53^a$

$v = -10$

22. $\dfrac{x}{8} + 1 = 8$ Check:

$$\frac{-1 \quad -1}{\dfrac{x}{8} + 0 = 7}$$

$\dfrac{56}{8} + 1 \stackrel{?}{=} 8$

$\dfrac{x}{8} = 7$

$7 + 1 \stackrel{?}{=} 8$

$8 = 8^a$

$8 \cdot \dfrac{x}{8} = 7 \cdot 8$

$x = 56$

24. $\dfrac{d}{7} - 3 = 2$ Check:

$$\frac{+3 \quad +3}{\dfrac{d}{7} + 0 = 5}$$

$\dfrac{35}{7} - 3 \stackrel{?}{=} 2$

$5 - 3 \stackrel{?}{=} 2$

$\dfrac{d}{7} = 5$

$2 = 2^a$

$7 \cdot \dfrac{d}{7} = 5 \cdot 7$

$d = 35$

26. $\dfrac{a}{4} - 4 = -6$ Check:

$$\frac{+4 \quad +4}{\dfrac{a}{4} + 0 = -2}$$

$\dfrac{-8}{4} - 4 \stackrel{?}{=} -6$

$-2 - 4 \stackrel{?}{=} -6$

$\dfrac{a}{4} = -2$

$-6 = -6^a$

$4 \cdot \dfrac{a}{4} = -2 \cdot 4$

$a = -8$

28. $2 - \dfrac{2}{9}y = 8$ Check:

$$\frac{-2 \qquad -2}{0 - \dfrac{2}{9}y = 6}$$

$2 - \dfrac{2}{9}(-27) \stackrel{?}{=} 8$

$2 + 6 \stackrel{?}{=} 8$

$-\dfrac{2}{9}y = 6$

$8 = 8^a$

$\left(-\dfrac{9}{2}\right)\left(-\dfrac{2}{9}y\right) = 6\left(-\dfrac{9}{2}\right)$

$y = -27$

30. $3d + 2 = 3$ Check:

$$\frac{-2 \quad -2}{3d + 0 = 1}$$

$3 \cdot \left(\dfrac{1}{3}\right) + 2 \stackrel{?}{=} 3$

$3d = 1$

$1 + 2 \stackrel{?}{=} 3$

$$\frac{3d}{3} = \frac{1}{3}$$

$3 = 3^a$

$d = \dfrac{1}{3}$

32. $\dfrac{x}{2} - \dfrac{1}{3} = \dfrac{1}{6}$ Check:

$$\frac{+\dfrac{1}{3} \quad +\dfrac{1}{3}}{\dfrac{x}{2} + 0 = \dfrac{1}{6} + \dfrac{1}{3}}$$

$\dfrac{1}{2} - \dfrac{1}{3} \stackrel{?}{=} \dfrac{1}{6}$

$\dfrac{3}{6} - \dfrac{2}{6} \stackrel{?}{=} \dfrac{1}{6}$

$\dfrac{x}{2} = \dfrac{1}{6} + \dfrac{2}{6} = \dfrac{3}{6} = \dfrac{1}{2}$

$\dfrac{1}{6} = \dfrac{1}{6}^a$

$2 \cdot \left(\dfrac{x}{2}\right) = \left(\dfrac{1}{2}\right) \cdot (2)$

$x = 1$

34. $\dfrac{5}{6}x + \dfrac{2}{3} = \dfrac{5}{6}$ Check:

$\dfrac{5}{6}x + \dfrac{2}{3} - \dfrac{2}{3} = \dfrac{5}{6} - \dfrac{2}{3}$

$\dfrac{5}{6}\left(\dfrac{1}{5}\right) + \dfrac{2}{3} \stackrel{?}{=} \dfrac{5}{6}$

$\dfrac{5}{6}x + 0 = \dfrac{5}{6} - \dfrac{4}{6}$

$\dfrac{1}{6} + \dfrac{2}{3} \stackrel{?}{=} \dfrac{5}{6}$

$\dfrac{5}{6}x = \dfrac{1}{6}$

$\dfrac{1}{6} + \dfrac{4}{6} \stackrel{?}{=} \dfrac{5}{6}$

$\dfrac{6}{5} \cdot \left(\dfrac{5}{6}x\right) = \left(\dfrac{1}{6}\right) \cdot \dfrac{6}{5}$

$\dfrac{5}{6} = \dfrac{5}{6}^a$

$x = \dfrac{1}{5}$

36.

$$7 + 2t = 18$$

$$\underline{-7 \qquad\quad -7}$$

$$0 + 2t = 11$$

$$2t = 11$$

$$\frac{2t}{2} = \frac{11}{2}$$

$$t = \frac{11}{2}$$

Check:

$$7 + 2\cdot\left(\frac{11}{2}\right) \overset{?}{=} 18$$

$$7 + 11 \overset{?}{=} 18$$

$$18 = 18^{a}$$

38.

$$2k - 3.1 = 6.9$$

$$\underline{+3.1 \quad\; +3.1}$$

$$2k + 0 = 10.0$$

$$2k = 10$$

$$\frac{2k}{2} = \frac{10}{2}$$

$$k = 5$$

Check:

$$2\cdot 5 - 3.1 \overset{?}{=} 6.9$$

$$10 - 3.1 \overset{?}{=} 6.9$$

$$6.9 = 6.9^{a}$$

40.

$$5y = 4y + 9$$

$$\underline{-4y \quad -4y}$$

$$y = 0 + 9$$

$$y = 9$$

Check:

$$5\cdot 9 \overset{?}{=} 4\cdot 9 + 9$$

$$45 \overset{?}{=} 36 + 9$$

$$45 = 45^{a}$$

42.

$$10r = 2r + 16$$

$$\underline{-2r \quad -2r}$$

$$8r = 0 + 16$$

$$8r = 16$$

$$\frac{8r}{8} = \frac{16}{8}$$

$$r = 2$$

Check:

$$10\cdot 2 \overset{?}{=} 2\cdot 2 + 16$$

$$20 \overset{?}{=} 4 + 16$$

$$20 = 20^{a}$$

44.

$$23 - 11b = 35b$$

$$\underline{+11b \quad +11b}$$

$$23 + 0 = 46b$$

$$23 = 46b$$

$$\frac{23}{46} = \frac{46b}{46}$$

$$\frac{1}{2} = b$$

Check:

$$23 - 11\cdot\left(\frac{1}{2}\right) \overset{?}{=} 35\cdot\left(\frac{1}{2}\right)$$

$$23 - \frac{11}{2} \overset{?}{=} \frac{35}{2}$$

$$23 - 5\frac{1}{2} \overset{?}{=} 17\frac{1}{2}$$

$$22\frac{2}{2} - 5\frac{1}{2} \overset{?}{=} 17\frac{1}{2}$$

$$17\frac{1}{2} = 17\frac{1}{2}^{a}$$

46.

$$2v = -6v + 5$$

$$\underline{+6v \qquad +6v}$$

$$8v = 0 + 5$$

$$8v = 5$$

$$\frac{8v}{8} = \frac{5}{8}$$

$$v = \frac{5}{8}$$

Check:

$$2\cdot\left(\frac{5}{8}\right) \overset{?}{=} -6\cdot\left(\frac{5}{8}\right) + 5$$

$$\frac{5}{4} \overset{?}{=} -\frac{15}{4} + 5$$

$$\frac{5}{4} \overset{?}{=} -\frac{15}{4} + \frac{20}{4}$$

$$\frac{5}{4} = \frac{5}{4}^{a}$$

48.

$$5c - 6 = 3c - 12$$

$$\underline{-3c \qquad -3c}$$

$$2c - 6 = 0c - 12$$

$$2c - 6 = -12$$

$$\underline{+6 \qquad +6}$$

$$2c + 0 = -6$$

$$\frac{2c}{2} = \frac{-6}{2}$$

$$c = -3$$

Check:

$$5\cdot(-3) - 6 \overset{?}{=} 3\cdot(-3) - 12$$

$$-15 - 6 \overset{?}{=} -9 - 12$$

$$-21 = -21^{a}$$

50.

$$5z + 3 = 6z - 6$$

$$\underline{-5z \qquad -5z}$$

$$0z + 3 = z - 6$$

$$\underline{+6 \qquad\quad +6}$$

$$9 = z + 0$$

$$9 = z$$

Check:

$$5\cdot 9 + 3 \overset{?}{=} 6\cdot 9 - 6$$

$$45 + 3 \overset{?}{=} 54 - 6$$

$$48 = 48^{a}$$

52. $5n + 2 = 3n - 6$ Check:

$$\underline{\ -3n \qquad\quad -3n}$$
$$2n + 2 = -6$$
$$\underline{\ -2 \qquad\quad -2}$$
$$\frac{2n}{2} = \frac{-8}{2}$$
$$n = -4$$

$$5(-4) + 2 \overset{?}{=} 3(-4) - 6$$
$$-20 + 2 \overset{?}{=} -12 - 6$$
$$-18 = -18^{a}$$

54. $41 - s = -1 - 7s$ Check:

$$\underline{\ +7s \qquad\quad +7s}$$
$$41 + 6s = -1$$
$$\underline{-41 \qquad\quad -41}$$
$$\frac{6s}{6} = \frac{-42}{6}$$
$$s = -7$$

$$41 - (-7) \overset{?}{=} -1 - 7(-7)$$
$$41 + 7 \overset{?}{=} -1 + 49$$
$$48 = 48^{a}$$

56. $3.4t - 3.9 = 2.1t + 1.3$

$$3.4t - 3.9 - 2.1t = 2.1t + 1.3 - 2.1t$$
$$1.3t - 3.9 = 1.3$$
$$1.3t - 3.9 + 3.9 = 1.3 + 3.9$$
$$1.3t = 5.2$$
$$\frac{1.3t}{1.3} = \frac{5.2}{1.3}$$
$$t = 4$$

Check:

$$3.4(4) - 3.9 \overset{?}{=} 2.1(4) + 1.3$$
$$13.6 - 3.9 \overset{?}{=} 8.4 + 1.3$$
$$9.7 = 9.7^{a}$$

58. $0.2y - 4.3 = 0.4y + 3.1$

$$0.2y - 4.3 - 0.2y = 0.4y + 3.1 - 0.2y$$
$$-4.3 = 0.2y + 3.1$$
$$-4.3 - 3.1 = 0.2y + 3.1 - 3.1$$
$$-7.4 = 0.2y$$
$$\frac{-7.4}{0.2} = \frac{0.2y}{0.2}$$
$$-37 = y$$

Check:

$$0.2(-37) - 4.3 \overset{?}{=} 0.4(-37) + 3.1$$
$$-7.4 - 4.3 \overset{?}{=} -14.8 + 3.1$$
$$-11.7 = -11.7^{a}$$

60. $6b + 5 = 3b + 6$ Check:

$$6b + 5 - 3b = 3b + 6 - 3b$$
$$3b + 5 = 6$$
$$3b + 5 - 5 = 6 - 5$$
$$3b = 1$$
$$\frac{3b}{3} = \frac{1}{3}$$
$$b = \frac{1}{3}$$

$$6\left(\frac{1}{3}\right) + 5 \overset{?}{=} 3\left(\frac{1}{3}\right) + 6$$
$$2 + 5 \overset{?}{=} 1 + 6$$
$$7 = 7^{a}$$

62. $8v - 3 = 3v + 9$ Check:

$$8v - 3 - 3v = 3v + 9 - 3v$$
$$5v - 3 = 9$$
$$5v - 3 + 3 = 9 + 3$$
$$5v = 12$$
$$\frac{5v}{5} = \frac{12}{5}$$
$$v = \frac{12}{5}$$

$$8 \cdot \left(\frac{12}{5}\right) - 3 \overset{?}{=} 3 \cdot \left(\frac{12}{5}\right) + 9$$
$$\frac{96}{5} - 3 \overset{?}{=} \frac{36}{5} + 9$$
$$\frac{96}{5} - \frac{15}{5} \overset{?}{=} \frac{36}{5} + \frac{45}{5}$$
$$\frac{81}{5} = \frac{81}{5}\,{}_{a}$$

64. $\quad 2h + 3 = \dfrac{1}{2}h + 9$

$2h + 3 - \dfrac{1}{2}h = \dfrac{1}{2}h + 9 - \dfrac{1}{2}h$

$\dfrac{3}{2}h + 3 = 9$

$\dfrac{3}{2}h + 3 - 3 = 9 - 3$

$\dfrac{3}{2}h = 6$

$\dfrac{2}{3} \cdot \dfrac{3}{2}h = 6 \cdot \dfrac{2}{3}$

$h = 4$

Check:

$2 \cdot 4 + 3 \overset{?}{=} \dfrac{1}{2} \cdot 4 + 9$

$8 + 3 \overset{?}{=} 2 + 9$

$11 = 11^{a}$

66. $\quad \dfrac{2}{5}k + \dfrac{1}{3} = \dfrac{2}{3}k - \dfrac{3}{5}$

$\dfrac{2}{5}k + \dfrac{1}{3} - \dfrac{2}{5}k = \dfrac{2}{3}k - \dfrac{3}{5} - \dfrac{2}{5}k$

$\dfrac{1}{3} = \dfrac{10}{15}k - \dfrac{6}{15}k - \dfrac{3}{5}$

$\dfrac{1}{3} = \dfrac{4}{15}k - \dfrac{3}{5}$

$\dfrac{1}{3} + \dfrac{3}{5} = \dfrac{4}{15}k - \dfrac{3}{5} + \dfrac{3}{5}$

$\dfrac{5}{15} + \dfrac{9}{15} = \dfrac{4}{15}k$

$\dfrac{14}{15} = \dfrac{4}{15}k$

$\dfrac{15}{4} \cdot \dfrac{14}{15} = \dfrac{4}{15}k \cdot \dfrac{15}{4}$

$\dfrac{7}{2} = k$

Check:

$\dfrac{2}{5} \cdot \left(\dfrac{7}{2}\right) + \dfrac{1}{3} \overset{?}{=} \dfrac{2}{3}\left(\dfrac{7}{2}\right) - \dfrac{3}{5}$

$\dfrac{7}{5} + \dfrac{1}{3} \overset{?}{=} \dfrac{7}{3} - \dfrac{3}{5}$

$\dfrac{21}{15} + \dfrac{5}{15} \overset{?}{=} \dfrac{35}{15} - \dfrac{9}{15}$

$\dfrac{26}{15} = \dfrac{26}{15}_{a}$

Guide Problems

68. Solve the equation $2(x + 9) = 3(3x - 1)$.

a. Apply the distribute property.

$2(x + 9) = 3(3x - 1)$

$2x + 18 = 9x - 3$

b. Use the addition property to get the variable term on one side of the equation.

$2x + 18 = 9x - 3$

$\underline{-2x -2x}$

$0x + 18 = 7x - 3$

$18 = 7x - 3$

c. Apply the addition property to isolate the variable term on one side of the equation.

$18 = 7x - 3$

$\underline{+3 +3}$

$21 = 7x + 0$

$21 = 7x$

d. Use the multiplication property to solve for the variable.

$\dfrac{21}{7} = \dfrac{7x}{7}$

$3 = x$

e.   Check the solution.

$$2(3+9) \overset{?}{=} 3(3 \cdot 3 - 1)$$

$$2(12) \overset{?}{=} 3(9-1)$$

$$24 \overset{?}{=} 3(8)$$

$$24 = 24^{\text{a}}$$

Use the method shown in the Guide Problem to solve problems 70 through 84. Be sure to check each solution.

70. $5(3x-4)=40$ Check:

$$15x - 20 = 40$$

$$15x - 20 + 20 = 40 + 20$$ $$5(3 \cdot 4 - 4) \overset{?}{=} 40$$

$$15x = 60$$ $$5(12 - 4) \overset{?}{=} 40$$

$$\frac{15x}{15} = \frac{60}{15}$$ $$5(8) \overset{?}{=} 40$$

$$x = 4$$ $$40 = 40 \,^{\text{a}}$$

72. $7(3p+4)=40$ Check:

$$21p + 28 = 40$$

$$21p + 28 - 28 = 40 - 28$$ $$7\left(3 \cdot \frac{4}{7} + 4\right) \overset{?}{=} 40$$

$$21p = 12$$ $$7\left(\frac{12}{7} + 4\right) \overset{?}{=} 40$$

$$\frac{21p}{21} = \frac{12}{21}$$ $$7\left(\frac{12}{7} + \frac{28}{7}\right) \overset{?}{=} 40$$

$$p = \frac{4}{7}$$ $$7\left(\frac{40}{7}\right) \overset{?}{=} 40$$

$$40 = 40 \,^{\text{a}}$$

74. $6(3t-7)=11t$ Check:

$$18t - 42 = 11t$$

$$18t - 42 - 18t = 11t - 18t$$ $$6(3 \cdot 6 - 7) \overset{?}{=} 11(6)$$

$$-42 = -7t$$ $$6(18 - 7) \overset{?}{=} 66$$

$$\frac{-42}{-7} = \frac{-7t}{-7}$$ $$6(11) \overset{?}{=} 66$$

$$6 = t$$ $$66 = 66 \,^{\text{a}}$$

76. $5p-(3p+4)=16$ Check:

$$5p - 3p - 4 = 16$$

$$2p - 4 = 16$$ $$5(10) - (3 \cdot 10 + 4) \overset{?}{=} 16$$

$$2p - 4 + 4 = 16 + 4$$ $$50 - (30 + 4) \overset{?}{=} 16$$

$$\frac{2p}{2} = \frac{20}{2}$$ $$50 - 34 \overset{?}{=} 16$$

$$p = 10$$ $$16 = 16 \,^{\text{a}}$$

78. $5(y+4)=6(y-2)$ Check:

$$5y + 20 = 6y - 12$$

$$5y + 20 - 5y = 6y - 12 - 5y$$ $$5(32 + 4) \overset{?}{=} 6(32 - 2)$$

$$20 = y - 12$$ $$5(36) \overset{?}{=} 6(30)$$

$$20 + 12 = y - 12 + 12$$ $$180 = 180 \,^{\text{a}}$$

$$32 = y$$

80. $5(4-3q)=-5(q-4)$

$$20 - 15q = -5q + 20$$

$$20 - 15q + 15q = -5q + 20 + 15q$$

$$20 = 10q + 20$$

$$20 - 20 = 10q + 20 - 20$$

$$0 = 10q$$

$$\frac{0}{10} = \frac{10q}{10}$$

$$0 = q$$

Check:

$$5(4 - 3 \cdot 0) \overset{?}{=} -5(0 - 4)$$

$$5(4 - 0) \overset{?}{=} -5(-4)$$

$$5(4) \overset{?}{=} 20$$

$$20 = 20^{\text{a}}$$

82. $\dfrac{5}{7}(v-2)=\dfrac{2}{7}v-4$ Check:

$\dfrac{5}{7}v-\dfrac{10}{7}=\dfrac{2}{7}v-4$ $\dfrac{5}{7}(-6-2)\overset{?}{=}\dfrac{2}{7}(-6)-4$

$\dfrac{5}{7}v-\dfrac{10}{7}-\dfrac{2}{7}v=\dfrac{2}{7}v-4-\dfrac{2}{7}v$ $\dfrac{5}{7}(-8)\overset{?}{=}-\dfrac{12}{7}-4$

$\dfrac{3}{7}v-\dfrac{10}{7}=-4$ $-\dfrac{40}{7}\overset{?}{=}-\dfrac{12}{7}-\dfrac{28}{7}$

$\dfrac{3}{7}v-\dfrac{10}{7}+\dfrac{10}{7}=-4+\dfrac{10}{7}$ $-\dfrac{40}{7}=-\dfrac{40}{7}$ a

$\dfrac{3}{7}v=-\dfrac{28}{7}+\dfrac{10}{7}$

$\dfrac{3}{7}v=-\dfrac{18}{7}$

$\dfrac{7}{3}\cdot\dfrac{3}{7}v=-\dfrac{18}{7}\cdot\dfrac{7}{3}$

$v=-6$

84. $\dfrac{1}{5}(y+4)=\dfrac{3}{5}y+3$ Check:

$\dfrac{1}{5}y+\dfrac{4}{5}=\dfrac{3}{5}y+3$ $\dfrac{1}{5}\left(-\dfrac{11}{2}+4\right)\overset{?}{=}\dfrac{3}{5}\left(-\dfrac{11}{2}\right)+3$

$\dfrac{1}{5}y+\dfrac{4}{5}-\dfrac{1}{5}y=\dfrac{3}{5}y+3-\dfrac{1}{5}y$ $\dfrac{1}{5}\left(-\dfrac{11}{2}+\dfrac{8}{2}\right)\overset{?}{=}-\dfrac{33}{10}+3$

$\dfrac{4}{5}=\dfrac{2}{5}y+3$ $\dfrac{1}{5}\left(-\dfrac{3}{2}\right)\overset{?}{=}-\dfrac{33}{10}+\dfrac{30}{10}$

$\dfrac{4}{5}-3=\dfrac{2}{5}y+3-3$ $-\dfrac{3}{10}=-\dfrac{3}{10}$ a

$\dfrac{4}{5}-\dfrac{15}{5}=\dfrac{2}{5}y$

$-\dfrac{11}{5}=\dfrac{2}{5}y$

$\dfrac{5}{2}\left(-\dfrac{11}{5}\right)=\dfrac{2}{5}y\cdot\dfrac{5}{2}$

$-\dfrac{11}{2}=y$

For problem 86, use the formula P = 2l + 2w.

86. *P = 2l + 2w, P = 16 in., l = 5 in.*

$16=2(5)+2w$

$16=10+2w$

$16-10=10+2w-10$

$6=2w$

$\dfrac{6}{2}=\dfrac{2w}{2}$

$3=w$

The width of the rectangle is 3 inches.

Cumulative Skills Review

2. $3x = 30$ Check

$$\frac{3x}{3} = \frac{30}{3} \qquad 3 \cdot 10 \overset{?}{=} 30$$

$$x = 10 \qquad 30 = 30^{a}$$

4. 30% of $\$1500 = 0.3 \times \$1500 = \$450$

6. $r = 5, f = -2$

$$(8r + 7f - 10)6 = 48r + 42f - 60$$

$$48 \cdot 5 + 42(-2) - 60 = 240 - 84 - 60 = 96$$

8. $C = \pi d \approx 3.14 \cdot 2.25 \approx 7.07$ in.

10. We must find the weighted average. A grade of B is worth 3 points and a grade of A is worth 4 points. The student took a total of 10 credits.

$$\text{GPA} = \frac{3 \cdot 3 + 3 \cdot 4 + 4 \cdot 3}{10} = \frac{9 + 12 + 12}{10} = \frac{33}{10} = 3.3$$

Section 10.5   Solving Application Problems

Concept Check

2.   Next, assign a __variable__ to the unknown quantity. Express other unknowns in terms of the chosen variable.

4.   Once you have an equation, __solve__ it.

6.   Once you have checked the solution, clearly __state__ the result using units, if necessary.

Guide Problems

8.   The product of 7 and a number is 12.

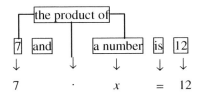

$$7 \qquad \cdot \qquad x \quad = \quad 12$$

For problems 10–20, use the key words and phrases found on page 738 in your text to translate each sentence into an equation. We let x = the unknown number in each problem; however, other variables may be used.

10. The difference of 8 and a number is –3.
$$8 - x = -3$$

12. The quotient of 48 and a number is 6.
$$\frac{48}{x} = 6$$

14. Five times a number is $-\frac{2}{3}$.

$$5x = -\frac{2}{3}$$

16. Ten subtracted from twice a number is 12.
$$2x - 10 = 12$$

18. Half of a number plus 19 is 15.

$$\frac{1}{2}x + 19 = 15$$

20. The quotient of 54 and the difference of a number and 6 is 9.

$$\frac{54}{x-6} = 9$$

For problems 22–48, use the six-step process to solve each problem.
> *1: Read and understand the problem.*
> *2: Assign a variable to the unknown quantity.*
> *3: Translate the problem into an equation.*
> *4: Solve the equation.*
> *5: Check the solution.*
> *6: Clearly state the result using units, if necessary.*

22. The difference between a number and 18 is 41. Find the number.
Let x = the number.

$$x - 18 = 41$$
$$x - 18 + 18 = 41 + 18$$
$$x = 59$$

Check
$$59 - 18 \overset{?}{=} 41$$
$$41 = 41^a$$

The number is 59.

24. The quotient of 63 and a number is 7. Find the number.
Let x = the number.

$$\frac{63}{x} = 7$$
$$x \cdot \frac{63}{x} = 7x$$
$$63 = 7x$$
$$\frac{63}{7} = \frac{7x}{7}$$
$$9 = x$$

Check
$$\frac{63}{9} \overset{?}{=} 7$$
$$7 = 7^a$$

The number is 9.

26. Seven subtracted from 5 times a number is 33. Find the number
Let x = the number.

$$5x - 7 = 33$$
$$5x - 7 + 7 = 33 + 7$$
$$5x = 40$$
$$\frac{5x}{5} = \frac{40}{5}$$
$$x = 8$$

Check
$$5(8) - 7 \overset{?}{=} 33$$
$$40 - 7 \overset{?}{=} 33$$
$$33 = 33^a$$

The number is 8.

28. The sum of 12 and twice a number is equal to four times the number. Find the number.
Let x = the number.

$$12 + 2x = 4x$$
$$12 + 2x - 2x = 4x - 2x$$
$$12 = 2x$$
$$\frac{12}{2} = \frac{2x}{2}$$
$$6 = x$$

Check
$$12 + 2(6) \overset{?}{=} 4(6)$$
$$12 + 12 \overset{?}{=} 24$$
$$24 = 24^a$$

The number is 6.

30. Six times the difference of a number and 3 is 2 less than twice the number. Find the number.
Let x = the number.

$$6(x - 3) = 2x - 2$$
$$6x - 18 = 2x - 2$$
$$6x - 18 - 2x = 2x - 2 - 2x$$
$$4x - 18 = -2$$
$$4x - 18 + 18 = -2 + 18$$
$$4x = 16$$
$$\frac{4x}{4} = \frac{16}{4}$$
$$x = 4$$

Check
$$6(4 - 3) \overset{?}{=} 2(4) - 2$$
$$6(1) \overset{?}{=} 8 - 2$$
$$6 = 6^a$$

The number is 4.

32. An exercise machine is on sale for $120 less than the regular price. The sale price is $599. Find the regular price.
Let x = the regular price.

$$x - 120 = 599$$
$$x - 120 + 120 = 599 + 120$$
$$x = 719$$

Check
$$719 - 120 \overset{?}{=} 599$$
$$599 = 599^a$$

The regular price is $719.

34. A trail begins at an altitude of 487 meters and ends at an altitude of 973 meters. If a hiker climbs from the beginning to the end of the trail, what is the net change in altitude?

Let x = the net change in altitude.

$$487 + x = 973 \qquad \text{Check}$$
$$487 + x - 487 = 973 - 487$$
$$x = 486$$
$$487 + 486 \overset{?}{=} 973$$
$$973 = 973^{a}$$

The net change in altitude is 486 meters.

36. One hundred thirty-five seniors made the honor roll. This represents one-fourth of the senior class. How many students are in the senior class?

Let x = the number of students in the senior class.

$$\frac{1}{4}x = 135 \qquad \text{Check}$$
$$4 \cdot \frac{1}{4}x = 135 \cdot 4 \qquad \frac{1}{4} \cdot 540 \overset{?}{=} 135$$
$$x = 540 \qquad 135 = 135^{a}$$

There are 540 students in the senior class..

38. An auditorium can seat 45 people in each row. How many full rows will be needed if 657 people are expected to attend a lecture?

Let r = the number of full rows needed.

$$45r = 657 \qquad \text{Check}$$
$$\frac{45r}{45} = \frac{657}{45} \qquad 45(14.6) \overset{?}{=} 657$$
$$r = 14.6 \qquad 657 = 657^{a}$$

The problem asks for the number of full rows, so round the answer up. 15 rows are needed.

40. One case of DVDs containing 48 units sold for $408.00. Find the cost of each DVD.

Let d = the cost of each DVD.

$$48d = 408.00 \qquad \text{Check}$$
$$\frac{48d}{48} = \frac{408.00}{48} \qquad 48(8.50) \overset{?}{=} 408.00$$
$$d = 8.50 \qquad 408.00 = 408.00^{a}$$

Each DVD costs $8.50.

42. At Phones West, long distance phone calls cost $0.55 for the first minute and $0.25 for each additional minute, plus an additional $1.50 service charge. If the total charge of a call is $10.30, how long did the call last?

Let m = the number of minutes the call lasted.

$$0.55 + 0.25(m - 1) + 1.50 = 10.30 \qquad \text{Check}$$
$$0.55 + 0.25m - 0.25 + 1.50 = 10.30$$
$$1.80 + 0.25m = 10.30 \qquad 0.55 + 0.25(34 - 1) + 1.50 \overset{?}{=} 10.30$$
$$1.80 + 0.25m - 1.80 = 10.30 - 1.80 \qquad 0.55 + 0.25(33) + 1.50 \overset{?}{=} 10.30$$
$$0.25m = 8.50$$
$$\frac{0.25m}{0.25} = \frac{8.50}{0.25} \qquad 0.55 + 8.25 + 1.50 \overset{?}{=} 10.30$$
$$m = 34 \qquad 10.30 = 10.30^{a}$$

The call lasted 34 minutes.

44. Marty's salary started at $26,000 per year with annual raises of $3000. Janice's salary started at $29,000 per year with annual raises of $2000. Marty and Janice were hired at the same time. After how many years will both employees earn the same salary.

Then y = the number of until they earn the same salary.

$$26,000 + 3000x = 29,000 + 2000x \qquad \text{Check}$$
$$26,000 + 3000x - 2000x = 29,000 + 2000x - 2000x$$
$$26,000 + 1000x = 29,000 \qquad 26,000 + 3000(3) \overset{?}{=} 29,000 + 2000(3)$$
$$26,000 + 1000x - 26,000 = 29,000 - 26,000 \qquad 26,000 + 9000 \overset{?}{=} 29,000 + 6000$$
$$1000x = 3000 \qquad 35,000 = 35,000^{a}$$
$$\frac{1000x}{1000} = \frac{3000}{1000}$$
$$x = 3$$

They will earn the same salary after 3 years.

46. A rectangle is such that its length is twice the difference of its width and 4 inches. The perimeter of the rectangle is 38 inches. Determine the length and the width.
Let w = the width in inches.
Then $2(w - 4)$ = the length.
$P = 2l + 2w = 2[2(w - 4)] + 2w$

$$2w + 2\left[2(w - 4)\right] = 38$$
$$2w + 2(2w - 8) = 38$$
$$2w + 4w - 16 = 38$$
$$6w - 6 = 38$$
$$6w - 16 + 16 = 38 + 16$$
$$6w = 54$$
$$\frac{6w}{6} = \frac{54}{6}$$
$$w = 9$$
$$2(w - 4) = 2(9 - 4) = 2(5) = 10$$

Check

$$2(9) + 2(10) \overset{?}{=} 38$$
$$18 + 20 \overset{?}{=} 38$$
$$38 = 38^a$$

The width is 9 inches and the length is 10 inches.

48. A 10-foot board is cut into three pieces. The second piece is twice as long as the first, and the third piece is a foot longer than the first. How long is each piece?
Let x = the length of the first piece. Then $2x$ = the length of the second piece, and $x + 1$ = the length of the third piece.

$$x + 2x + (x + 1) = 10$$
$$4x + 1 = 10$$
$$4x + 1 - 1 = 10 - 1$$
$$4x = 9$$
$$\frac{4x}{4} = \frac{9}{4}$$
$$x = \frac{9}{4} = 2\frac{1}{4}$$
$$2x = \frac{9}{4} \cdot 2 = \frac{9}{2} = 4\frac{1}{2}$$
$$x + 1 = 2\frac{1}{4} + 1 = 3\frac{1}{4}$$

Check

$$2\frac{1}{4} + 4\frac{1}{2} + 3\frac{1}{4} \overset{?}{=} 10$$
$$9\frac{4}{4} \overset{?}{=} 10$$
$$10 = 10^a$$

The three boards are $2\frac{1}{4}$ feet, $4\frac{1}{2}$ feet, and $3\frac{1}{4}$ feet.

Cumulative Skills Review

2. $2\frac{1}{2} \cdot 9\frac{2}{3} = \frac{5}{2} \cdot \frac{29}{3} = \frac{145}{6} = 24\frac{1}{6}$

4. $\dfrac{\$1.00}{12\text{-ounces}} = \$0.08$ per ounce

6. $5 \text{ yards} = 5 \text{ yards} \times \dfrac{3 \text{ feet}}{1 \text{ yard}} = 15 \text{ feet}$

8. $-\dfrac{1}{5} - \left(-\dfrac{2}{3}\right) = -\dfrac{1}{5} + \dfrac{2}{3} = -\dfrac{3}{15} + \dfrac{10}{15} = \dfrac{7}{15}$

10.
$$15h + 5 = 72.5$$
$$15h + 5 - 5 = 72.5 - 5$$
$$15h = 67.5$$
$$\frac{15h}{15} = \frac{67.5}{15}$$
$$h = 4.5$$

Check
$$15(4.5) + 5 \overset{?}{=} 72.5$$
$$67.5 + 5 \overset{?}{=} 72.5$$
$$72.5 = 72.5^a$$

Chapter 10 Numerical Facts of Life

2. The ratio in the equation $T = P + \dfrac{10}{91}t$ tells us that 10 people are added to the population every 91 seconds.

Manipulating this ratio, we find that 1 person is added every 9.1 seconds: $\dfrac{10 \text{ people}}{91 \text{ seconds}} = \dfrac{1 \text{ person}}{9.1 \text{ seconds}}$

Chapter 10 Review Exercises

In Problems 1 through 4, evaluate each algebraic expression when x = 2 and y = 3.

1. $2x - 3y$
   $2(2) - 3(3) = 4 - 9 = -5$

2. $x^2 - y$
   $2^2 - 3 = 4 - 3 = 1$

3. $xy + 6y - 3x - 18$
   $2 \cdot 3 + 6 \cdot 3 - 3 \cdot 2 - 18 = 6 + 18 - 6 - 18 = 0$

4. $8x + 12y - 5xy$
   $8 \cdot 2 + 12 \cdot 3 - 5 \cdot 2 \cdot 3 = 16 + 36 - 30 = 22$

In exercises 5 through 12, combine like terms. Remember that like terms have the same variables and same exponents.

5. $9a - 4b + 2a + 8b = (9a + 2a) + (-4b + 8b)$
   $= 11a + 4b$

6. $4x + 7y - 5y + 12x = (4x + 12x) + (7y - 5y)$
   $= 16x + 2y$

7. $4z + 5v + 6z - 8v = (5v - 8v) + (4z + 6z)$
   $= -3v + 10z$

8. $2rt + 4r - 7rt + 5t - 6r$
   $= (4r - 6r) + (2rt - 7rt) + 5t$
   $= -2r - 5rt + 5t$

9. $a^2 + 5a - 4a - 8a^2 = (a^2 - 8a^2) + (5a - 4a)$
   $= -7a^2 + a$

10. $m^3 + m^2n - 4m^3 + 8mn^2$
    $= (m^3 - 4m^3) + m^2n + 8mn^2$
    $= -3m^3 + m^2n + 8mn^2$

11. $gh + g^2 - gh + h^2 = g^2 + (gh - gh) + h^2$
    $= g^2 + h^2$

12. $7x^3y + 3x^2y - 36x^3y + 5x^2y$
    $= (7x^3y - 36x^3y) + (3x^2y + 5x^2y)$
    $= -29x^3y + 8x^2y$

For problems 13–16, apply the associative property of multiplication and the commutative property of multiplication as necessary to multiply the expression.

13. $2(3x) = 6x$

14. $-5(5y) = -25y$

15. $2.1(3a) = 6.3a$

16. $\dfrac{1}{2}(8d) = 4d$

For problems 17–24, use the distributive property $a(b + c) = ab + ac$ or $(a + b)c = ac + bc$.

17. $3(x - 15) = 3x - 45$

18. $8(2k^2 + 1) = 16k^2 + 8$

19. $-(b - 7) = -b + 7$

20. $-(4z + 8 - y) = -4z - 8 + y$

21. $-3(8p+7) = -24p-21$

22. $-4(5t^2-2) = -20t^2+8$

23. $-2(-3m^2+2mn-9n^2) = 6m^2-4mn+18n^2$

24. $-5(7y^2-3yz+2z^2) = -35y^2+15yz-10z^2$

In problems 25 through 32, determine whether the given value is a solution to the given equation by substituting the value for the unknown in the equation.

25. $x=2; \; 7x+15=29$

$$7(2)+15\overset{?}{=}29$$
$$14+15\overset{?}{=}29$$
$$29=29^a$$
2 is a solution.

26. $y=2; \; 4-(2y+6)=-8$

$$4-(2\cdot2+6)\overset{?}{=}-8$$
$$4-(4+6)\overset{?}{=}-8$$
$$4-10\overset{?}{=}-8$$
$$-6\neq-8$$
2 is not a solution.

27. $b=6; \; 5b-9=7b+3$

$$5(6)-9\overset{?}{=}7(6)+3$$
$$30-9\overset{?}{=}42+3$$
$$21\neq45$$
6 is not a solution.

28. $k=-20; \; k+20=0$

$$-20+20\overset{?}{=}0$$
$$0=0^a$$
-20 is a solution.

29. $p=3; \; p^2-3=5$

$$3^2-3\overset{?}{=}5$$
$$9-3\overset{?}{=}5$$
$$6\neq5$$
3 is not a solution.

30. $m=4; \; m^2+9=25$

$$4^2+9\overset{?}{=}25$$
$$16+9\overset{?}{=}25$$
$$25=25^a$$
4 is a solution.

31. $a=8; \; 63-a^2=1$

$$63-8^2\overset{?}{=}1$$
$$63-64\overset{?}{=}1$$
$$-1\neq1$$
5 is not a solution.

32. $t=10; \; 109-t^2=9$

$$109-10^2\overset{?}{=}9$$
$$109-100\overset{?}{=}9$$
$$9=9^a$$
10 is a solution.

Be sure to check each solution for problems 33–56.

33. $v+15=34$ Check

$$v+15-15=34-15$$
$$v=19$$
$$19+15\overset{?}{=}34$$
$$34=34^a$$

34. $x+21=8$ Check

$$x+21-21=8-21$$
$$x=-13$$
$$-13+21\overset{?}{=}8$$
$$8=8^a$$

35. $\quad m - 2.3 = 5.4 \qquad$ Check

$m - 2.3 + 2.3 = 5.4 + 2.3$

$\qquad\qquad m = 7.7 \qquad 7.7 - 2.3 \overset{?}{=} 5.4$

$\qquad\qquad\qquad\qquad\qquad 5.4 = 5.4^{a}$

36. $\quad b - 5.7 = 8.4 \qquad$ Check

$b - 5.7 + 5.7 = 8.4 + 5.7$

$\qquad\qquad b = 14.1 \qquad 14.1 - 5.7 \overset{?}{=} 8.4$

$\qquad\qquad\qquad\qquad\qquad 8.4 = 8.4^{a}$

37. $\quad 12 + p = 4 \qquad$ Check

$12 + p - 12 = 4 - 12$

$\qquad\qquad p = -8 \qquad 12 + (-8) \overset{?}{=} 4$

$\qquad\qquad\qquad\qquad 4 = 4^{a}$

38. $\quad 20 + r = 7 \qquad$ Check

$20 + r - 20 = 7 - 20$

$\qquad\qquad r = -13 \qquad 20 + (-13) \overset{?}{=} 7$

$\qquad\qquad\qquad\qquad 7 = 7^{a}$

39. $\quad a + \dfrac{1}{3} = \dfrac{1}{2} \qquad$ Check

$a + \dfrac{1}{3} - \dfrac{1}{3} = \dfrac{1}{2} - \dfrac{1}{3} \qquad \dfrac{1}{6} + \dfrac{1}{3} \overset{?}{=} \dfrac{1}{2}$

$\qquad\qquad a = \dfrac{3}{6} - \dfrac{2}{6} = \dfrac{1}{6} \qquad \dfrac{1}{6} + \dfrac{2}{6} \overset{?}{=} \dfrac{1}{2}$

$\qquad\qquad\qquad\qquad\qquad \dfrac{3}{6} \overset{?}{=} \dfrac{1}{2}$

$\qquad\qquad\qquad\qquad\qquad \dfrac{1}{2} = \dfrac{1}{2}^{a}$

40. $\quad n + \dfrac{2}{5} = \dfrac{1}{2} \qquad$ Check

$n + \dfrac{2}{5} - \dfrac{2}{5} = \dfrac{1}{2} - \dfrac{2}{5} \qquad \dfrac{1}{10} + \dfrac{2}{5} \overset{?}{=} \dfrac{1}{2}$

$\qquad\qquad n = \dfrac{5}{10} - \dfrac{4}{10} = \dfrac{1}{10} \qquad \dfrac{1}{10} + \dfrac{4}{10} \overset{?}{=} \dfrac{1}{2}$

$\qquad\qquad\qquad\qquad\qquad \dfrac{5}{10} \overset{?}{=} \dfrac{1}{2}$

$\qquad\qquad\qquad\qquad\qquad \dfrac{1}{2} = \dfrac{1}{2}^{a}$

41. $4k = 48 \qquad$ Check

$\dfrac{4k}{4} = \dfrac{48}{4} \qquad 4 \cdot 12 \overset{?}{=} 48$

$\qquad k = 12 \qquad 48 = 48^{a}$

42. $7q = 56 \qquad$ Check

$\dfrac{7q}{7} = \dfrac{56}{7} \qquad 7 \cdot 8 \overset{?}{=} 56$

$\qquad q = 8 \qquad 56 = 56^{a}$

43. $2z = 25 \qquad$ Check

$\dfrac{2z}{2} = \dfrac{25}{2} \qquad 2 \cdot \dfrac{25}{2} \overset{?}{=} 25$

$\qquad z = \dfrac{25}{2} \text{ or } 12\dfrac{1}{2} \qquad 25 = 25^{a}$

44. $3h = 47 \qquad$ Check

$\dfrac{3h}{3} = \dfrac{47}{3} \qquad 3 \cdot \dfrac{47}{3} \overset{?}{=} 47$

$\qquad z = \dfrac{47}{3} \text{ or } 15\dfrac{2}{3} \qquad 47 = 47^{a}$

45. $\quad -\dfrac{2}{5}t = 12 \qquad$ Check

$\left(-\dfrac{5}{2}\right)\left(-\dfrac{2}{5}t\right) = 12\left(-\dfrac{5}{2}\right) \qquad -\dfrac{2}{5}(-30) \overset{?}{=} 12$

$\qquad\qquad\qquad t = -30 \qquad\qquad 12 = 12^{a}$

46. $\quad -\dfrac{3}{7}t = 24 \qquad$ Check

$\left(-\dfrac{7}{3}\right)\left(-\dfrac{3}{7}t\right) = 24\left(-\dfrac{7}{3}\right) \qquad -\dfrac{3}{7}(-56) \overset{?}{=} 24$

$\qquad\qquad\qquad t = -56 \qquad\qquad 24 = 24^{a}$

47. $0.3p = 3.9 \qquad$ Check

$\dfrac{0.3p}{0.3} = \dfrac{3.9}{0.3} \qquad 0.3 \cdot 13 \overset{?}{=} 3.9$

$\qquad p = 13 \qquad\qquad 3.9 = 3.9^{a}$

48. $0.5x = 4.5 \qquad$ Check

$\dfrac{0.5x}{0.5} = \dfrac{4.5}{0.5} \qquad 0.5 \cdot 9 \overset{?}{=} 4.5$

$\qquad p = 9 \qquad\qquad 4.5 = 4.5^{a}$

49.
$$12t + 3 = 39$$
$$12t + 3 - 3 = 39 - 3$$
$$12t = 36$$
$$\frac{12t}{12} = \frac{36}{12}$$
$$t = 3$$

Check
$$12 \cdot 3 + 3 \overset{?}{=} 39$$
$$36 + 3 \overset{?}{=} 39$$
$$39 = 39^a$$

50.
$$8b - 9 = 31$$
$$8b - 9 + 9 = 31 + 9$$
$$8b = 40$$
$$\frac{8b}{8} = \frac{40}{8}$$
$$b = 5$$

Check
$$8 \cdot 5 - 9 \overset{?}{=} 31$$
$$40 - 9 \overset{?}{=} 31$$
$$31 = 31^a$$

51.
$$9x = 5x + 40$$
$$9x - 5x = 5x + 40 - 5x$$
$$4x = 40$$
$$\frac{4x}{4} = \frac{40}{4}$$
$$t = 10$$

Check
$$9 \cdot 10 \overset{?}{=} 5 \cdot 10 + 40$$
$$90 \overset{?}{=} 50 + 40$$
$$90 = 90^a$$

52.
$$7s = 3s + 52$$
$$7s - 3s = 3s + 52 - 3s$$
$$4s = 52$$
$$\frac{4s}{4} = \frac{52}{4}$$
$$s = 13$$

Check
$$7 \cdot 13 \overset{?}{=} 3 \cdot 13 + 52$$
$$91 \overset{?}{=} 39 + 52$$
$$91 = 91^a$$

53.
$$2(m + 6) = 4(2m + 3)$$
$$2m + 12 = 8m + 12$$
$$2m + 12 - 2m = 8m + 12 - 2m$$
$$12 = 6m + 12$$
$$12 - 12 = 6m + 12 - 12$$
$$0 = 6m$$
$$\frac{0}{6} = \frac{6m}{6}$$
$$0 = m$$

Check
$$2(0 + 6) \overset{?}{=} 4(2 \cdot 0 + 3)$$
$$2(6) \overset{?}{=} 4(0 + 3)$$
$$12 \overset{?}{=} 4(3)$$
$$12 = 12^a$$

54.
$$6(z - 5) = 3(4z + 8)$$
$$6z - 30 = 12z + 24$$
$$6z - 30 - 12z = 12x + 24 - 12z$$
$$-6z - 30 = 24$$
$$-6z - 30 + 30 = 24 + 30$$
$$-6z = 54$$
$$\frac{-6z}{-6} = \frac{54}{-6}$$
$$x = -9$$

Check
$$6(-9 - 5) \overset{?}{=} 3(4(-9) + 8)$$
$$6(-14) \overset{?}{=} 3(-36 + 8)$$
$$-84 \overset{?}{=} 3(-28)$$
$$-84 = -84^a$$

55.
$$5(2n - 11) - 7n = 5$$
$$10n - 55 - 7n = 5$$
$$3n - 55 = 5$$
$$3n - 55 + 55 = 5 + 55$$
$$3n = 60$$
$$\frac{3n}{3} = \frac{60}{3}$$
$$n = 20$$

Check
$$5(2 \cdot 20 - 11) - 7 \cdot 20 \overset{?}{=} 5$$
$$5(40 - 11) - 7 \cdot 20 \overset{?}{=} 5$$
$$5(29) - 140 \overset{?}{=} 5$$
$$145 - 140 \overset{?}{=} 5$$
$$5 = 5^a$$

56. $7(3c + 10) + 2c = 1$

    $21c + 70 + 2c = 1$

    $23c + 70 = 1$

    $23c + 70 - 70 = 1 - 70$

    $23c = -69$

    $\dfrac{23c}{23} = \dfrac{-69}{23}$

    $c = -3$

Check

$7(3(-3) + 10) + 2(-3) \overset{?}{=} 1$

$7(-9 + 10) + 2(-3) \overset{?}{=} 1$

$7(1) + 2(-3) \overset{?}{=} 1$

$7 + (-6) \overset{?}{=} 1$

$1 = 1$[a]

For problems 57–60, use the six-step process to solve each problem.

    1: Read and understand the problem.

    2: Assign a variable to the unknown quantity.

    3: Translate the problem into an equation.

    4: Solve the equation.

    5: Check the solution.

    6: Clearly state the result using units, if necessary.

57. Write an algebraic expression to represent twelve subtracted from twice the difference between ten and a number.

Let x = the number.

$2(10 - x) - 12$

58. An airplane flying at an altitude of 32,000 feet suddenly has to change altitude to 29,500 feet. What is the net change in altitude.

Let x = the net change in altitude..

$32,000 - 29,500 = x$ Check

    $2500 = x$ $32,000 - 29,500 \overset{?}{=} 2500$

                  $2500 = 2500$[a]

The net change in altitude is 2500 feet.

59. A new radio sells for $58.99. If this is $17.68 above the wholesale price, find the wholesale price.

Let x = the wholesale price.

    $x + \$17.68 = \$58.99$

$x + \$17.68 - \$17.68 = \$58.99 - \$17.68$

              $x = \$41.31$

Check

$\$41.31 + \$17.68 \overset{?}{=} \$58.99$

    $\$58.99 = \$58.99$[a]

The wholesale price is $41.31

60. Martha was paid $348.75 for 45 hours of work. Find her rate of pay.

Let x = Martha's hourly rate of pay.

    $45x = \$348.75$ Check

    $\dfrac{45x}{45} = \dfrac{\$348.75}{45}$ $45 \cdot \$7.75 \overset{?}{=} \$348.75$

        $x = \$7.75$ $\$348.75 = \$348.75$[a]

Martha earned $7.75 per hour.

61. There are 32 students in a beginning algebra class. The number of males is seven less than two times the number of females. Find the number of each.

Let f = the number of females in the class. Then $2f - 7$ = the number of males.

$$f + (2f - 7) = 32$$

$$f + 2f - 7 = 32$$

$$3f - 7 = 32$$

$$3f - 7 + 7 = 32 + 7$$

$$3f = 39$$

$$\frac{3f}{3} = \frac{39}{3}$$

$$f = 13$$

$$2f - 7 = 2(13) - 7 = 26 - 7 = 19$$

Check

$$13 + 19 \overset{?}{=} 32$$

$$32 = 32^a$$

There are 13 females and 19 males in the class.

Chapter 10 Assessment Test

1. $a^2 + 7(b - 4)$; $a = 3$, $b = 8$

   $3^2 + 7(8 - 4) = 9 + 7(4)$

   $\qquad = 9 + 28 = 37$

2. $4b - a^2 + (a - b)^2$; $a = 3$, $b = 8$

   $4 \cdot 8 - 3^2 + (3 - 8)^2 = 4 \cdot 8 - 9 + (-5)^2$

   $\qquad = 32 - 9 + 25$

   $\qquad = 48$

3. $6m^4n^3 + 8m^4n - m^4n^3 + 12m^4m + 3m^4n^3 = \left(6m^4n^3 - m^4n^3 + 3m^4n^3\right) + \left(8m^4n + 12m^4n\right) = 8m^4n^3 + 20m^4n$

4. $a^2 + 2ab - b^2 + 5ab - 8a^2 + 3b^2 = \left(a^2 - 8a^2\right) + \left(2ab + 5ab\right) + \left(-b^2 + 3b^2\right) = -7a^2 + 7ab + 2b^2$

5. $-3(9d - 8) = -27d + 24$

6. $5(8m - 7) = 40m - 35$

7. $x = 12$, $2x + 3(2x - 4) = 9x$

   $2 \cdot 12 + 3(2 \cdot 12 - 4) \overset{?}{=} 9 \cdot 12$

   $2 \cdot 12 + 3(24 - 4) \overset{?}{=} 9 \cdot 12$

   $2 \cdot 12 + 3(20) \overset{?}{=} 9 \cdot 12$

   $24 + 60 \overset{?}{=} 108$

   $84 \neq 108$

   12 is not a solution.

8. $y = -7$, $6y + 14(y + 5) = 10y$

   $6(-7) + 14(-7 + 5) \overset{?}{=} 10(-7)$

   $6(-7) + 14(-2) \overset{?}{=} 10(-7)$

   $-42 + (-28) \overset{?}{=} -70$

   $-70 = -70^a$

   -7 is a solution.

9. $\quad x + 45 = 38$

   $x + 45 - 45 = 38 - 45$

   $\quad x = -7$

   Check

   $-7 + 45 \overset{?}{=} 38$

   $38 = 38^a$

10. $\quad p + 12.5 = 9.5$

    $p + 12.5 - 12.5 = 9.5 - 12.5$

    $\quad p = -3$

    Check

    $-3 + 12.5 \overset{?}{=} 9.5$

    $9.5 = 9.5^a$

11. $9q = 108$ Check

$$\frac{9q}{9} = \frac{108}{9} \qquad 9 \cdot 12 \overset{?}{=} 108$$

$$q = 12 \qquad 108 = 108^{a}$$

12. $\dfrac{1}{5}w = \dfrac{2}{3}$ Check

$$5 \cdot \frac{1}{5}w = \frac{2}{3} \cdot 5 \qquad \frac{1}{5} \cdot \frac{10}{3} \overset{?}{=} \frac{2}{3}$$

$$w = \frac{10}{3} \text{ or } 3\frac{1}{3} \qquad \frac{2}{3} = \frac{2}{3}{}^{a}$$

13. $\qquad 7(x-8) = 3(2x-5)$ Check

$$7x - 56 = 6x - 15$$

$$7x - 56 - 6x = 6x - 15 - 6x$$

$$x - 56 = -15$$

$$x - 56 + 56 = -15 + 56$$

$$x = 41$$

$$7(41-8) \overset{?}{=} 3(2 \cdot 41 - 5)$$

$$7(33) \overset{?}{=} 3(82 - 5)$$

$$231 \overset{?}{=} 3(77)$$

$$231 = 231^{a}$$

14. $\qquad 7(2t+3) = 3(t-4)$ Check

$$14t + 21 = 3t - 12$$

$$14t + 21 - 3t = 3t - 12 - 3t$$

$$11t + 21 = -12$$

$$11t + 21 - 21 = -12 - 21$$

$$11t = -33$$

$$\frac{11t}{11} = \frac{-33}{11}$$

$$t = -3$$

$$7(2(-3)+3) \overset{?}{=} 3(-3-4)$$

$$7(-6+3) \overset{?}{=} 3(-7)$$

$$7(-3) \overset{?}{=} -21$$

$$-21 = -21^{a}$$

15. $\qquad 8y + 3 = 12y$ Check

$$8y + 3 - 8y = 12y - 8y$$

$$3 = 4y$$

$$\frac{3}{4} = \frac{4y}{4}$$

$$\frac{3}{4} = y$$

$$8 \cdot \frac{3}{4} + 3 \overset{?}{=} 12 \cdot \frac{3}{4}$$

$$6 + 3 \overset{?}{=} 9$$

$$9 = 9^{a}$$

16. $\qquad 24(p+1) = 3p$ Check

$$24p + 24 = 3p$$

$$24p + 24 - 24p = 3p - 24p$$

$$24 = -21p$$

$$\frac{24}{-21} = \frac{-21p}{-21}$$

$$-\frac{8}{7} = p$$

$$24\left(-\frac{8}{7} + 1\right) \overset{?}{=} 3\left(-\frac{8}{7}\right)$$

$$24\left(-\frac{8}{7} + \frac{7}{7}\right) \overset{?}{=} 3\left(-\frac{8}{7}\right)$$

$$24\left(-\frac{1}{7}\right) \overset{?}{=} 3\left(-\frac{8}{7}\right)$$

$$-\frac{24}{7} = -\frac{24}{7}{}^{a}$$

Write an algebraic expression to represent the given expression in problems 17 and 18.

17. Three times a number decreased by 24.
    Let x = the number.
    $3x - 24$

18. The product of three and the sum of the square of a number and 15.
    Let x = the number.
    $3\left(x^2 + 15\right)$

19. The temperature this morning was 34 degrees. By noon, the temperature had risen 7 degrees. Find the new temperature.
    Let t = the new temperature.
    $34 + 7 = t$ Check
    $41 = t$
    $$34 + 7 \overset{?}{=} 41$$
    $$41 = 41^{\text{a}}$$
    The new temperature was 41 degrees.

20. A jet flew a distance of 3300 miles in 6 hours. What was the average speed of the jet in terms of miles per hour?
    Let s = the average speed of the jet in miles per hour.
    $$s = \frac{3300 \text{ miles}}{6 \text{ hours}} = 550 \text{ miles per hour}$$
    The average speed of the jet was 550 miles per hour.

21. You are planning to advertise your car for sale on the Internet. *Car Showroom* charges \$1.80 for a photo plus \$0.09 per word. *Car Bazaar* charges \$1.00 for the photo plus \$0.11 per word. For what number of words will the charges be the same?
    Let w = the number of words.

    $$1.80 + 0.09w = 1.00 + 0.11w$$
    $$1.80 + 0.09w - 0.09w = 1.00 + 0.11w - 0.09w$$
    $$1.80 = 1.00 + 0.02w$$
    $$1.80 - 1.00 = 1.00 + 0.02w - 1.00$$
    $$0.80 = 0.02w$$
    $$\frac{0.80}{0.02} = \frac{0.02w}{0.02}$$
    $$40 = w$$

    Check
    $$1.80 + 0.09(40) \overset{?}{=} 1.00 + 0.11(40)$$
    $$1.80 + 3.60 \overset{?}{=} 1.00 + 4.40$$
    $$5.40 = 5.40^{\text{a}}$$

    The charges will be the same for 40 words.